BRAIN BEAT

Scientific Foundations and Evolutionary
Perspectives of Brain Health

Michael Hoffmann MD, PhD

PAGE PUBLISHING, INC.
New York, NY

First originally published by Page Publishing, Inc. 2015

ISBN 978-1-68139-739-9 (pbk)
ISBN 978-1-68139-740-5 (digital)
ISBN 978-1-68213-319-4 (hardcover)

Printed in the United States of America

Cover Designed and drawn by Devon Lesley Brasler, Artist,
Johannesburg, South Africa, home of the
Cradle of Humankind, UNESCO.

To my family—Bronwyn, Jenna-Leigh, and Michael—the thousands of researchers referenced in this book, and the millions of animals sacrificed in the name of science

Brain Beat Cover Explanation

Key events in human evolution included an increase brain size that followed the adoption of bipedalism. This occurred in the African Rift Valley region depicted in the right upper image of Africa. Our lineage stems from primates, and the many extant primates of today represent traces of our evolutionary origins in terms of our dependency on frugivorous diet (critical for brain health), the musicality of gibbon communication, and the musical protolanguage origins and chimpanzees representative of level 2 working memory, compared to the level 7 of humans. Archeological discoveries point to the increase in brain size having occurred in Eastern, Central, and Northern Africa. The skull of *Sahelanthropus tchadensis*, the world's oldest man, was found in the Chad region of Africa in 2002, Northern Africa, where the brain image is depicted. The face, right lower part, signifies captivating data (dietary, genetic linguistic), suggesting that Southern Africa was the region where the human mind became "super connected'. The background of water ripples on the cover impart the concept of vibrations, rhythm, and movement that also expands to astrophysical forces such as the sun and moon and their place in pacing certain rhythms in nature. The blue background and ripples also have a fingerprint-like appearance, which symbolize one's identity and speak to the uniqueness of the individual. The blue also signifies the special place of blue open water expanses, lacustrine and coastal, wherein humans evolved. The position of the head with eyes closed eyes suggests meditation, becoming more in tune with the rhythm of breathing, heartbeat, and the stream of consciousness, increasingly used in brain and mind therapies.

Contents

Illustrations 6

Tables 9

Preface 13

Acknowledgments 15

1. Our Brains Evolved, Attuned to Rhythms in the
   Natural World 17

2. Physical Exercise, Neurogenesis, Evolutionary
   Origins, and Implications for Brain Health 95

3. Brain Foods: Evolutionary Insights into Nutrition
   and Advantageous Biocultural Changes 141

4. Sleep Health 255

5. Social Intelligence, Sociality, and Brain Health 292

6. Cognitive Exercise and Cognitive Reserve 310

7. Putting It All Together: What May Be the
   Benefits of Adhering to All Five Components of
   Brain Health? 357

Index 365

Illustrations

Figures

1.1 Interrelationships
1.2 Natural Rhythms
1.3 Your Golden Opportunity
1.4 The Band-Aid Effect
1.5 Disciplines That Interacted and Contribution to the Study of Human Evolution
1.6 Dirt Archeology and Cognitive Archeology
1.7 Brodmann Areas, Primary Areas, Unimodal and Tertiary Association Areas
1.8 Isolated Frontopolar Lesion (Midline Dark Area) Due to a Discreet Brain Hemorrhage
1.9 *Dunkleosteus terrelli*
1.10 Key Innovation of Mammals
1.11 Hominin Proliferation, Brain Enlargement, and Ice Ages
1.12 Brain Size
1.13 Parietal Lobe Expansion and Increased Globularity Enabled Improved Intracerebral Connectivity
1.14 Orbitofrontal Subcortical Circuit
1.15 The Brain, Mind, Cognitive Evolution Sequence
1.16 The Frontopolar Cortex (BA10) and Related Frontal Regions
1.17 Hohlenstein Stadel Figurine: The *Lion Man*
1.18 Franco-Cantabrian Cave Art
1.19 The Major Tectonic Plates

1.20 The Planet's "Geological Heartbeat"
1.21 Plate Tectonic Movements of Earlier Supercontinents
1.22 Cold Dense Water Travel Due to Sea Ice Formation
1.23 Global Cooling Trend
1.24 Himalayan Mountains, Tibetan Plateau Formation
1.25 "Pacemaker of the Ice Ages"
1.26 Pacific and Atlantic Water Mixing
   Through the "Old" Panama Canal
1.27 Atlantic Meridional Overturning Circulation
1.28 Equatorial to Interpolar Circulation
1.29 Factors Impacting the Evolution of Hominins:
   Paleogeological, Paleoclimatological, Astrophysical
2.1 The Laetoli Footprint Trace Fossils
2.2 Chase Hunting and Power Scavenging
2.3 Hominin Cognitive Evolution Sequence
2.4 Hippocampal Dentate Gyrus Neurogenesis in Exercising
   Mice
2.5 Mice Exercise and Green Fluorescent Protein Indicate
   New Neurons in the Hippocampus
2.6 Aerobic Exercise Increases Gray Matter Volume
   and White Matter, Fiber Tracts in Older Adults
2.7 Mental and Physical (MAP) Training
   Combined More Effective
3.1 Complex Systems
3.2 Multiple Connections Exist to Transmit Effects from the
   Gut, Feeding, and Food on Cognition
3.3 Cognition, Energy Homeostasis, and the BDNF Link
3.4 The Brain-Microbial-Gut Communication Systems
3.5 The Principal Dopaminergic Systems
3.6 Diet Quality Versus Log Body Weight
3.7 Primate Species
3.8 Mean BMI
3.9 A Classification of Fats
3.10 Arachidonic Acid Metabolism
3.11 Arachidonic Acid Cyclooxygenase cascade
3.12 Arachidonic Acid Cyclooxygenase Cascade Functions
3.13 Arachidonic Acid Lipoxygenase Pathway
3.14 Arachidonic Acid Lipoxygenase Leukotriene Functions

3.15   Predilection of Atherogenic Sites in
       the Cerebrovascular Tree
3.16   Fish Consumption and Major Depression
3.17   Brain Size
3.18   Honey Seeker Images from the Levantine Rock Art
4.1   Natural Light Varies Throughout the Day
4.2   Light Impinges on the Retinal ipRGCs
4.3   The Chemistry of the Wake-Sleep Cycle
4.4   Wake-Producing Systems
4.5   Sleep-Wake Flip-Flop Switch
4.6   Restorative Function of Sleep
4.7   Tree-to-Ground Transition Improved
       Sleep in Early Hominins
4.8   Microglia and Topiary
4.9   Quantitative EEG and Lucid Dreaming
4.10   3-D State Space AIM Model
5.1   Vasopressin and the Prairie Role
5.2   Grooming Baboons
5.3   Schematic Social Brain Circuitry Hubs
5.4   Social Group Size for Monkey and Ape Species
6.1   Glial Cells Outnumber Neurons
6.2   Brain Reserve and Cognitive Reserve
6.3   Treatment of Vascular Risk Factors
6.4   Lascaux Painting
6.5   Categories of Simple Geometric, Visual
       Hallucinations (Entoptics)
6.6   Spirituality, Mysticism, and Religion
6.7   Intensified Consciousness Trajectory and
       Neurological Bridge Hypothesis
6.8   Ecology of Human Health and the Biosphere
6.9   Default Mode Network and Attentional Network
6.10   Metacognitive Ability
6.11   Meditation "Brain Builds"
6.12   Musicality and the Brain
7.1   Brain Box Dashboard
7.2   Natural Rhythms

Tables

1.1   Human mind Evolution
1.2   The Beat and Pulsing of Ocean Currents
1.3   Relationship of Physical Events
1.4   Brain Statistics: Anatomical
1.5   The Majority of the Energy Used by the Brain
2.1   Conditioning
2.2   Musculoskeletal, Metabolic, and Cerebral Adaptations of Humans to Running
2.3   Exercise-Induced Trophic Factors Influencing Adult Neurogenesis
2.4   Terminology of Physical Activity Measures
2.5   PAR Activities in Men (Women)
2.6   Measuring VO$_2$ Max
3.1   The Enteric Nervous System
3.2   Hormonal Communication Channels Between the Brain and Gut
3.3   BDNF and Neuropsychiatric Disease
3.4   The Six Different Taste Senses
3.5   Macronutrient Requirements
3.6   Micronutrient Requirements
3.7   Common medications for Micronutrient Deficiencies
3.8   Micronutrient Subtypes
3.9   Omega-6 to Omega-3 Ratios in Various Populations
3.10 Long-Chain Fatty Acid Classification, Carbon Atom Number, and Double Bonds

3.11   DHA Beneficial Effects

3.12   Mechanisms Whereby Ketones Exert Their Effects

3.13   Classification of Sugars

3.14   The BMI Categories from Severe Undernutrition

3.15   Adverse Effects Soft Drink

3.16   Deleterious Effects of Alcohol

3.17   Alcohol Level and Effects on Neurological Function

3.18   Salt-Intake Variation and Some Food Salt Contents

3.19   Antioxidant Classification Substance
        Found in Phytochemicals

3.20   Definition of Terms

3.21   The Legacy Diet

4.1   Neurological Sleep Disorders

4.2   Prevalence of Moderate to Severe SDB in Cardiovascular
        and Cerebrovascular Diseases

4.3   Slow Wave and REM Sleep Electrical
        Activity and Neurotransmitters

4.4   The Biological and Neurological Merits of Sleep

4.5   The Benefits of Dreaming

5.1   Functions of the Hormones AVP and Oxytocin

6.1   Epidemiological Studies Have Delineated
        Several Cognitive Reserve Factors

6.2   Hypothetical Components of Brain/
        Cognitive Reserve Capacity

7.1   Personalized Medicine

Notice to the Readers

Medicine, both as a science and art, is a field that is undergoing constant and increasingly rapid changes. These include changes in the treatment of diseases and conditions that include not only drug treatment but also other types of managements, including device therapies. The author of this book, together with Page Publications, has reviewed the sources of the information, referenced in this book, for accuracy and reliability. Because of the rapid change of knowledge inherent in medicine and the ever present chance of human error, the author and publisher cannot mandate that all information is completely accurate and comprehensive in scope. The readers are encouraged always to check the information gleaned from this book and compare to other reliable authorities and sources. This should include product information from pharmaceutical companies when medications are concerned and checking particular practices with their local physician groups as these can vary across cultures and countries.

Preface

Our brains have been befittingly described as complex systems, as indeed are many other natural and man-made systems such as the stock market, airline routes, and hubs, our 20 trillion resident germs (microbiota), and scientific networks, for example. A hallmark feature of complex systems are interconnected hubs. A major ambition of this book is that it might come to represent a small hub of knowledge about brain health and fitness implications. The many references embody the spokes emanating from the hub that can be interrogated further with the help of web-based searches through medical and scientific sites. Although the book is aimed primarily at the clinicians of many health-related disciplines, students of medicine and science, sportswomen and -men, the large majority of the content should be comprehensible by those without such backgrounds. However, because of the plenteous disciplines cited, there may be many terms or concepts that are foreign to students entrenched in one particular field of study. I have, nevertheless, taken the liberty of introducing the exact scientific and medical terms, as these are still the least ambiguous, and if they appear unfamiliar or alien, reliance on smart phones or web access helps unscramble these by accessing sites such as Pubmed, Google search, Wikipedia, and disease-specific websites for example. Each chapter concludes with many references as these have been chosen from many more as the most pertinent to the particular topic. No doubt many equally or more important references may have been missed, and from month to month as new information is published, this will further increase the deficit of whatmight have been included. However, as with the brain, there needs to be continuous plasticity and molding of our knowledge.

In evolutionary terms, although the concept of survival of the fittest conjures up peak attributes and performance, we are instead a product of a long list of compromises in response to the changing forces in nature. Walking upright comes at a price of low-back pain, large brains create difficulty in giving birth, and food choices today may suffer from our more ancient needs linked to our hedonic reward brain circuitry. Chapter 1 deals with the intricate web of our evolution in the context of environment, climate, the Earth, and the universe. Chapters 2–6 deal with the major components of brain health and dispel knowledge about *how* and *why*. However, we are prone to developing silent diseases that include silent stroke, silent heart attacks, cryptogenic atrial fibrillation, insidious dementia; we may even deny our own disease or weakness (anosognosia), and the initial onset of frontotemporal dementia might be first apparent by excessive credit card use or behavior noticed only by the family (frontotemporal lobe dementia). This necessitates monitoring of our body functions, and this is the focus of chapter 7.

Acknowledgments

The singling out of individuals for thanks no doubt will leave out many others that were instrumental in my training and conceptualization of brain health and fitness, and for this I apologize in advance. The evolution of my thinking and ultimately this book is tribute to many friends and colleagues who helped me in my formative years. I was very fortunate to have Professor Phillip Tobias as my anatomy professor and dean of the medical school at the University of Witwatersrand. He taught us human anatomy from not one but three large books called man's anatomy parts 1, 2, and 3 and more importantly enkindled in his students a fascination for human origins that he was so famous for.

Professors Pierre Bill, John Cosnett of the University of KwaZulu Natal, Durban, for their patient and expert teaching in clinical neurology, guiding my early career development.

Professor John Robbs, head of surgery and vascular surgery, University of Kwa-Zulu Natal, Durban, for his enthusiastic support and promotion of my early forays into cerebrovascular medicine and helping form the Durban Cerebrovascular Group.

Professor Bill Pryse-Phillips helped land my first neurology job at Memorial University, Canada, while he researched and wrote his book *Neurology Dictionary*.

Professors JP Mohr and Ralph Sacco enthusiastically guided me through my stroke fellowship and instilled the fervor for computerized registry analyses, while at Columbia University, New York.

I am very fortunate to have the continued guidance and mentorship in cognitive neurology and cognitive neuroscience from Professor Frederick Schmitt of the Sanders Brown Aging Institute at the University of Kentucky and Professor Ken Heilman of University of Florida.

I am indebted to the ever-buoyant Professor Joseph Berger for assisting me with my neurological career in the USA.

I am grateful to Dr. Fiona Crawford and Dr. Michael Mullen for providing me with a platform for launching neuroarcheological seminars at the Roskamp Institute in Sarasota and promoting clinical cognitive neurology to flourish side by side with their high-level neuroscience research. Finally, I am grateful to Kamie Butler of Page Publishing, New York, who was exceptionally efficient and helpful, in shepherding this book into publication.

1

Our Brains Evolved, Attuned to Rhythms in the Natural World

The Concept of the Brain Beat

There is a beat, a rhythm, or a cycle to all living things. Our bodies have heartbeats. Our brains beat with a so-called heart beating at the center of the brain,[1] resulting in the growth of new brain cells (neurogenesis), the growth of connections between brain cells (synapses), triggered by activities and pruning of synapses during sleep. Circadian (day-night) rhythms determined by the brain's hypothalamus, in turn, are linked to the Earth's rotation and our evolutionary third eye, now transformed into the pineal gland, secretes soporofic (sleep-inducing) melatonin. This pulsing in the body and brain is intimately tied to the pulsing in the climate, the Earth's plate tectonic movement, in turn, engendered by the circulating inner magma, with continent movement and the Earth's movement around the sun according to the three different cycles, first described by Milankovitch (see below). The planet too has a heartbeat and an EKG, a term first coined by Neil Shubin in his book *The Universe Within Us*.[2] Even our solar system adheres to cycles within our galaxy, which in turn has correlations to comet and asteroid genesis.[3] Ultimately all these natural processes influence each other albeit with vastly different time frames. Not only does acknowledging our subservience to this pulsing convey health and vitality, but also, ultimately, these processes over millennia are what formed our own existence and caused us to evolve into the species *Homo sapiens*. Tracing the sequence of events takes us far back in time, but each leap in complexity has some message or relevance for healthy living today.

A fundamental part of being human is to question the cause of things that happen to us, or the environment, particularly those that are adverse. As an evolutionary adaptation, this would allow us to learn from the experience, preempt and be prepared with a strategy for avoiding future incidents. A primary objective of this book is based on the premise that "if you know how it's constructed, you might better know how to fix it." All living things are related to one another, and all are, in turn, influenced by the natural world rhythms, as well as those beyond, such as astrophysical forces (figure 1.1).

Fig. 1.1 Interrelationships

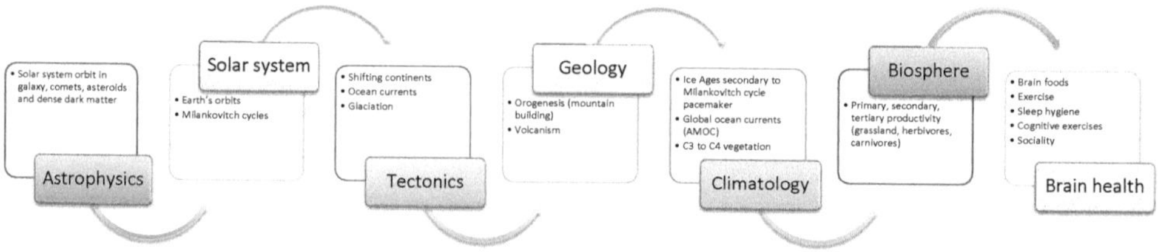

Although we cannot influence astrophysical or geological factors, a gradation exists from these more distant forces to those of the environment, to those of our biosphere, to our bodies, and ultimately to our minds. The closer we are to the inner circles, the more impact we have on our own health and vitality (figure 1.2).

Fig. 1.2 Natural rhythms

Ranges from direct control, encompassed by brain fitness components, to factors that made us human to no control at all

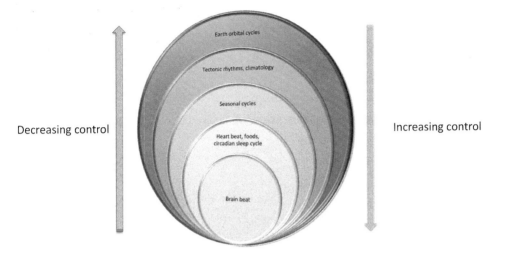

Whether currently considered brain healthy or not, we have a choice to improve or maintain the status quo (figure1.3).

Fig. 1.3 Your golden opportunity

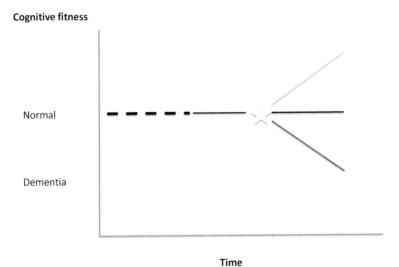

Few people have the time, commitment, or resources to pursue an optimally brain-healthy lifestyle, but that should not prevent us from losing sight of the ideal. Too often, once we incur ailments, medical interventions may include one or many medications, frequently for chronic use, and the underlying cause remains, leading to the Band-Aid effect (figure 1.4).

Fig. 1.4 The Band-Aid effect
Artwork by Todd Soper, concept and design by author

The challenge of convincing people to change in the face of symptoms, impending illness, or diagnostic certainty of dementia or other brain malady is formidable. Issuing a laundry list of dos and don'ts may work for some, but as a clinician it has long been apparent to me that conviction to change lifestyle choices comes with understanding the underlying reasons or the *why* question. Clinical medical education primarily addresses the how-to issue; rarely are discussions devoted or concerned with the why issue.

This book is about not only how but also *why* we are destined to pursue a particular mode of existence—why we need to exercise, eat certain foods, stimulate our brains, sleep fitfully, and socialize. It all relates to the various beats in our bodies and, in the broader sense, to the pulsing, ebbs and flows, not only of our bodies, but also of the natural world. The interconnectedness of these beats and rhythms too are important. The formation of the African Rift Valley, our place of origin, ten to five million years ago, transformed Eastern Africa from a flat landscape to one that is complex in topography, with mountains, valleys, and lakes. The increasing aridity, in turn, due to polar ice formation and secondary Indian Ocean monsoonal climate changes led to a drier East Africa, compounded by the influence of the Earth's orbital variations (see below). Together, this constellation of adversity factors led to the emergence of humans, one very likely hypothesis being the pulsed climate variability hypothesis expounded by Maslin et al.[4]

Piecing together this intricate web of interaction of the natural world and the evolution of life spans are many disciplines. Each has contributed major insights, and each has had the opportunity to catapult our evolutionary knowledge forward from time to time. Whether a neuroscientist, philosopher, or geneticist, every discipline has stumbled on to discoveries that place a decisive or critical piece in the puzzle (figure 1.5).

Fig. 1.5 Disciplines that interacted and contributed to the study of human evolution

Clinical; Neurology, Neurosurgery, Psychiatry, Psychology, Psychopharmacology, Speech/Language

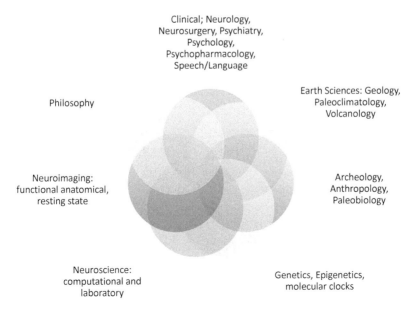

Clinical; Neurology, Neurosurgery, Psychiatry, Psychology, Psychopharmacology, Speech/Language

Philosophy

Earth Sciences: Geology, Paleoclimatology, Volcanology

Neuroimaging: functional anatomical, resting state

Archeology, Anthropology, Paleobiology

Neuroscience: computational and laboratory

Genetics, Epigenetics, molecular clocks

Neuroarcheology: From Fragments of Skull to Fragmented Behavior

So-called dirt archeologists excavate sites around the world—finding skulls, bones, and stone tools—and have arguably made the most significant contributions to human evolution (figure 1.6).

Fig. 1.6. Dirt archeology and cognitive archeology

Archeological unearthing of skulls such as *Sahelanthropus tchadensis* (left), the world's oldest man, approximately 7 million years old. Brain lesions decoupling brain circuits that hint at our evolutionary past (right).

Figure credit (left) with permission: Wood B. Hominid revelations from Chad. Nature 2002; 418:133–135.

 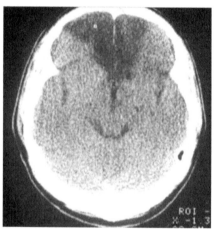

In 1924 Raymond Dart was credited with finding the missing link, embodied by a skull he found in Taung, Southern Africa. With a volume of 400–500 cc, the estimated brain size was comparable to a chimpanzee. However, the evidence of smaller canine teeth and the foramen magnum (skull and spinal cord junction) trajectory that was unmistakably more downward supported bipedalism. These features and the dry, savannah habitat location of the find, unsuited for present-day apes, all conspired to support the notion of bipedalism having occurred before an increase in brain size reflected by this specimen that he subsequently called *Australopithecus africanus*, or African Southern ape.[5] Frequently, only fragments of a skull, stone implements, or imprints are found, but much can be deduced and extrapolated. One of the more dramatic examples is represented by the fossilized Laetoli footprints discovered near the famous Olduvai gorge in northern Tanzania in 1978 by Mary Leakey, dated at 3.6 million years ago (mya). It again implied bipedality in our ancestral australopithecines. The well-preserved imprints are—thanks to one of many eruptions of the adjacent African Valley Rift volcano, Sadiman, with ash deposition blanketing the landscape on which the tracks were made, with subsequent hardening by a fortuitous episode of infrequent rainfall—covered by soil from the nearby river flooding and fossilized.[6] However, piecing together the apologue of human evolution is accredited to the contributions from many, sometimes disparate, disciplines. This includes neurology.

Brain Lesion and Behavior Analysis Formed the Basis of Neurology and Functioning of the Mind

The *neuro* part of *neuroarcheology* has been heavily invested in brain lesion studies. Such studies still steer neurological sciences today by rendering us brain areas that are necessary for certain functions. Although this has been complemented by functional MRI studies, these provide ancillary information in what participatory circuits are active with a particular function. The single case report by John Harlow of Phineas Gage's survival and marked behavioral impairment after a three-and-a-half-foot, one-inch-diameter tamping rod inadvertently traversed his frontal lobes in 1848 is one of the most cited cases in the neurosciences.[7] The traumatic brain injury studies by Luria and his meticulous studies and neuropsychological investigations helped launch the science that is at best only a few decades old, gaining momentum only by the 1980s.[8] Paul Broca's expressive aphasia, pathological study implicating the posterior, inferior frontal lobe in expressive speech, is another landmark lesion study.[9] Despite this, the study of brain function has been particularly challenging. People with frontal lobe damage rarely initiate clinical evaluation, and clinicians test what we have tests for. There are many behaviors and syndromes that may be associated with facetious, puerile, irascible, profane behavior or aspontaneity and lack of foresight, for which we have no tests.

My own fascination and contributions to the inner workings of the brain and their possible origination relate to the protean clinical presentations of the injured brain. The particular brain dysfunction presentation or fragmented behavior was chronicled by a young man who, during a hospital stay, imitated almost every action that occurred in front of him, much to the consternation of his physicians. The cause was an unusual bifrontal stroke as a complication of vasculitis (inflammation) of his brain arteries. He displayed a number of field-dependent behavioral syndromes that have since been labeled the environmental dependency syndrome, imitation behavior, and utilization behavior (figure 1.6).[10] During the same year, Professor Francois Lhermitte from France published his two-part series on the imitation behavior syndromes in neurology, which aptly described my patient.[11, 12] A specific frontal brain circuitry presumably had been lesioned, with resultant field-dependent behavior or stimulus-bound behavior as the predominant finding, with minimal accompanying neurological deficit. In essence, his mirror neuron circuitry had been affected, perhaps uncoupled, leaving him to unquestioningly imitate limb movements, facial expressions, and behaviors of those around him. The mirror neuron concept has been a relatively recent discovery and implicated in much of our higher cognitive function abilities, including theory of mind, language, praxis, and learning.[13] Being able to imitate dramatically reduces the time and energy associated with learning by trial and error. From an evolutionary point of view, the mirror neuron system (MNS) is deemed a versatile learning mechanism that ultimately translated into enhanced survival of early hominins. It is regarded as the system of brain networks that have made the greatest contributions to our cultural revolution. In Ramachandran's words, "The MNS will do for psychology what DNA has done for biology."[14] Arbib has since proposed a six-grade system of increasing complexity of the MNS in primate and hominid evolution, with stages 1–3, associated with primates and our last common ancestor and stages 4–6 presumed to have developed in the hominin line leading to modern humans.[15]

This so-called uncoupling of the MNS gives us unique insights into brain circuitry. In a follow-up study some twenty-five years later, a series of such patients (73 out of a larger series of 1,436 people with stroke) were studied with a wide range of presentations discovered. In essence, a loss of personal autonomy occurs and may take many forms. These are more fully elaborated in the publication but included imitation behavior (dutifully copying actions without being instructed to do so), utilization behavior (compulsion to fiddle with objects in immediate vicinity), echolalia (repeating of words or sentences spoken by others), environmental dependency syndrome (environmental cues causing stereotyped incongruous comportment and behavior), forced hyperphasia (compulsion to read out aloud road signs and other signboards), Zelig-like syndrome (adjust appearance or behavior to people they interact with to become acceptable to them), command-automatism and echopraxia to television (talking to actors while watching television and taking part in the discussion), and excessive television watching. In addition, the neuropsychiatric syndromes of obsessive-compulsive disorder and Tourette's syndrome are regarded as manifestations of field-dependent behavior impairment of the mirror neuron system.[16] Fortunately most people afflicted by the sudden onset of field-dependent behavior recover in days to weeks. This fracturing of the MNS by brain various lesions gives us some insights into human mind evolution. In primate and human evolution, increasing frontoparietal integration provided the foundation for the more elaborate mirror neuron system (MNS) circuitry, which, in turn, enabled conversion of visual information into knowledge. The mosaic cognitive evolution theory posits that this evolved in the general cognitive domains such as memory, attention, and also within specific cognitive domain hierarchies, represented by tool use and language.[17]

At the most anterior part of the brain, the frontopolar cortex (FPC) or Broca's area 10 (figure 1.7) is one of the few brain regions that is markedly enlarged in humans, compared to our closest primate relatives. The functions of the FPC are regarded as the most apical of all human cognitive qualities. The core functions of the FPC include the simultaneous considerations of a number of options or tasks to optimize output selection and the switching between internally and externally disposed thoughts. These data derive from functional magnetic resonance imaging studies and some from frontal lobe lesions in general.[18, 19]

Fig. 1.7. Brodmann areas, primary areas, unimodal and tertiary association areas

Red and blue areas depict primary motor and primary sensory areas such as tactile, visual, and auditory. Orange depicts supplementary motor areas and pale blue unimodal association areas. The white regions depict higher-order, heteromodal association areas or tertiary association areas.

Figure credit with permission from: Fuster JM. The Prefrontal Cortex. Philadelphia Lippincott Raven 1997.

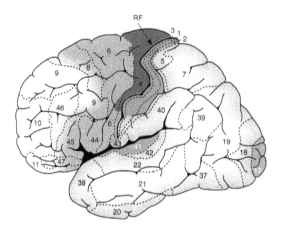

To date, the only isolated FPC lesion study reported was that of relatively young women whom I was consulted for a stroke syndrome, who incurred a small hemorrhage solely confined to this region (figure 1.8).

Fig. 1.8. Isolated frontopolar lesion (midline dark area) due to a discreet brain hemorrhage (red arrow)

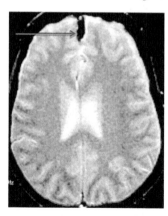

Extensive cognitive testing revealed no deficits other than emotional intelligence subtest score abnormalities. This supported the role of the medial FPC being a necessary component for the emotional processing of internal states.[20] The FPC is also the premise of metacognition or introspection, something we strongly suspect only humans are able to do. Such examples from brain lesion studies further our understanding of the highest cognitive function of human brain development and some of the key regions.

A brief survey of the accomplishments by the Earth and life sciences to date is pertinent. Each stage in the evolutionary tree informs us about something in our own body or what may have happened in prehistory or history. Sometimes it is merely a discovery of notable interest, such as that our diminutive middle ear bones were derived from the jaws of early fishes. Other times the information is more critical such as imparting insights and clues to diseases that we are grappling with today. These include the obesity, metabolic, cardiovascular, and dementia epidemics as well as mitochondrial diseases that date to prokaryote cells 3.5 billion years ago.

Setting the Stage: From Unicellular to Multicellular Life, from Molecular to Gravitational Forces, Migration from Waterto Land, and Remodeling from Small to Larger Brains the First Life-Forms Evolve

The age of the Earth is estimated at over 4.5 billion years, and life evolved on Earth approximately 3.8 billion years ago (bya); the first 500–700 million years are thought to have been "sterile" with ocean temperatures over 100 degrees Celcius. Early life probably evolved adjacent to hydrothermal systems, with the evolution of hyperthermophile (heat liking) organisms, termed the submarine alkaline hydrothermal theory for the emergence of life.[21] This underscores the hydrothermal heritage of our basic proteins and biochemical processes evolution that are part of the modern biological processes today. These were initially chemical and anoxygenic (not photosynthetic) and later became oxygen associated and photosynthetic with the replication of nuclei acids.[22, 23]

Unicellular organisms appeared at about 3.5 billion years ago (bya) with the most ancient cells (prokaryotes) containing circular, anuclear (no nuclear envelope), free-floating DNA and sixty-four possible codons, in turn accounting for the production of twenty amino acids for protein building. This indicates that the genetic code is redundant (many different codons can code for the same amino acid). Prokaryotes are usually considered unicellular organisms, but they can aggregate and exist in an amorphous (shapeless) mass, such as blue-green algae, slime molds that are present today. These are capable of cell-to-cell signaling.[24]

Complex Cells Evolve Followed by Multicellular Life-Forms (Metazoans)

With the advent of eukaryote cells about 1.7 bya, thanks to acquiring mitochondria powerhouses that generated ATP, we surmise, due to symbiosis with prokaryotes, acritarchs appeared. Acritarchs represent the remains of three forms of earliest life-forms—archaea, bacteria, and eukaryotes. This new ability of eukaryotic cells allowed change of shape and movement in response to the environment and represented a key evolutionary feature. Amoebae are representative of nature's simplest organisms. In response to stressors, dispersed amoebae may aggregate and communicate via cyclic AMP (which plays a crucial signaling role in us today), revealing how an existing life form today reveals the transition to unicellularity to multicellularity. By this time, the basic cell machinery that included ion channels, receptors, and neurotransmitters that is shared by all life forms were in place.[25]

The Ediacarans, which are spongy, matlike life-forms on the seabed, emerged about 585 million years ago (mya) only to vanish again around 542 mya. Multicellular life-forms (metazoans) appeared about 600 mya, having had to wait almost 3 by for an adequately formed oxygenated atmosphere. Today oxygen makes up 21% of the atmosphere but used to be only 0.001 % of the levels present today until the great oxygen event (GOE) 2.4–2.1 bya. Oxygen provided the impetus for building larger animal bodies. The emergence of oxygen-producing photosynthesis, the source of all oxygen in the atmosphere, allowed more energy expensive tissues, such as collagen, for building bigger bodies and neural tissue ultimately for bigger brains[26]

Multicellular Systems Evolve Symmetrical Forms and Elementary Nervous Systems

Not much happened until the receding glaciers that reached the equator during a period called snowball Earth, about 600 mya. Early metazoans (multicellular life) and the ancestral urbilaterian (worm-like, 1 cm long) represented the next step in animal evolution with the achievement of bilateral symmetry and cephalization (head formation). In addition, centralization of the nervous system occurred, evolving from the neural net-type arrangement of previous organisms such as the hydra. A nerve net is the simplest type of nervous system. In addition to a simple two-layer nervous system, consisting of a sensory and motor neuron, a third neuron layer was also present, an interneuron. This allowed increasing complexity of responses.[27] Existing in a marine environment roughly 600 mya, they had a basic nervous system with neurotransmitters and intracellular signaling present in our cells today.[28] Urbilaterians evolved into bilaterians, which gave rise to two major branches, the deuterostomes that included the chordates and subsequently lancelets (amphioxus), vertebrates and mammals and the protostomes that give rise to arthropods (insects) and flatworms and annelids.

The First Brain Evolves

The first true brain is represented by the extant amphioxus (lancelet forms), representing the origin of vertebrate forms, with a small anterior brain blister, a notochord, but without a backbone. The archetypal vertebrate was formed about 520 mya, with the notochord and dorsal nerve cord extending into the head where the nerve cord was slightly larger, a swelling, and regarded as the first true brain. During the early Cambrian period (541–485 mya), the overall structure of the vertebrate brain and neurotransmitter systems we have in common were shared with jawless fish. The missing link between jawless and jawed vertebrates is represented by Galeaspid (435–370 mya), an extinct, jawless, bony vertebrate, considered a precursor to jawed vertebrates. Tomographic study of their cranium revealed that they had twin nostrils instead of one. This feature implies that the development of the cranium of vertebrates was not associated with jaw development but occurred in steps with the rostrally extending mesenchyme growth that is representative of vertebrate cranial development currently appreciated.[29]

The development of myelin was a major event in evolution and set the foundation of our future human connectome. It was closely associated with development of jaws and complex head structures allowing predation to evolve.

Structures that gave an evolutionary advantage included a head, eyes, and rapid nerve conduction to control the body, which were functions associated with embryonic neural crest cells. These constituted some of the features that made vertebrates successful. The relatively small size of invertebrates, with unmyelinated nerve conduction velocities of around one meter per second sufficed. However, with an increase in size, much more rapid nerve conduction and reaction time was required, for effective predation and evasion. Hence, it is no surprise that myelin developed in step with jaw development and the neural crest, during the Devonian period first with the placoderms (including *Dunkleosteus*). Myelin enabled up to a one-hundred-fold increase in conduction velocity along nerve fibers at fifty to one hundred meters per second. Other advantages of myelinization of nerve fibers included more advantageous placement of sensory organs, such as the eyes enabled by longer optic nerves. In addition, a more com pact nervous system is possible because of the smaller size of nerve fibers, now feasible, together with improved metabolic efficiency due to more proficient nerve impulse propagation, which account up to 50% of the metabolic energy demands.[30] These become all the more important with larger brain size.

Placoderms were the first jawed fish and the first superpredators, evolved about 420 mya, one of which was *Dunkleosteus* (380–360 mya) (figure 1.9).

Fig. 1.9 Dunkleosteus terrelli

An apex predator with one of the most powerful bite forces in vertebrate history. The distinct four bar jaw linkages, depicted in the figure enabled both rapid opening of the jaws creating suction that expedited predation in addition to a bite force of about 5300 N, the greatest among all fossil and living fishes. Up to 36 ft long, weighing 4 tons and bite force of ~ 8,000 pounds per square inch, it was in a league with Tyrannosaurus Rex and Megalodon Image with permission: Andeslon PSL, Westneat MW. Feeding mechanics and bite force modelling of the skull of *Dunkleosteus terrelli*, an ancient apex predator. Biol Lett 2007; 3:76–79.

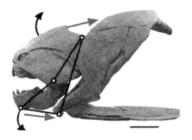

Dunkleosteus grew up to thirty-six feet in length, weighing up to four tons, rivaling the dimensions of the massive shark, megalodon, that appeared much later during evolution, surviving until about 1.5 mya.[31] The physical space constraints of vertebrates of a skull and vertebral column was overcome by the markedly increased speed of conduction due to myelination of nerve fibers and enabled a leap in the size of bodies.[32]

"Fishapods" Occupy the Terrestrial Environment and Several Major Extinctions Followed

Perhaps fish wars or the prospects of meeting up with Dunkeosteus prompted the move to land. *Panderichthys* (397 mya), *Tiktaalik* (375 mya), and *Acanthostega* (365 mya) were vertebrates with recognizable limbs, representing anatomical intermediates between the fishes with lobe-fins and the first terrestrial tetrapods. They were also termed "fishapods" by Neil Shubin, the discoverer of Tiktaalik.[33] The Hangenberg event was an anoxic period, which occurred at the end of the Devonian period (358 mya) associated with a rapid sea-level fall, due to Southern Hemisphere glaciation.[34] Romer's gap refers to the subsequent void in the tetrapod fossil record ranging from 360–345 mya, blamed on massive extinctions of the Hangenberg event. This was responsible for the disappearance of primitive and armored fishes such as the placoderms, *Dunkleosteus, Panderichthys*, and *Tiktaalik*.[35, 36] After this gap, domination by the ray-finned fish (including sharks) occurred and another wave of amphibians invaded land. However, the most devastating of all extinctions occurred about 252 mya, termed the Permian-Triassic extinction event, obliterating approximately 96% of marine and about 70% of terrestrial vertebrates. The cause was attributed to the massive volcanic eruption of the Siberian traps, a large continental size area of land of about 7 million km² covered in basaltic lava. Life on Earth took about 30 million years to recover where after, archosaurs (reptiles) evolved, that ultimately gave rise to dinosaurs, pterosaurs, birds, and crocodiles.[37] Mammal-like reptiles, called synapsids, were the dominant terrestrial vertebrates during the Permian period (299–251 mya), most of which died during the Permian-Triassic extinction except for Lystrosaurus, which survived in most parts of the world. Mammals and dinosaurs evolved at approximately the same time during the Triassic period (251–199 mya).[38] However, the Archosaurs became dominant during this time, perhaps due to more rapid limb development compared to the synapsids and better at water conservation, allowing them to tolerate the aridity associated with the ancient continent of Pangea at the time.[39]

The Jurassic Period: A Two-Hundred-Million-Year Subsequent Dinosaur Dominance with Palm Trees in Antarcticaand Mammals Small, Insignificant, and Nocturnal

During the Jurassic period (201–145 mya), the Earth looked very different with the continents all clumped together in masses called Gondwanaland in the south and Laurasia in the north, separated by the ancient Tethys Sea, with the rifting apart from the ancient supercontinent Pangea, preceded by the earliest acknowledged continents, Rodinia and Panotia. This configuration was associated with a tropical climate evidenced by the most common terrestrial vertebrate at the time, Lystrosaurus, a reptilian lizard whose fossils have been found in most continents, including Antarctica. The physiology of Lystrosaurus is thought to have allowed it to survive the major

Permian-Triassic extinction event with markedly elevated CO_2 levels and so become the dominant species.[40] Tropical trees and palms were also recovered in fossilized form in Antarctica. Accruing information has portrayed the dinosaurs as extraordinarily successful, their 200-million-year reign notwithstanding, that was terminated by something catastrophic, thought to be an asteroid impact sixty-six million years ago, itself in turn perhaps coupled to the 35-million-year comet cycle.[41] One reason for the dinosaur success may been their unique ability, at least at the time of their existence, to be mesothermic, or in between mammalian endothermy (self-regulate body temperature) and reptilian ectothermy (body temperature regulated by the environment). This ability, it is presumed, enabled dinosaurs to grow to their enormous size and body mass, requiring lower energy costs in the much more tropical environment. This capability may have allowed them to outcompete both ectothermic and endothermic animals.[42, 43]

Mammals Evolved During This Time, but They Were Small, Used Smell and Hearing Rather Than Vision, Were Nocturnal, and Developed Their Crucial SixLayer Cortex and Enlarged Brain (figure 1.10)

Fig. 1.10. Key innovation of mammals: the six-layer neocortex and comparison to fish, amphibian, and reptile cortices
Abbreviation: P pallium, which refers to both paleocortex or neocortex. With permission from: Fuster JM. The Prefrontal Cortex. Philadelphia Lippincott Raven 1997 and von Bonin G. Essays on the cerebral cortex of man. Charles C Thomas, Springfield Illinois, 1948.

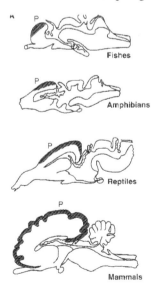

The mammalian lineage (synapsida) diverged from other reptilian tetrapods in the Carboniferous about 300 mya. These early cynodonts possessed low level hearing and olfaction (smell), poor vision, only coarse tactile reactivity, relatively crude motor coordination. Notably, their brains had relatively sparse representation for the sensorimotor integration circuitry seen in later mammals, primates, and humans. Mammalia arose in or before the early Jurassic about 200 mya, and one of the first mammals recognized, Morganucodon, featured increased olfactory resolution and improved tactile sensitivity that stemmed from body hair. In addition, there was improved sensorimotor coordination, reduced middle ear ossicle size that remained attached to the lower jaw, and a prolonged cochlea (hearing organ).

Further, brain enlargement was primarily due to olfactory enhancement, represented by Hadrocodium (~150 mya). In addition, the middle ear ossicles were now detached from the lower jaw, and the cerebellum and spinal cord enlargement indicated augmented further sensorimotor integration. Advanced sensorimotor integration denotes the foundation of the future circuitry for higher cortical functions seen in humans.

A third pulse of mammalian evolution represented by the crown mammalia was also driven by increasing olfactory enlargement, ossified ethmoid turbinals that allowed a tenfold increase in the nasal cavity olfactory epithelium. Aside from olfaction, hearing and sensorimotor integration, other drivers for increased encephalization (brain enlargement) and origin of the neocortex included feeding habits (insectivory), miniaturization, viviparity, elevated metabolism, and milk. Early mammals possessed fur (evolved from hair initially used for tactile function), implying they were also endothermic and partook in parental care. Mammalian hair would later be expected for the evolution of fur and pelts that would be critical for the subsequent cooling of the planet and glacial cycles. Endothermy was likely consequent to the high metabolism required by a larger brain.[44]

The Catastrophic KT Event (Cretaceous Tertiary) Allowed Mammals to Become Diurnal and Proliferate in the Aftermath of Dinosaur Near Extinction

Although some controversy remains, an asteroid impact is the most likely cause of the KT event about 66 mya, suggested by the discovery of the underwater Chicxulub crater in the Gulf of Mexico. Geological evidence bolstered this find by the discovery worldwide of a band of iridium (typical of asteroids but rare on Earth) that can be found throughout the world in terrestrial and marine rock strata.[45] The ensuing global climactic perturbations caused by the ash, sulphuric acid, dust, and other aerosols ejected into the atmosphere, blocking the solar radiation for an estimated several decades causing an impact winter. This has since been termed the Alvarez bolide impact theory.[46]

However, it is also possible that massive volcanic eruptions of the Deccan traps (akin to the Siberian traps and the Permian Triassic extinction) in India with superplume effects were responsible. These erupted over a period of several millions of years and may correlate better with the temporal sequence of events of the more gradual dinosaur extinction process over the twenty million years before the KT event.[47, 48] A combination of the bolide (meteor) impact as well as Deccan trap eruptions is also a current consideration of the KT event. These events, or event, led to the extinction of approximately 75% of animal and plant life, including all nonavian dinosaurs. The branch of dinosaurs that pursued miniaturization (as mammals did previously), over the last 200 mya, about 50 million years before the evolution of the first bird fossil find, archaeopteryx, survived. These dinosaur survivors led to the further evolution of birds and flight evolution. The main impetus for smaller size, which is a requirement for arboreal habitation, were the niche opportunities of both food and safety, similar to that which ancestral primates would pursue about 100 million years later. Instead of fur, these dinosaurs developed feathers for insulation and allowed nocturnal living that would later be elaborated to permit flight.[49, 50]

Although at least four orders of mammals had started to diversify before this impact, rapid mammalian diversification occurred in the millions of years after the impact with the earliest ancestral primate, Archicebus Achilles, dating to about 55 mya.[51]

Primates Evolve and Develop Trichromatic Color Vision, Stereoscopic Vision, Prehension, and Further Sensorimotor Integration

A very warm period about fifty-five million years ago termed the Paleocene-Eocene thermal maximum (PETM) was associated with extensive tropical forests covering most of the early continents, including Antarctica. The cause of this particularly warm period is not clear, but a leading contender is methane release perhaps from the seafloor, or methane clathrate eruption, a more potent greenhouse gas than carbon dioxide.[52] Toward the end of the Cretaceous period (145–66 mya) after several radiations, angiosperms became dominant over cycads, ferns, and large canopy configuration trees.[53] This near-global arboreal environment and the available fruit, thanks to the angiosperm (produce seeds, flowers, and fruit) evolution, provided a new environmental niche opportunity. Primate evolution over the last fifty-five million years molded the brain by virtue of a high-quality diet due to frugivory (fruit eating). Vision became the predominant sense, necessitated by the need for stereoscopic, three-dimensional, and color vision in the arboreal environment. Vision replaced olfaction as the principal sense organ, and trichromatic color vision was selected for by some primates, specifically those that inhabited Africa (catarrhines) and to a lesser extent those in South America (platyrrhines). The Madagascan primates (strepsirrhines—lemurs and lorises) remained with poor color vision. Lynne Isbell proposed the snake detection theory, which correlates with an evolutionary advantage endowed by excellent color vision, for detection of the patterning and coloring typically associated with poisonous snakes. She posited that the numerous poisonous snakes in Africa, less so in South America and nonexistent in Madagascar, accounts for this variation. Modern primates therefore redeveloped trichromatic color vision that had been lost by the early nocturnal mammals.[54] The eyes became more frontally situated for improved stereoscopic and depth perception, useful in the three-dimensional arboreal environment. The predominantly arboreal (tree-dwelling) nature of these primates with grasping extremities that featured nails rather than claws further honed their sensorimotor circuits in our brain that would later be adapted for other complex brain functions such as working memory and language, as well as our dietary, sleep, and physical exercise requirements. With vision the dominant sense, but concentrated on the frontal fields, with restriction of the lateral and posterior fields of vision, predation from behind, was perhaps partly solved by living in groups. Other primate brain developments different to their mammalian ancestors included a doubling in brain size attributed to their complex social life requiring facial expression, eye signal detection, and emotion perception as well as the high-quality diet afforded by eating fruit.

The best preserved, primitive, primate fossil ever found, *Darwinius masillae*, dated to 47 mya ("Ida"), was from the Messel Pit (maar lake) in Germany due to remarkably unique environmental circumstances. A maar lake forms when either hot magma or volcanic lava below the lake forms chimneys that occasionally disgorge CO_2 through the subterranean layers that kill animals or birds that might be flying over the lake or residing nearby trees, dying immediately and preserved in the depths of oxygen-deprived water. Subsequently, in this particular circumstance, there was coating by iron carbonate, which forms a thin protective layer that preserves even fine detail, including colors. A similar modern-day example occurred in northwest Cameroon in 1986 where Lake Nyos emitted a CO_2 cloud that killed 1,700 people and 3,500 domestic animals.[55]

These are called limnic eruptions, due to CO_2 building up in the lakes. A solution currently pursued in Cameroon and other West African lakes (Lakes Nyos, Kivu, and Monoun) involves the insertion of siphons that allow the degassing of the lake.[56]

Evolution of the Mind Takes Off: General Intelligence and Social Intelligence Develop

General Intelligence (Learning from Experience as Opposed to Hardwired Behavioral Responses)

The three-dimensional forest environment (spatial dimension), the flowering plants and their fruit offerings, the timing of fruit ripeness (a temporal dimension) were challenges that faced one of the earliest primates, *Purgatorius* (pleasiadapiform), 65 mya. This species was associated with a general increase in brain size and presumably general intelligence, which increased to more than predicted for body size, which is correlated with being able to learn from experience. Notharctus (a lemur-like mammal) at 50 mya had elongated fingers and the development of a thumb for more precise gripping onto branches, indicating further sensorimotor development. Aegytopithecus at 35 mya and *Proconsul* (23 mya) were subsequently represented by fossil finds with overall further increase in body and brain size, particularly *Proconsul*, who may have even reached a modern human body size. *Proconsul* had notable features of old-world monkeys and apes but lacking a tale. The increase in both general intelligence and evolution of social intelligences were associated with a reproductive advantage.[57, 58]

The Body Changed Before the Brain: Bipedalism Came Before an Increase in Brain Size

There was a dearth of fossils in the late Oligocene period (30–23 mya) and until 4.5 mya attributed to global cooling and drying. Australopithecines were now widespread and pursued a joint arboreal and terrestrial lifestyle, yet brain size remained stable. It remains uncertain why the escalating brain size halted, for about two million years, during the Australopithecine period, a characteristic that is termed evolutionary stagnation. The skeletal fossil finds of Lucy (*Australopithecus afarensis*) of a widened pelvis, slightly valgus knee-joint angle, the presence of foot arches as well as the Tanzanian Laetoli fossilized footprints all indicate that bipedalism had developed, but their brain size at 450 cc remained similar to that of an extant chimpanzee.[59] Perhaps the profusion of large African predators at the time (sabertoothed cats, dinofelis) forced this dual habitation of both the arboreal and terrestrial habitat. This changed relatively abruptly (punctuated) due to an Ice Age at about 2.4 mya. Not only did global cooling result in increased aridity in the equatorial regions, but also the instability of the African tectonic plate and the African Rift Valley (ARV) formation 10–5 mya made the East African climate particularly unstable. For example, the eastern fault mountain ranges prevented moisture-laden air from the Indian Ocean from traversing over Eastern Africa, with consequent aridity. Stable climates and environments were associated with minimal evolutionary changes. Importantly these precipitous climate changes were correlated with evolutionary surges in mammalian species, most particularly the hominids, which Elizabeth Vrba termed the "principal engine of evolutionary change and forcing agent of speciation" in her turnover pulse hypothesis.[60]

In contradistinction to unstable environments, stable environments may maintain the status quo. The most extreme evidence we have of evolutionary stasis is the recent discovery of sulfur cycling fossil bacteria almost 2 billion years old! These were discovered by Shopf et al. in the Western Australian Turee Creek Group.[61]

Extreme climate variability occurred three times during the last three million years, which has been assigned to orbital forcing (the Earth axis wobbling and orbital-shape Milankovitch cycles). This coincided with Ice Ages waxing and waning, in addition to the occurrences of stadials (colder temperatures during interglacial warm periods) and interstadials (warmer temperatures during an Ice Age). More specifically these three periods were consonant with the following:

1. Intensification of the Northern Hemisphere glaciation at about 2.7 mya
2. The onset of the Walker circulation at about 2 mya
3. The mid-Pleistocene revolution about 1 mya (see below) [62]

The Periods of Severe Climactic Change and Adversity in the Last Three Million Years Were Associated with Human Brain Enlargement (figure 1.11)

Fig. 1.11. Hominin proliferation, brain enlargement, and Ice Ages

Figure credit with permission: deMenocal PB, Bloemendal J. Plio-Pleistocene Climatic Variability in Subtropical Africa and the Paleoenvironment of Hominid Evolution: A Combined Data-Model Approach. In: Vrba ES, Denton GH, Partridge TC, Burckle LH (eds). Paleoclimate and Evolution with Emphasis on Human Origins. Yale University Press, New Haven, 1995

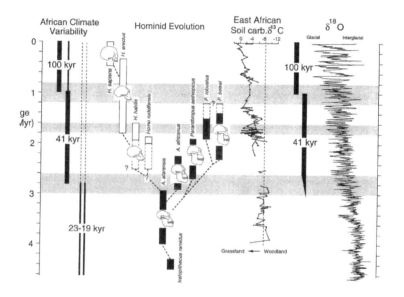

Global tectonic changes ultimately resulted in first Antarctic and more recently Arctic glaciation (see below). The Walker circulation is a Pacific Ocean wind and water phenomenon, whereby the western Pacific is relatively moist and warmer with resulting low pressure. This, in turn, draws surface trade winds to blow from the drier, cooler eastern Pacific, which return west to east, higher up in the atmosphere. When this circulation is relatively strong, it is termed a La Niña phase. Periodic weakening of this pressure gradient occurs, whereby warm water spreads east, resulting in an El Niño phase, with widespread global weather system ramifications such as droughts, flooding, and tropical storms in various parts of the world.

Climatically, the mid-Pleistocene transition represented a shift to more extensive Northern Hemisphere ice cover at approximately

920 kya. Proposed responsible mechanisms include a change in dominance of the 41 ky Milankovitch to the 100 ky year periodicity.[63]

Brain size (in cubic centimeters, cc) increased from *Australopithecus* (~450) to *Homo erectus* (~850), to *Homo heidelbergensis* (~1100), Neanderthal man (~1500 cc), and *Homo sapiens* (~1350) (figure 1.12).

Fig. 1.12. Brain size (cc): Australopithecus **(~450),**
Homo erectus **(~850),** Homo sapiens **(~1200)**
Gibbons A. Food for thought. Did the first cooked meals
help fuel the dramatic evolutionary expansion of the
human brain? Science 2007; 316:1558–1560.
Figure credit with permission: Klein RG. The Human Career
3rd ed. University of Chicago Press, Chicago 2012.

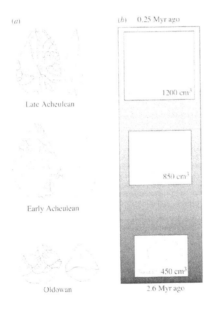

The following are factors associated with increase in brain size

1.   Bipedalism
2.   Running
3.   Meat diet
4.   Smaller gut
5.   Cooking

This has been attributed to a sequence of events that started with bipedalism, the development of endurance running, and an increased meat diet from about 2.5 mya onward. At 1.9 mya *Homo erectus*, with both larger body and brain but smaller gut and teeth, has been associated with archeological evidence of mechanical (stone tools) and chemical (fire and cooking of foods) processing of food, both of which allow for a higher-quality diet.[64]

Evolution of the Different Intelligences: Technical, Procedural Memory, Visuospatial Working Memory, Conceptual Thought

Early technical abilities have been deduced from the archeological finds to date. For example, the more primitive stone tools found in Eastern Africa (Oldowan gorge), termed flakes, indicate the initial development of basic sensorimotor (parieto-frontal) coordinated activities, primarily in the dorsal stream of the visual system that assists in the control of actions. These were brain areas involved in the pounding of rocks to produce the initial flakes, about 2.6 mya.[65] There was also an overall reduction of the visual area at the expense of parietal cortex relative to chimpanzees during this time of the australopithecines, evidenced by a posterior excursion of the lunate sulcus.[66]

Later Technical Intelligence Development: The Dorsal and Ventral Visual Streams Are Further Developed

The subsequent manufacture of more sophisticated stone tools such as the symmetrical blades, or hand axes, implicated further development. These included the dorsal visual stream that mediates visuospatial and visuomotor abilities, ventra visual stream with the left posterior temporal region, the site of knowledge of tool use at the semantic level. In addition, the left posterior-inferior parietal lobule, the region for stored motor programs, were engaged.[67]

An approximate sequence of events is proposed as follows:

1. *Homo erectus* (1.9 MYA)

Stone tool knapping and the manufacture of hand axes may be correlated with procedural memory and conceptual thought development. In addition, there is evidence for visuospatial and visuomotor abilities (parietal) and shape identification (temporal lobe) development. Complex tool use places demands on both the ventral and dorsal visual pathway streams that convey object dimensional data (object recognition and semantic knowledge) and visuomotor ability respectively. Neuroimaging studies with PET scans has shown that complex tool use engages a more extensive network of the prefrontal (action planning and execution), inferior parietal (motor programs for tool use), posterior temporal (semantic knowledge of tools) network, bilaterally, but predominantly of the left hemisphere primarily.[68] This praxis circuit for toolmaking and tool use is considered to have formed the basis of the neural circuitry that would later be accepted for language development.[69]

As a motor task, the more elementary stone knapping requires coordination of the parietal spatial, dorsal pathway, and shape appreciation, the ventral temporal lobe pathway. This was achieved through procedural memory in *Homo erectus*, whose artifacts remained unchanged for about 1 mya. There was no innovation or creativity, which are both considered integral to advanced working memory capacity. *Homo erectus* is thought to have learned by direct observation and emulated the sequences and then incorporated these into procedural memory rather than episodic memory, which developed later.[70]

2. *Homo heidelbergensis/rhodesiensis*(~500 KYA)

The discovery of the exquisitely preserved wooden Shoeningen spears dated to 400 kya supported a postulated improvement in the visuospatial sketchpad component of working memory (WM) as well as further improvements in complex technical ability. *Homo heidelbergensis* is also attributed with symbolic thinking (they buried their dead with pink quartzite 300 kya), and their bigger brains were mostly due parietal lobe expansion and increase in globularity, which facilitated intracerebral connectivity (figure 1.13).[71]

Fig. 1.13. Parietal lobe (left figure) expansion and increased globularity enabled improved intracerebral connectivity.
This began with *Homo heidelbergensis* who had bigger brains than *Homo erectus* and became even more obvious with modern humans (CroMagnons) when compared to the less globular brain of Neanderthals.
Figure (right) credit with permission: Klein RG. The Human Career 3rd ed. University of Chicago Press, Chicago 2012

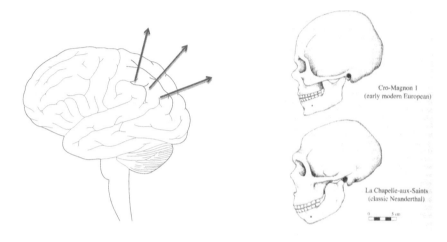

3. Neanderthals (500–30 KYA)

Further technical intelligence ability is evidenced by archeological finds such as the invention of hafting, which was a significant technological advance. Hafting involves taking two or more separate elements such as bone or stone and attached a handle device to form a single weapon that improves that weapon's capability. However, despite this technical advance, Neanderthals likely did not have shared attention and theory of mind (TOM), which suggests no modern language, no significant working memory enhancement, and no episodic memory formation.[72] Bruner's endocast research supports primarily parietal lobe expansion resulting in a more globular brain in *Homo sapiens*, compared to Neanderthals with no obvious frontal lobe differences, termed an evolutionary stasis of the frontal lobes.[73, 74]

Modern Human Intelligences: Enhanced Working Memory (EWM), Executive Function (EF), and Episodic Memory (EM)

Working Memory

Enhanced working memory capability forged the semblance of the modern mind. Although there was a reduction in brain volume of about 9% in *Homo sapiens* compared to Neanderthals, an overall corticocortical connectivity took place. EWM is integral to attention, language, inhibition, theory of mind, episodic memory, autonoesis (subjective experience of time), fluid intelligence (novel problem solving), and mental time travel. Working memory is thought to have undergone progressive expansion, and the leap to enhanced working memory may have been due to a microcephalin 1 gene mutation. Microcephalin 1 regulates brain size.[75]

Other important gene candidates in molecular evolution as they relate to human cognition include the following:

1. FOXP2—improves speech and language capabilities
2. RNF213—improves blood supply (primate brain) to brain, increased intelligence
3. MYH16—protein involved in jaw muscle reduction allowing brain expansion
4. ASPM—gene implicated in human brain expansion
5. CDK5RAP2—gene involved in neuronal differentiation CENJP—cytoskeletal gene involved in brain expansion
6. SRGAP2—gene that speeds up neural migration and forming more connections
7. AMY1—salivary amylase enables improved starch ingestion
8. HACNS1—forepaw activation, possible opposable thumb development in humans
9. PCDH11X and PCDH11Y—genes associated with laterality
10. USF1—gene controls a transcription factor that regulates synaptic plasticity, neuronal survival, and differentiation. Also involved in the transcriptional machinery of APOE.

11. RUNX2—controls closure of cranial sutures, clavicle, rib cage, and dental development

12. DLX1—controls skull morphology, thalamic development, and connectivity

13. DLX2—controls thalamic connectivity with neocortical regions, craniofacial development

14. DLX5/DLX6—skull and brain development, neuronal migration, forebrain GABA ergic neurons

15. BMP2—skull development, differentiation of GABA and dopamine neurons, astrocyte generation

16. BMP7—skull and brain development, osteogenesis, mutations associated with learning disabilities

17. DISP1—key component of thalamic development, positive selection in humans

18. MEF2A—increase in mRNA of synaptic genes especially in prefrontal cortex, thalamus

19. TSC1—involved in thalamocortical circuitry development, mutations lead to tuberous sclerosis, epilepsy

20. OTX2—thalamic development, abnormalities associated with language disorder and bipolar disorder.[76, 77]

Notwithstanding the above important, so far known genetic alterations that enabled the human mind and body, there has been an overly protein centric view in the fields of cell biology, molecular biology and genetics. The human genome contains ~20,000 genes for protein coding that is similar in number to the nematode *Caenorhabiditis elegans*, with ~1000 somatic cells, also has ~20,000 protein coding genes, similar to that in the human who have approximately 10^{14} somatic cells. In contrast, the nonprotein-coding DNA regions increase as the complexity of the organism does, and these regions occupy a staggering 98.8% of the genome in humans. These sequences are transcribed into nonprotein-coding RNAs (ncRNA) that number several hundred thousand. The major function of these ncRNAs is in the regulation of epigenetic processes. Primates in particular have evolved plasticity within RNA regulatory networks, particularly in the brain. Therefore, in addition to genetic information being transcribed into mRNA and proteins, it may also be transacted by this ncRNA system in many other ways. A marked increase has been shown to have occurred) in the intensity of RNA editing in humans as compared to the mouse, estimated at ~35% increase.

Most of the information human genome, therefore, is now considered to be contained within these complex regulatory processes. Mattick proposed that a more appropriate view of the genome may be that DNA can be regarded as a kind of hard drive, proteins as the analog effectors and RNA the operating system.[78]

The increase in the association cortical areas, particularly the prefrontal cortex is regarded as a pivotal development in cognition in humans. Not so much the size of the brain but the evolution of the extensive cortical networks (~100 000 miles of fiber tracts) is considered the key factor in human cognition.[79] The synapse is a central component in these networks and synaptopathies are integral to many different brain diseases (dementia, schizophrenia, autism). The micro-RNA (miRNA) effects at the synapse include synapse maturation, dendritic modeling, and arborization and may be viewed as a kind of fine tuning of the gene expression systems. As each individual mRNA has up to several hundred different miRNAs, which, in turn, fine-tune hundreds of genes, there exists profound potential in the treatment of these complex brain diseases through miRNA control.

Some examples of the diverse micro-RNA (miRNA) and target mRNA interactive systems include the following:

1. miR 134—dendritic spine maturation and cytoskeletal formation
2. miR 284—glutamate receptor subunit composition
3. miR 132—circadian rhythm and transcription
4. miR 9—alcohol tolerance
5. miR 219—NMDA receptor signaling and schizophrenia 80.

The current working memory model is based on Baddeley's model, which could also be termed working attention and includes a central executive, an episodic buffer, a phonological loop and visuospatial store.[81] The phonological loop is concerned with acoustic information, and its evolution is regarded as key to language acquisition enabling temporary acoustic storage. The visuospatial sketchpad is concerned with visual information such as locations and shapes of objects. Working memory and executive functions are embodied in five frontal-subcortical circuits that course between the prefrontal cortices, basal ganglia, thalamus, and circuit back to the PFC.[82] Although the individual constituents of the modern human mind evolved at different times over the last two to three million years (table 1.1), the last component was probably working memory. Wynn and Coolidge have proposed that the final enhancement of WM took place about thirty thousand years BP.[83]

The modern human mind trajectory departed from their closest ancestors *Homo heidelbergensis* and Neanderthals (*HH* and N) with allometric enlargement of the parietal cortex and a more globular brain about 200 kya. EWM expansion followed sometime after 50 kya that led to more advanced executive function ability. Working memory in humans has been graded at a level 7 compared to a level of 2 in chimpanzees, *Pan paniscus*. The underlying calculations for this gradation utilized both direct and indirect methods. Nut cracking, regarded as a capability of manipulating three objects (nut, stone, anvil), is an ability that most chimpanzees (about three quarters) are not able to perform, even though chimpanzees perceive each other's attempts. Because of them being able to perform only a two-step procedure, they are awarded grade 2 working memory level by Read et al. Comparison to human children, using several studies of verbal, imitation, and visuospatial abilities implies that at the age of three to four years children have a working memory level of 2, and at age twelve they attain a grade of 7.[84–87]

Executive Function

Executive functions include a wide array of supervisory cognitive abilities but can be simplified by considering core features. These include initiation of action or behavior, inhibition of action or behavior, monitoring of activities, abstraction, attention, planning, being cognizant of the temporal sequence of events and emotional self-regulation. Neurobiologically these are embodied in the five recognized frontal-subcortical circuits that impart the following:

1.   Executive function—temporal organization of information, contingency planning – dorsolateral prefrontal cortex – striatum – thalamus – cortex (figure 1.14)

Fig. 1.14. Orbitofrontal subcortical circuit

Legends: OFC - orbitofrontal cortex, DLPFC - dorsolateral prefrontal cortex, C - corpus callosum, VS - ventral striatum, DS - dorsal striatum, GP - globus pallidus, T - thalamus, A - amygdala

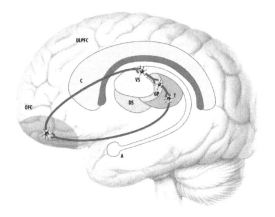

2.   Motivation and attentional aspects of behavior (central executive component of WM)—dorsal anterior cingulate cortex – striatum – thalamus – cortex

3.   Empathic and socially appropriate behavior—medial orbitofrontal cortex subgenual anterior cingulate gyrus – nucleus accumbens – thalamus to cortex

4.   Impulsivity/compulsivity control—lateral orbitofrontal cortex – caudate – thalamus – cortex

5.   Motor circuitry—oculomotor (frontal eye fields BA 8) and preparatory premovement circuits that originate in the supplementary motor cortex (BA 6) – striatum-thalamus – cortex.

These frontal subcortical circuits have connections to other cortical regions that include (1) dorsolateral prefrontal cortex DLPFC to parietal; (2) anterior cingulate to specific temporal lobe areas such as the hippocampus, amygdala, and entorhinal cortex; (3) medial orbitofrontal cortex to temporal lobe; and (4) lateral orbitofrontal cortex to tertiary association sensory cortex.[88] These circuits form the basis of conditions that are today recognized as psychiatric disorders such as obsessive-compulsive disorders, bipolar disease, depression, anxiety, Tourette's, attention-deficit hyperactivity as well as many neurological disease states.

Theory of Mind

The mirror neuron systems (MNS) is regarded as a plausible framework for a number of our higher cognitive function faculties such as praxis, language, and learning from others. Arbib has proposed a succession of progressively more complex MNS networks evolving to explain our cognitive developments, in particular language. His seven-stage extended mirror neuron system hypothesis includes stage 1–3 occurring within primates leading to our last common ancestor (LCA) and stages 4–7 incorporating the stage from the LCA to modern humans:

- i. Grasping
- ii. Mirror system for grasping
- iii. Simple imitation (shared with chimpanzees but not macaques)
- iv. Complex imitation (beyond chimpanzees)
- v. Protosign (key innovation, open repertoire)
- vi. Protospeech (key innovation, neocortical vocal control via collateralization)
- vii. Modern language[89]

Fig. 1.15. The brain, mind, cognitive evolution sequence

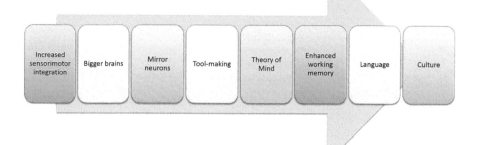

Beyond Executive Function— Metacognition

Metacognition refers to the human ability of introspection and ability to arbitrate with respect to our own judgments and is a function of the frontopolar cortex (BA 10) (figure 1.16).

Fig. 1.16. The frontopolar Cortex (BA10) and related frontal regions

Figure credit with permission: Petrides M. The middorsolateral prefrontal parietal network and epoptic process. In: Stuss DT, Knight RT. Principles of Frontal Lobe Function. Oxford University Press, Oxford, 2012.

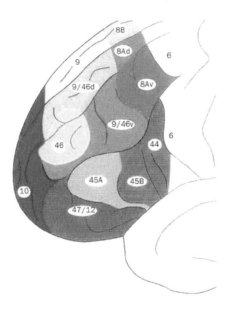

Important changes in the frontal lobes during human evolution included elaboration of BA10 and 13, white matter density, and spindle cells. BA10 is twice as large in humans compared to any of the other great apes, and BA13 is relatively reduced in humans. The neuronal density of the important BA10 and 13 in humans are about half (human BA10 ~32,000, chimpanzee 60,000 neurons per cubic millimeter). This neuropil (axons, dendrites, glial cells) increase in BA10 relates to increased connectivity with other cortical regions.[90] Spindle cells in BA10, frontoinsular cortex, and anterior cingulate cortex occur only in humans, African great apes, and cetaceans and are ~ 30% more abundant in the right hemisphere.[91]

Archeological evidence for the oldest evidence of modern executive function include animal traps, foraging activity (managing food supplies, agriculture), and more complex, reliable weapon manufacture (hafting, harpoons) dating to ~18000 kya. The earliest reliable archeological evidence of abstract reasoning as a form of executive function is represented by the therianthropic (animal and human figure combinations) figurine discovered in Southern Germany, Hohlenstein-Stadel, about 32,000 years ago, called the *Lion Man*. The figurine comprises of a man's body with a lion's head and is representative of form of abstraction, perhaps, related to existential contemplations (figure 1.17).[92]

Fig. 1 17. The most compelling artifact ever found, the Hohlenstein Stadel figurine: the Lion Man, **Upper Paleolithic Period (40,000–35,000 years before present), considered the oldest evidence for modern executive function.**

Figure credit with permission: Photographer Yvonne Mühleis, copyright, Ulmer Museum, Stadt Ulm, Germany.

Episodic Memory—Enabled Mental Time Travel

Tulving has proposed that imagination of future scenarios has been an impelling force in episodic memory evolution. *Autonoesis* is a term he introduced to refer to the human ability to become aware of time-stamping events, which then allows contemplation of the past and future. The ability to ponder future events is considered to underlie the concept of mental time travel.[93] The overlap of working memory and episodic memory may be represented by the episodic buffer component of working memory. In the episodic buffer, attention allows long-term memory traces and image assembly. Shepard argued that semantic memory accumulation on its own would not have sufficed to further and allow progress in human knowledge, and he proposed the need of so-called thought experiments that would then be followed by real-time rendition.[94] Through the recall of episodic memories, this allows simulation of future scenarios and autonoesis (mental time travel), which has survival value. The episodic buffer proposed by Baddeley and episodic memory (which has both long- and short-term components) have an important relationship that awaits more precise delineation. The episodic buffer is seen as the principal route by which the central executive retrieves long-term memories. Various episodic memories that may constitute visuospatial, phonological, or other long-term traces are assembled in the episodic buffer, with the help of attention, provided by working memory. Theories about what may have precipitated this change include a fortuitous epigenetic event or genetic mutation that impacted the episodic buffer.[95] As Coolidge and Wynn emphasized, the archeological record of the last 40 kya is replete with examples of episodic memory, autonoetic, and mythic examples. In addition to the *Lion Man* figurine, another notable one stems from the Lascaux cave painting of the a human figure with a bird head, disemboweled bison, and bird on a shaft. This has been interpreted as an example of our ancestor's contemplation of the afterlife.[96, 97]

The Downside of Mental Time Travel

Through expanded working memory capacity and increased episodic memory processing of past events, possible negative events may be recalled and imagined. The most obvious is one's own mortality and may have served as the neurobiological circuitry for incipient anxiety, depression, and other stressors in humans.[98]

Language Evolution

Learning and memory, in particular episodic memory, are faculties that may have allowed improved adaptability of responses to the environment using past experiences as one of the information sources. This ability of imaging future scenarios as well as drawing on the past, referred to as mental time travel, probably required the coevolution of recursive language by enabling sharing of episodic knowledge with conspecifics (others of us) and benefiting from their experiences. Hence, one of the language theories proposals include the coevolution of language with episodic memory as well as emotional intelligence. The evolution of emotions, by the development of sensitivity to others, or social emotion, is postulated to have improved information sharing. Language may have played an important role regulating emotions, both intrapersonal as well as interpersonal.[99]

Emotional Intelligence (EI)

Processing of internal states, especially emotive ones, involving mentalizing and being concerned with one's own emotions and the emotions of others, has been attributed to the frontopolar cortex (BA10). Another core frontopolar function is the simultaneous consideration of several task options for optimum response and the ability to switch between internally and externally orientated thoughts.[100, 101] There is some support for the intrapersonal EI function of frontopolar cortex from a case study where the lesion was exclusively confined to BA10, the sole case report, as such, to date.[102]

Spirituality

Archeological evidence supports spirituality in humans before language evolution. The Franco Cantabrian cave art (40–30 kya) suggests that imagistic communication was used for conveying spirituality and that cave art and religion are closely related human mind operations and attempts at abstract thought interpretations. The basis may have been triggered by various forms of hallucinations, from simple to complex, that may occur in all humans as stereotyped responses. Archeological findings further imply that both spirituality and art developed together, relatively suddenly, thought to have been initially shamanistic based and supporting the expression of creativity in humans.[103] The Lascaux paintings generally depict groups of bison and horses predominantly, less often other animals. Theorists of cave art contend that these sophisticated forms of art represented deliberate configurations of alliances among social groups (figure 1.18).[104]

Fig. 1.18. Franco-Cantabrian Cave art: The Lascaux Bulls, Lascaux Cave, France

Figure credit with permission: French Ministry of Culture and Communication (http://www.culture.gouv.fr).

Table 1.1. Human mind evolution: Approximate sequences

1. Frontoparietal circuitry, dorsal and ventral visual streams development
   Oldowan stone tools, flakes, australopithecines Estimated ~2.6 mya[105]
2. Technical intelligence, procedural memory, conceptual thought
   Archeulean hand axes, blades, *Homo erectus* Estimated ~1.9 mya[106]
3. Symbolic thought Estimated ~500–300 kya[107]

4. Enhanced working memory to stage 7 Estimated ~30 kya[108]
5. Executive function
    Estimated 40–30 kya Hohlenstein-Stadel Lionman
6. Mirror neuron circuit to stage 7 and theory of mind Since ~50 kya? [109]
7. Autonoesis, mental time travel since ~50 kya?[111, 112]
8. Spirituality, shamanism, cave art, imagisticcommunication Since ~30 kya[113]
9. Emotional intelligence and social emotion time (?)[114]
10. Recursive language ~50 kya115,116
11. Metacognition (introspection) time?[117]

What Caused the Climate Changes That Prompted the Punctuated Rather Than Gradual Growth in Brain Size? Evidence of Further Natural Beats and Rhythms?

A Shift from a Warm Earth to a Cool Earth and Evolutionary Consequences

A puzzlelike configuration of about twenty major and ten minor tectonic plates envelop the Earth, which are in continuous motion transforming continents, building mountains, modifying ocean currents, and secondarily cause major climate changes (figure 1.19).

Fig. 1.19. The major tectonic plates

Figure credit: http://pubs.usgs.gov/publications/text/slabs.html.

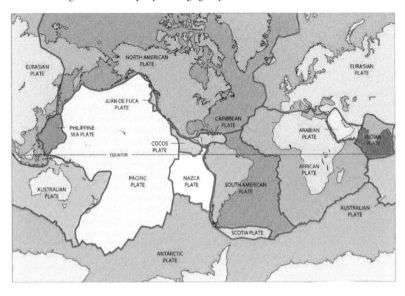

These impinge on each other (convergent boundaries), an example being the formation of the Himalayas. Or they may drift apart (divergent boundaries), an example being the mid-Atlantic Ridge. There are also sideways glancing actions (transform boundaries) as exemplified by the California faults, all driven by the mantle below (figure 1.20).

Fig. 1.20. The planet's "geological heartbeat"

Plate tectonics mechanisms: New crust formation added from the ocean ridges (red, orange, yellow newer and blues and purple oldest), driven by mantle convection currents.

Figure credit with permission: Müller RD, Sdrolias M. Age, spreading rates and spreading asymmetry of the world's ocean crust. Geochemistry Geophysics Geosystems 2008; 9:1525–1527 (left figure) and http://www.platetectonics.com/book/page_11.asp (right figure).

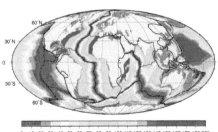

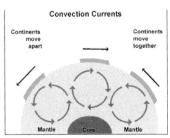

The newly formed ocean currents subsequently became significant in moving heat around the globe. Any factor impeding the flow of ocean currents from the tropics to the poles cause the latter to progressively cool and freeze, compounded by the polar ice and snow reflecting sunlight and associated heat (albedo effect).

Antarctic and Arctic Ice Sheet Formation

The Earth's climate cooled dramatically over the last fifty million years and involved multiple components. Gondwanaland broke up into Africa, India, and South America, and Australia and Antarctica in the south from ~34 mya ago (figure 1.21).

Fig. 1.21. Plate tectonic movements of earlier supercontinents: Rodinia, Pangea, Laurasia, and Gondwanaland from ~250 million years ago (mya) to the present time.
Figure credit: United Stages Geological Survey.org.

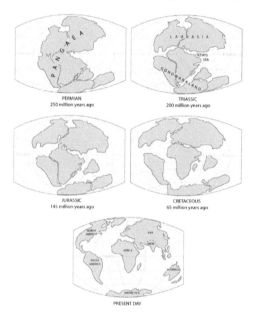

The continental separations led to the opening of the Drake passage and Tasmanian passages in the Southern Hemisphere termed the "Southern Ocean gateway opening." This set up new ocean currents, one of which encircled Antarctica, which gradually moved toward the south pole and became progressively colder with glaciation occurring at about 30 mya. The cold currents were trapped around Antarctica, forming a progressively colder gyre, in the absence of warming influence from equatorial currents. In addition, the deep water of the oceans became colder and denser and generally remained close to freezing. This cold water flows into the deep-sea water regions of most parts of the world and remains cold (figure 1.22).

Fig. 1.22. Cold dense water (dark blue) travelling northward from Antarctica through the sea troughs and basins due to sea ice formation (red crosses) that helps form Antarctic bottom water.

Figure credit with permission: Bradley RS. Paleoclimatology. *Reconstructing Climates of the Quaternary* (3rd edition). Elsevier, Amsterdam, 2015.

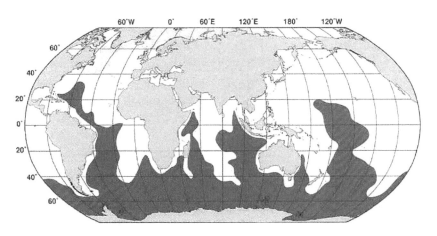

In certain places in the lower latitudes such as the coasts of western South Africa, western Chile, western Australia, and California, upwelling of these waters occurs leading to cooler surface waters with colder air above it with resultant rich sea life and Mediterranean-type climates.[118, 119] Other explanations for the Antarctic ice sheet formation 34 mya include a marked decline in atmospheric CO_2 levels, the exact cause of lower CO_2 remaining uncertain. However, the profound continental reorganization that included India breaking away from Africa, Australia moving north and breaking away from Antarctica, which moved south, may have played a role. The ensuing ocean circulation changes, and extensive upwellings consisting of plankton may also have been responsible, as with their demise they could have drawn significant amounts of carbon with them into the oceans, one of several forms of carbon sequestration.[120]

The Earth Further Cooled Markedly at about 14 MYA Due to the Further Extension of the Antarctic Ice Sheet and AgainSince about 6 MYA with the Formation of the Arctic Glaciation

A further significant temperature drop occurred at 14 mya as a result of extension of the Antarctic ice sheet (figure 1.23).

Fig. 1.23. Global cooling trend over the last 50 million years (y axis) deduced from deep-sea foraminifera 18O/16O ratios.
The time span of first Antarctic glaciation and later Arctic glaciation is shown by the vertical bars. The temperature change from generally ice free to glacial ice appears on the x axis.
Figure credit with permission from: Klein RG. *The Human Career*, "Human Biological and Cultural Origins." Third Edition. University of Chicago Press, Chicago, 2009.

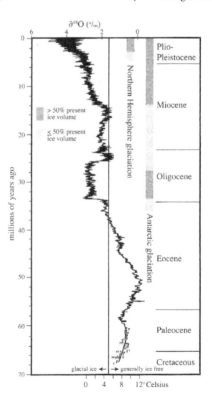

Additional temperature drops 6 mya and 2.8 mya coincided with glaciation in the Northern Hemisphere as a consequence of the Arctic ice cap formation due to a combination of the Panama isthmus formation, Asian orogenesis with formation of the Tibetan Plateau and Himalayas mountains due to the Indian subcontinent precursor colliding with the Asian continent (figure 1.24).[121]

Fig. 1.24. Himalayan mountains, Tibetan Plateau formation.
Collision of the Indian continent with Eurasia occurred at about 55 mya with most of the uplift occurring ~ 8 mya. Atmospheric circulation over Africa changed with drier summer air and loss of two moisture bearing winds.
Figure credit: www.usgs.org.

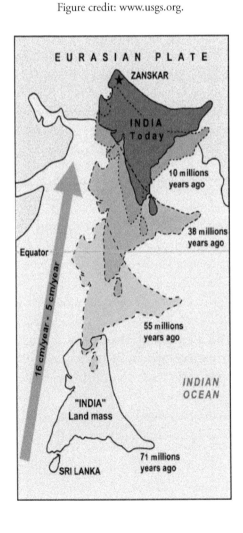

Recurrent warmer periods also occurred during the Pliocene epoch warm intervals (5.33–2.58 mya) associated with relatively high global temperatures and elevated CO_2 levels in the atmosphere and sea levels up to twenty meters higher than today. These were correlated with the retreat of the East Antarctic ice sheet together with melting of the Western Antarctic and Arctic ice. Recurrent melting between 5 and 3 mya took place during this Pliocene era.[122]

After the glaciation of Antarctica 34 mya, for over thirty million years many parts of the planet became not only cooler but also drier followed by the reduction in forest environments, the spread of savannah with grasses. During this time the Arctic region remained ice free, but at about 2.5 mya, a much more profound so-called glacial maximal occurred, and the modern Ice Age began. This resulted in further cooling affecting the Northern Hemisphere with glaciation of Scandinavia, Greenland, North America, and Europe but which also impacted the East African climate.

The Astrophysical Beat: The Periodicity of Ice Ages Correspond to the Earth's Orbit Shape, Its Tilt and Wobble—the Pacemaker of Ice Ages

These have been implicated to having played an important role and took effect after the global cooling 45 mya, first described by Serbian mathematician astronomer, climatologist, and geologist Milutin Milankovitch. He postulated at least three cycles of the Earth's orbital variations that are now considered a principal cause of Ice Ages (figure 1.25).[123]

The Earth's orbit changes in three major ways with five periods:

1. The orbit alternates from an oval configuration to a more circular pattern over both 100 ky and 400 ky cycles.
2. The Earth rocks back and forth about two degrees over 41 ky cycles.
3. The Earth's tilt wobbles akin to that of a spinning top over 23 ky and19 ky cycles.

Fig. 1.25. "Pacemaker of the Ice Ages."
The three main orbital variations of the Earth and its five periods.
Figure with permission from Zachos J, Pagani M Sloan L, Thomas
E, Billups K. Trends, Rhythms, and Aberrations in Global Climate
65 Ma to Present. Science 2001; 292:686–693.

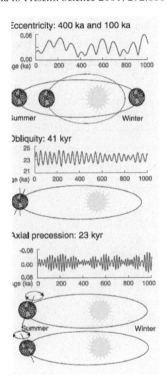

These cycles are correlated with Ice Ages at those intervals and are followed by warming periods termed interglacial periods. There is also a correlation of increased volcanic activity following the melting of ice attributed to crustal stress changes secondary to the ice mass.[124]

The Unique Role of the Atlantic Meridional Overturning Circulation (AMOC) and the Closure of the Old Panama Canal

The Pacific and Atlantic Oceans communicated through the old Panama Canal twenty million years ago, but subsequently the collision of the Pacific and Caribbean plates caused underwater volcanic activity and uplift of the seafloor. Eventually by 3 mya, a narrow land mass isthmus had formed, and the important rerouting of both Atlantic and

Pacific Ocean currents occurred, regarded as one of the most important geological incidents over the last sixty million years (figure 1.26).

Fig. 126. The "Old" Panama Canal allowed Pacific and Atlantic water mixing with overall lower salinity in the Atlantic waters.
With the Panama isthmus forming about 3 mya, this resulted in more saline, warm North Atlantic water (via the AMOC) and sinking before it reached the Arctic Pond and so isolating the Arctic Pond with resulting year round ice. The circum-Antarctic gyre persistent cold water has the same effect with glaciation and cooling polar air masses.
Figure credit with permission: Stanley SM. *Children of the Ice Age*. WH Freeman and Company, New York, 1998.

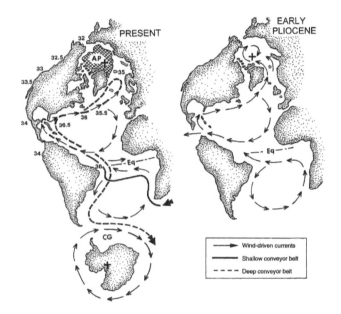

The Atlantic currents, the Florida current, and Gulf Stream were forced to flow northward, markedly influencing the northwest European climate with an overall ten-degree Celsius warmer than would otherwise be the case. For example, Oslo, at latitude 60, has an ice-free harbor year-round. The Atlantic also became saltier with respect to the Pacific. The massive warm water, relatively salty (35% salinity), Gulf Stream current moves north, becoming the North Atlantic current, flows north to the Greenland and Labrador where, upon cooling, the increased density causes it to sink and ultimately return to the Southern Hemisphere via the deep ocean currents. This is termed the thermohaline circulation. Two of the fastest ocean currents in the world are the Agulhas (off the Southern African coast) at seventy to eighty-five million cubic meters per second (m³/sec) and the Gulf stream at 150 m³/ sec. In comparison, the Amazon River flows at million m³/sec.

Any interruption of the North Atlantic flow can cause sudden cooling (bereft of the warming effects of the warm trop-ical waters) of the Northern Hemisphere, with increase in glaciation. Almost par-adoxically this occurs when Greenland glaciers melt and cause a large influx of relatively hypodense freshwater into this critical area (a type of Achilles's heel) where the now colder and denser Atlantic waters descend to become a deep ocean circulation that tracks back to the Southern Hemisphere. This system is termed the Atlantic meridional overturning circulation (AMOC).[125, 126] It is estimated that during the twenty-first century the AMOC will slow an estimated 25–30% due to greenhouse gas increase, largely anthropogenic.[127] The multidecadal AMOC fluctuations have caused sudden climate changes, impacted climate globally, particularly in Africa, the monsoons in India, and the Atlantic tropical atmospheric circulation relevant to hurricane genera-tion. With the closure of the Central American Seaway by the Panama isthmus formation between approximately 4.6 and 3 mya, diversion of the North Atlantic current occurred with warming of the northern Atlantic regions particularly Western Europe (figure 1.27).

Fig. 1.27. Atlantic meridional overturning circulation (AMOC).
Figure credit: Kuhlbrodt T, Griesel A, Montoya M, Leverman A, Hoffman M, Rahmstorf S. On the driving processes of the Atlantic meridional overturning circulation. Reviews of Geophysics 2007. doi:10.1029/2004RG000166

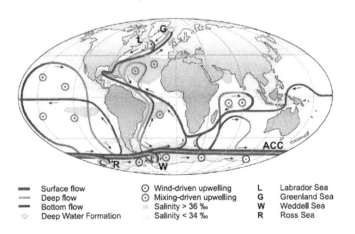

However, it also subsequently caused worldwide cooling as well as major climate fluctuations.[128]

A Key Event Transpired from Approximately 36 MYA with the Ocean Circulation Changing from an Equatorial to an Interpolar Type

Relatively warm oceanic waters had flowed unimpeded around the broad expanse of the equatorial Tethys Ocean (figure 1.28). This progressively changed as cold waters built up, encircling the isolated Antarctica with ice beginning to form on land and sea and on land during winter. The Antarctic waters became particularly cold and subsequently became denser, which caused their sinking. They also spread into the ocean trenches and basins northward. These bottom waters inhabiting the higher latitudes at certain periods encountered undersea barriers in the same way mountain ranges present barri ers on land. A notable one is the submarine waterfall flowing over the Greenland-Iceland Ridge underlying the Denmark Strait. About five million cubic meters per second surge over a vertical drop of more than 3,500 meters, down into the northern part of the Atlantic basin. The Greenland-Iceland-Scotland (GIS) was a ridge formed by basaltic lavas and had presented an initial barrier to mixing of the cold, deep waters of the Atlantic and Arctic about 30 mya, the trans-gression of which caused further overall global cooling.[129]

Fig. 1.28. Equatorial to interpolar circulation.
The ancient Tethys Ocean was associated with a warm equatorial ocean circulation. With tectonic plate movements gradually obliterating the Tethys Ocean, the ocean circulations changed to an interpolar meridional type.
Illustration adapted from Stow D. *Vanished Ocean: How Tethys Reshaped the World*. Oxford University Press, Oxford, 2010

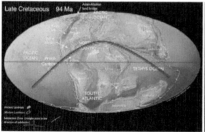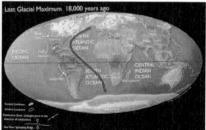

In Addition to the Long-Term Ice Age Cycles, Short, Abrupt Climate Inversions Occur

The whiplash climate changes were discovered, thanks to the ice core drilling in the Arctic region, and has provided us with "two-mile time machine," both appropriate terms suggested by William Calvin. Ice core drilling data comes from Greenland and Antarctica. In Greenland, both the USA sponsored GISP2 (Greenland Ice Sheet Project 2) and the nearby GRIP (Greenland Ice Core Project, European) delivered ice cores of over 3 km in depth representing ice and climate data up to 250 kya.[130] The Antarctica Vostok ice sheet drilling data spans the last 400 kya incorporating four climate cycles, which confirm a strong correlation between atmospheric greenhouse gas concentrations (CO_2, methane) and Antarctic temperatures and orbital cycles.[131]

The whiplash climate changes are due to Dansgaard-Oeschger (D-O), Heinrich, and Bond events that can cause sudden cooling and warming within decades or just a few years. D-O events are attributed to AMOC fluctuation and are short-lived with fluctuation from a stadial (lower temperatures during a warm period) to interstadial (warm period during a glacial period) period and reverting back again in a period of less than one thousand years. Heinrich events have a more global impact, are more pronounced than D-O events, lasting centuries, consequent to more marked AMOC reductions, and attributed to continental ice melting. They were discovered by ocean-floor drilling whereby boulders were noted that originated mostly from Hudson Bay and presumably dropped by iceberg movements, predominantly in the Labrador Sea area. Heinrich events are less frequent, associated with a stronger reduction of the AMOC, in turn related to large quantities of freshwater from the Laurentide ice sheet being added. However, another speculation is that they could also be due to the collapse of the Western Antarctic ice sheet.[132,133] For example, during the last Ice Age (110–12 kya), twenty-five such events occurred, and there is some evidence of a cycle time of 1,470 years. Similar North Atlantic climate fluctuations during the Holocene period (11700 kya to the present time) are referred to as Bond events with comparable climate cyclicity (8 to date with a cyclicity of ~1,470 years). These are also termed the interglacial comparative of the D-O glacial events but with lower maximum temperature changes (table 1.2).[134]

Oxygen Isotope Fingerprints Serve as an Important Record of Ice Ages and Warm Periods

Microscopic plankton shells termed foraminfera, when alive, concentrate regular oxygen 16 in their carbonate (CaCO) shell as well as oxygen 18. Snow and ice contain more oxygen 16, while seawater contains relatively enriched oxygen 18, the heavier molecule. This ratio is reflected in the carbonate shells of foraminfera. For example, the last Ice Age contained a warm period between 130 and 117 kya (Eemian period or marine isotope stage 5e) ago that encompassed several D-O cycles. There are 104 described marine isotope stages (MIS), odd numbers indicating warm, even numbers cold, dating back to 2.6 mya, with MIS2 (cold) dating to the last glacial maximum 29 kya and MIS1 (warm) having started 14 kya and continuing to the present time. These have been derived from marine bed core drilling with evaluation of the oxygen 16 to oxygen 18 ratios that correlates with terrestrial glaciation and interglacial evidence.[135] The abrupt cooling event of 8200 ya ago, called the Younger Dryas period, was due to a D-O event, discovered by drilling of lake cores and examination of pollen that has been contained in the sediment. In addition to ice core, marine cores such as pollen and dust cores are useful in the evaluation of the paleoclimate.[136]

Ultimately, the interaction of astrophysical and geological factors are responsible for changes relating to humans and animals. The tectonic changes in Africa as well as adjacent Asia made East Africa particularly sensitive to climatic changes. A recently proposed theory, the pulsed climate variability hypothesis, combines tectonic forcing (orbital motions influencing tectonic movements) with climate variability, linking both orbital variation and the new topographical aspects (e.g., Rift Valley formation), proposed by Martin Trauth of the University of Potsdam in Germany and Mark Maslin.[137]

Table 1.2. The beat and pulsing of ocean currents (Atlantic and Pacific) leading to major and minor climate changes and their influence on human history

1. **Atlantic meridional overturning circulation related**

    Bond events (selected events over the last 12 ky of B0–B8)

    B8—Younger Dryas, 12.8–11.5 kya "big freeze" event due collapse of N. American ice sheets, may have initiated agriculture with cereal cultivation

    B3—Collapse of the Egyptian Old Kingdom, 4.2 kya

    B2—Eastern Mediterranean drought, ~3 kya collapse of Bronze Age cultures

    B1—Migration period 1.4 kya, extreme weather 535–536, Barbarian invasion

    B0—Little Ice Age (during years 1250–1650)

    D-O Events (about twenty-five events since the last 110 ky)

    Sahara pump theory supports several waves of human evolution out of Africa.*

    Homo erectus ~1.8 mya

    Homo heidelbergensis ~500 kya

    Homo sapiens leaves Africa ~70 kya

    Formation of Sahara ~6 kya – followed by the Saharasia period, a hypothesized origin of violent, armored human conflict and patriarchism Heinrich

    Events may follow an approximate 7,000-year cycling (selected events H0-H6)

    H0 (~12 kya) H6 (~60 kya)

2. **Pacific decadal oscillation every fifteen to thirty years between El Niño and La Niña**

    El Niño

    Atmospheric warming phase (increase in global extreme weather)

La Niña
Atmospheric cooling phase (Haiyan 2013,
    strongest typhoon recorded)

Legend
*The Sahara pump theory relates to intermittent wet and
dry phases of the present-day Sahara and Middle East that
enabled migration during wet periods lasting up to thousands of years, of fauna between Africa and Eurasia.[138–140]

Tectonic Uplift, Himalayan and Tibetan Plateau Formation, and the Formation of a Major Carbon Elimination Process

The Tibetan plateau and Himalayan mountain formation started 70
mya at a relatively fast rate of 15 cm per year and is still ongoing
with the plateau rising about 5 mm per year. It was formed by the
Indomadagascar plate (India) colliding with the Asian plate, obliterating the ancient Tethys Ocean (by 50 mya). This orogenic process
formed the biggest mountainous region on Earth, rising on average
5 km above sea level with an approximate area of 2.5 million km^2,
also termed the third pole because of extensive glacier formation. It
also comprises of ~82% of the Earth's rock surface and functions as
an atmospheric CO_2 extractor, with carbon containing rock erosion
by river action flushing it into the ocean.[141, 142] With the prospect of a
possible doubling of atmospheric CO_2 by the end of the twenty-first
century accompanied by an estimated average six degrees Celsius elevation in global warming, weathering processes and CO_2 cycling may
be very important. For example, CO_2 consumption due to weathering processes increased > 50% for the Mackenzie River Basin (Arctic)
underscoring the key role that weathering may play in the future
global carbon cycling.[143]

The Oceans Play an Important Role in Carbon Sequestration and Heat Regulation

Oceans are capable of storing heat as well as carbon, and hence, the
ocean climate bond is critical to understanding climatology. For
example, the Gulf Stream conveys 2,300 trillion joules per second

of heat to Europe, predominantly the northwestern parts, but the effects are felt much farther afield as well. Oceans are also capable of holding fifty times more CO_2 than the atmosphere as well as being able to absorb approximately 30–40% of anthropogenic CO_2. Hence, oceans regulate global temperatures as well as greenhouse gases in the atmosphere.[144]

Astrophysical Factors: Sun Storms, Tectonic, Geomagnetic, and Paleoclimatological Events That Worked Together in Intricate Interrelationships

Solar Storms

The most extensive solar storm recorded to date was the Carrington event of 1859 with auroras visible as far south as Hawaii and Cuba in the Northern Hemisphere and Santiago in the Southern Hemisphere.[145] Events of this magnitude are thought to occur every five hundred years but lesser incidents are more frequent. There is a direct connection between the sun's solar storms, coronal mass ejections (CMEs), and human biology. CMEs are brief episodes, and for example, strokes have been strongly associated with these as have influenza epidemics been correlated to solar storms.[146, 147] The charged particles have also been linked to neuropsychiatric symptoms such as anxiety, depression, bipolar disorder, impaired cognition, and increased sleepiness. The latter is ascribed to electromagnetic activity affecting the pineal gland, which increased melatonin secretion as a result.[148] The eleven-year solar cycle has been proposed to be a trigger for human diseases such as the neuropsychiatric conditions and increased incidences of autoimmune disease, metabolic disease, and cancer. The mechanism whereby the solar radiation cycle causes human diseases is postulated to be due to ultraviolet light radiation damaging the human genome. In particular, the introns, which modulate gene control, may be affected. From an evolutionary perspective, Davis and Lowell further speculate that instances of past, beneficial genetic mutations may have also occurred, such as those that mediated higher consciousness and creativity.[149]

Geomagnetic (Pole Reversals)

The Earth's magnetic field periodically changes from normal polarity to reversed polarity, with the positions of magnetic north and magnetic south interchanged. The last geomagnetic reversal took place 780,000 years ago, referred to as the Brunhes-Matumaya reversal. Reversed polarity periods are termed chrons, and reversals take between one thousand to ten thousand years to form. The planet's magnetic fields are created by a type of dynamo action whereby molten iron convections in turn give rise to electric currents that in turn induce magnetic fields.[150]

Other geomagnetic phenomena include magnetic excursions, rather than magnetic reversals. These may last a few years, and one example is the Gothenburg magnetic excursion or Gothenburg "flip" that occurred about 12,000 years ago. The reason these are important for human evolution and human existence is the association with radiation effects on biological systems. Life on Earth is protected by the magnetic field, shielding it from solar radiation, which may cause DNA damage, mutations, and cancers. Periods of weak magnetic fields, by allowing increased radiation such as ultraviolet, may have influenced evolution with some evidence that there is an 11,500-year cycle of evolution events that were, in turn, triggered by radiation exposure. Some examples include the extinction of the woolly mammoths 11,500 years ago in relation to the Gothenburg magnetic reversal that took place 12,400–12,350 years before the present time. This event coincided with a relatively short Ice Age period.[151] Other speculative events include the Mono Lake magnetic reversal 23,000 kya and a major Ice Age. The last major eruption of Campi Flegrei (eight-mile-wide volcanic caldera near Naples, Italy) was 12 kya at the same time of the Gothenburg magnetic reversal 12 kya, which was relatively rapid lasting about 440 years with the field strength about 25% of today's. The largest Northern Hemisphere volcanic eruption over the last 100 ky took place at Campi Flegrei 39,400 years ago, coincident with the Laschamp magnetic reversal. This caused extensive climate change in Europe and may have been a factor in Neanderthal extinction. The Lake Mungo magnetic reversal 33,500 years ago was also hypothesized to be correlated to the disappearance of the Neanderthals. The Earth's field strength had decreased to about 5% of today's field strength with a loss of protection against cosmic rays with elevated radiation exposure. [152, 153]

Solar System and Galactic Beats: Dark Matter and Comet Formation

Lisa Randall and Matthew Reece, Harvard physicists, have proposed that our solar system has orbital variations within its own galaxy that have a 35-million-year cycle. The presence of so-called dark matter disc formation in the galaxy is correlated with the escalation in comet collisions with the Earth that take place approximately every thirty-five million years. The Chicxulub asteroid impact ~66 mya that caused the extinction of all nonavian dinosaurs may have been due to one of these comets and paved the way for mammalian diversification and ultimately primate and human evolution.[154, 155]

The Coalescing of Many Events: Rift Valley Formation and Complex Topography Formation in East Africa—the Pulsed Climate Variability Hypothesis

This theory combines the effects of tectonic forcing, climate variability, orbital variation, and new topography. The unique East African climate fluctuations in turn are considered the main driver of hominid evolutionary change with up to fifteen hominid species appearing in the period from 5–0.5 mya associated with phases of inventiveness and creativity.[156]

These Climate Changes First Led to the Development of Modern Bodies and Ultimately Initiated the Changes for the Modern Mind

We evolved to be endurance runners. Being neither big nor fast, our species exploited an environmental niche activity of endurance activity in the midday heat. A particularly poignant quote from Raymond Dart in 1925 was insightful into the connection between physical exercise and cognition:

For the production of man a different apprentice-ship (from forests) was needed to sharpen the wits and quicken the higher manifestations of intel-lect—a more open veldt country where competi-tion was keener between swiftness and stealth and where adroitness of thinking played a preponder-ating role in the preservation of the species.

There are well over two dozen recognized major astrophysi-cal, geological, and biosphere circumstances that steered the various stages in our evolution. A representation of these factors and how they impacted the final common path, emphasizing the pulsed cli-mate variability hypothesis whereby the complex topography of the African Rift Valley and orbital forcing impacted climate to give us what has been termed the east side story of human origins[157] (figure 1.29).

Fig. 1.29. Paleogeological, paleoclimatological, astrophysical, and other factors that impacted events in Eastern Africa leading to the evolution of hominins

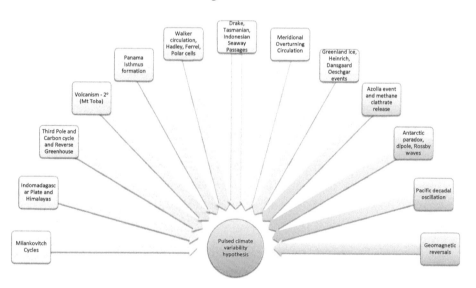

The table below represents a summary of those that are known, some very important, others less so, and some merely interest-ing associations.

Table 1.3. Relationship of physical events (global, major, and minor) and key events relating to mammalian and human evolution for life (global, major, and minor)

Event and Time Period	Evolutionary or Historic Event
Tethys Ocean, equatorial ocean circulation 260–35 mya	Warm, tropical planet, no polar ice
Period ~200 -65 mya	Mammalian 6 layer cortex, olfaction, fur
Asteroid impact (~66 mya), Deccan traps eruptions?	Dinosaur extinction, mammals set free
Paleocene–Eocene Thermal Maximum 55 mya	Tropical Earth, methane clathrates?
Warm Miocene climate 55–45 mya?	Earth tropical, primate evolution
Circumpolar ocean circulation, polar ice caps form	Progressive cooling since 50mya
Tasmania/Antarctic and Drake passages open	Thermal isolation of Antarctica
Greenland-Iceland-Scotland ridge breached 30 mya	Further global cooling
Antarctic glaciation ~30 mya	Marked increase in global cooling
Himalayan/Tibetan orogenesis (50–5 mya)	East African climate cooling, aridity
African Rift Valley formed 10–5 mya.	Markedly variable topography
Panama Isthmus formation, "Old Canal" closes fluctuations	AMOC formation, climate
Pulsed Climate Variability, 3 periods in 5 my	Hominid species appear, 15 in 5 my
Increase in N. hemisphere glaciation 2.7 mya	Australopithecines arboreal, terrestrial
Onset of the Walker circulation 2 mya	*Homo habilis, Homo erectus* appear
mid-Pleistocene revolution 1 mya	Out of Africa exodus

Marine Isotope Stage 6 (195–120 kya)	Ice Age, marine/USO diet in S. Africa
Volcanism – Mt Toba eruption (~73 kya)	Volcanic winter, Homo exits Africa?
Geomagnetic reversals, Laschamp event 41 kya	Radiation, Neanderthal extinction?
Dansgaard Oeschgar events (Younger Dryas)	Agriculture, mini– Ice Age 8200 ya
African Humid period (Holocene)	Human expansion in Saharasia
End of African Humid period (6–5 kya)	Riverine cultures, Nile, Euphrates, Tigris
Increased aridity in Saharasia	Recurrent warfare, patriarchism
Volcanism, Mt Samalas eruption 1257	Little Ice Age, black death in Europe
Volcanism, Mt Tambora 1815	Famine, "Year without a summer"
Carrington Event Solar Storm 1861 (largest)	Night sky illumination in tropics

Where We Are Now and Where We Are Going

The evolutionary history of our brain, literally honed by fire, ice, and adversity has left us with an approximately 1,350 cc organ that is frequently referred to as the most complex entity in the universe. However, the large brain and extensive connectome (circuitry) with 150,000 km of fibers uses an incommensurate amount of energy and, at the same time, also makes us prone to human specific diseases. Larger brains have more synapses per neuron and have disproportionately more white matter than gray matter. Larger brains are metabolically more expensive, as most of the energetic cost involves neuronal signaling, synaptic activity, and electrochemical gradients. The human brain vital statistics include some formidable numbers that are difficult to conceive of.

Table 1.4. Brain statistics: Anatomical

Brain

Neurons	10^{11}	(100 billion)
Glia	10^{12}	(1 trillion)
Synapses	10^{15}	(1 quadrillion)
Connectome	150,000	km of axons
Blood vessels	700 km	

One mm^3 brain comprises of

Neurons	50,000
Synapses	50×10^6
Dendrites	150 m
Axons	100 m

Microbiome

Microbes	2×10^{14}	(200 trillion)
Microbiome	1.5 kg	

All our cells	10^{13}	(10 trillion)

Neurophysiological Perspectives

The human sensory systems receive ~11 million bits of information per second.[158] However, the conscious mind is unable to process this amount of data, and it is estimated to process only about 16–50 bits per second.[159] Hence, most incoming information is processed subconsciously. Estimates of conscious activity is considered to comprise of only ~5% of all cognition with the other 95% of processing occurring beyond our awareness. Even willed movement is initially nonconscious, with the readiness potential preceding awareness of the movement by one second and by up to eight seconds prior in the frontopolar cortex. Hence, so-called free will actually has a significant, initial, nonconscious component.[160] Nonconscious activity uses most of the energy and is the dominant brain activity.

Table 1.5. The majority of the energy used by the brain is attributed to action potentials and synaptic activity[161]

Neural electrochemical process	Brain energy consumption %
Action potentials brain energy consumption	47
Postsynaptic processing	34
Resting neuronal potential	13
Glutamate recycling	3

Other Brain Processing Dimensions in Three-Dimensional Space and Time Include Gliotransmission and Epigenetic Mechanisms Astroglial Networks or Gliotransmission

Glial cells enabled mammals' increasing speed of reaction and more complex brain functions. As animals became more complex, there is an increase in glial cells to neuron ratio. In humans, the glia to neuron ratio is ~6:1, with more glia in prefrontal cortex than any other animal. Astrocytic processes are intimately associated with synapses and blood vessels and form the blood-brain barrier, control potassium homeostasis as well as uptake of cellular waste after brain insults. Astrocytes have receptors for the principal neurotransmitters (glutamate and GABA), hence the name tripartite synapse.[162]

Epigenetics

Epigenetic alterations have a long-term effect on gene regulation and behavior but are generally reversible. This is the process that links nature and nature in developing diverse biological organisms and systems. During this process, a change occurs in gene expression without altering the actual DNA sequence. Some epigenetic alterations extend beyond an individual's lifetime, termed transgenerational epigenetic alterations such as may occur from parent to offspring. The neurobiological mechanisms are via DNA methylation, histone acetylation, and micro-RNA interference.[163]

Are We at Our Limits in Brain Size and Function?

There is speculation that we may have reached the physiological as well as physical limits of brain size and processing ability. The fundamental impediment to further increases in intelligence are the limits of interneuronal communication capability and physics laws.[164] Functional brain network efficiency and intellectual performance are correlated. For example, the efficiency of the resting state functional connectivity (such as the default mode network) patterns is predictive of cognitive performance. Intellectual performance is related to how effectively our brain assimilates information between many different brain sectors.[165]

The Human Connectome Has Hot Spots That Are Susceptible to Metabolic Injury

Brain networks connect with many others, and these areas of interconnectivity or so-called hubs have relatively extended connections over longer distances, compared to other brain regions. These hubs are the brain regions that subserve higher cognitive processes and have been shown to be high-energy consuming regions of the brain. Accordingly, these are regions that are first affected in brain disorders, termed "hots pots," or the hub vulnerability hypothesis by Crossley et al. This has been shown for ten syndromes thus far (Alzheimer's disease, frontotemporal lobe disorder, posttraumatic stress disorder, schizophrenia, Asperger's syndrome, juvenile myoclonic epilepsy, temporal lobe epilepsy, and progressive supranuclear palsy as well as migraine.)[166, 167] These brain regions are therefore more likely affected, no matter what the pathophysiological process (causative disease), because of their particular liability to oxidative stress secondary to elevated metabolism, in turn a consequence of the concentration of neuronal spiking and synaptic activity.[168, 169]

Transfer of information across an expanse of cortical regions, in those with large brains, such as primates and humans, can be facilitated by limiting the length and number of long-range axons. This has been achieved by modular circuits, or the so-called small world topography of brain connectivity. These modular circuits are connected in turn by the long-range axons. In addition, folding of the cortex into gyri and a more globular brain configuration with parietal enlargement allows for improved cortical connectivity.[170]

Information Acquisition Is Key, as Is the Method of Acquisition

From an evolutionary point of view, the more information that an animal can process about the environment per unit time, the better its chances for survival or success in a particular circumstance. The amount of information that can be processed and matched to as many stored memory traces as possible, all with extreme rapidity, would also correlate with survival success.

The drive within us to acquire knowledge continues unabated. The link with the hedonic reward centers of the brain underscores this key role in our brain circuitry. Merely seeking novelty information, though, leads to what has been termed diversive curiosity, such as occurs in particular with electronic media. Epistemic (knowledge) curiosity leads to more integrative knowledge storage with that which is already present in the brain. This involves more extensive brain circuitry being activated which is then more likely to be transmodally available.[171, 172] The better informed we are in today's world, the better the decisions we make and outcome—usually.

We Have a Legacy That We Have to Abide By

The earthly and astrophysical factors detailed in this introduction forged our bodies and brains in a particular way. We have no choice but to respect this legacy and live accordingly as best as we can. In the next chapters, the known factors that influence brain health and impairment are deliberated upon as well as proposed recipes to keep this 1.5 kilogram organ with 20 billion neurons; 150,000 km of fibers; and 700 km of blood vessels functioning in optimum capacity. Five principal realms may be identified for specific attention and maintenance: physical exercise, brain foods (or foods that are best for the brain and body), cognitive exercises, sociality, and sleep health. These topics are now discussed in the following chapters.

References

1. Kazanis I., "The Subependymal Zone Neurogenic Niche: A Beating Heart at the Center of the Brain." *Brain* 2009; 132:2909–2921.

2. Neil Shubin, *The Universe Within* (New York: Pantheon Books, 2013).

3. Fan J1, Katz A., Randall L., Reece M., *Dark-disk universe. Phys Rev Lett.* 2013; 110(21):211302.

4. Maslin MA, Christensen B. Tectonics, orbital forcing, global climate change, and human evolution in Africa. *Journal of Human Evolution* 2007; 53: 443–464.

5. Dart RA, *Australopithecus africanus*: The man-ape of Southern Africa. *Nature* 1925; 115:195–199.

6. Leakey MS, Haley RL. Pliocene footprints in the Laetoli beds at Laetoli, northern Tanzania. *Nature* 1979; 278:317–323.

7. Harlow JM, "Passage of an iron rod through the head." *Boston Medical and Surgical Journal* 1848; 39:389–393.

8. Luria AR, *Higher Cortical Functions in Man* (New York: Basic Books, 1972).

9. Broca P. ,Nouvelle observation d'aphémie produite par une lésion de la moitié postérieure des deuxième et troisième circonvolution frontales gauches. *Bulletin de la Société Anatomique* 1861; 36:398–407.

10. Hoffmann M., Bill PLA, The environmental dependency syndrome, imitation behaviour and utilisation behaviour as presenting symptoms of bilateral frontal lobe infarction due to Moyamoya disease. *South African Medical Journal* 1992; 81:271–273.

11. Lhermitte F., Pillon B., Seradura M., Human Autonomy and the Frontal Lobes. Part 1: Imitation and Utilization Behavior. A Neuropsychological Study of 75 patients. *Ann Neurol* 1986; 19:326–334.

12. Lhermitte F. Human, "Autonomy and the Frontal Lobes. Part II: Patient Behavior in Complex and Social Situations: The "Environmental Dependency Syndrome." *Ann Neurol* 1986; 19:335–343.

13. Rizzolatti G., Fadiga L., Fogassi L., Gallese V., Resonance behaviors and mirror neurons. *Arch Ital Biol* 1999; 137:85–100.

14. Ramachandran VS, *The Tell Tale Brain* (New York: W.W. Norton & Company, 2011).

15. Arbib M., From Mirror Neurons to Complex Imitation in the Evolution of Language and Tool Use. *Ann Rev Anthropol* 2011; 40:257–273.

16. Hoffmann M. The panoply of field dependent behavior in 1436 stroke patients. The Mirror Neuron System uncoupled and the consequences of loss of personal autonomy. *Neurocase* 2014; 20(5):556–68. doi: 10.1080/13554794.2013.82668.

17. Subiaul F., Mosaic Cognitive Evolution: The Case of Imitation Learning. In Broadfield D, Yuan M, Schick K, Toth N. The Human Brain Evolving. Stone Age Institute Press 2010, Gosport, IN.

18. Koechlin E., Hyafil A., Anterior Prefrontal Function and the Limits of Human Decision Making. *Science* 2007; 318:594–598.

19. Burgess PW, Durmontheil I., Gilbert SJ. The gateway hypothesis of rostral prefrontal cortex (area 10) function. *Trends Cogn Sci* 2007; 11(7):290–298.

20. Hoffmann M., Bar-on R., Isolated Frontopolar Cortex Lesion—a Case Study. *Cognitive and Behavioral Neurology* 2012; 25:50–56.

21. Russell MJ, Barge LM, Bhartia, R., The Drive to Life on Wet and Icy Worlds. *Astrobiology* 2014; 14:308–343.

22. Nisbet EG., Sleep NH. The habitat and nature of early life. *Nature.* 2001 Feb. 22; 409(6823):1083–91.

23. Kreysing M., Keil L, Lanzmich S., Braun D., Heat flux across an open pore enables the continuous replication and selection of oligonucleotides towards increasing length. *Nat Chem.* 2015; 7:203–8. doi: 10.1038/nchem.2155.

24. Fuqua C, White D., Prokaryotic intercellular signaling Mechanistic diversity and unified themes. In Fairweather I (ed). Cell Signalling in Prokaryotes and Lower Metazoa 2004. Kluwer Academic Publishers, Dordrecht, 2004.

25. Caveney S., Cladman W., Verellen LA, Donly C., Ancestry of neuronal monoamine transporters in the Metazoa. *The Journal of Experimental Biology* 2006; 209:4858–4868.

26. Lyons TW, Reinhard CT, Planavasky NJ, The rise of oxygen in Earth's early ocean and atmosphere. *Nature* 2014; 506:307–315.

27. Squire LR, Berg D., Bloom FE, Du Lac S., Ghosh A., Spitzer NC. *Fundamental Neuroscience*, Fourth edition (Elsevier, Amsterdam: Academic Press, 2013).

28. Denes AS, Jekely G, Arendt D et al., Conserved mediolateral molecular architecture of the annelid trunk neuroectoderm reveals common ancestry of bilateral nervous system centralization. *Cell* 2007; 129:277–88.

29. Gai Z. Donoghue PC, Zhu M, Janvier, Stampanoni M. Fossil jawless fish from China foreshadows early jawed vertebrate anatomy. *Nature* 2011; 476: 324–327.

30. Zalc B, Goujet D, Colman D. The origin of the myelination program in vertebrates. *Curr Biol* 2008; 18:R511–R512.

31. Anderson PSL, Westneat MW. Feeding mechanisms and bite force modeling of the skull of Dunkleosteus terelli, an ancient apex predator. *Biology Letters* 2007; 3:77–80. Doi 10.1098/rsbl.2006.0569.

32. Zalc B. Origins of vertebrate success. *Science* 2000; 288: 5464 p. 271.

33. Daeschler EB, Shubin NH, Jenkins FA Jr. A Devonian tetrapod-like fish and the evolution of the tetrapod body plan. *Nature*. 2006; 440:757–63.

34. Sandberg CA, Morrow JR, Ziegler W. Late Devonian sea level changes, catastrophic events and mass extinctions. In: Koeberl C, MacLeod KG (eds). Catastrophic Events and Mass Extinctions: Impacts and Beyond: Boulder, Colorado. Special Paper. Geological Society of America 2002; 356:473–487.

35. Boisvert, C. A. 2005. The pelvic fin and girdle of Panderichthys and the origin of tetrapod locomotion. *Nature* 438: 1145–1147.

36. Niedzwiedzki G, Szrek P, Narkiewicz K, Narkiewicz M, Ahlberg P. Tetrapod trackways from the early Middle Devonian period of Poland. *Nature* 2010; 463:43–48.

37. Nesbitt SJ. The early evolution of archosaurs: relationships and the origin of major clades. *Bulletin of the American Museum of Natural History* 2011:352; 1–292. Doi:10.1206/352.1.

38. Kemp TS. The origin and early radiation of the therapsid mammal-like reptiles: a palaeobiological hypothesis. European Society of Evolutionary Biology 2006; 19:1231–1247.

39. De Bakker MA, Fowler DA, den Oude K. et al. Digit loss in archosaur evolution and the interplay between selection and constraints. *Nature* 2013; 463:445–448.

40. Sahney, S, Benton, MJ. Recovery from the most profound mass-sextinctionofalltime. *Proc Biol Sci* 2008; 275: 759–765.

41. Fan J, Katz A, Randall L, Reece M. Dark-disk universe. *Phys Rev Lett.* 2013; 110(21):211302.

42. Grady JM, Enquist BJ, Dettweiler-Robinson E, Wright NA, Smith FA. Evidence for mesothermy in dinosaurs. *Science* 2014; 344:1268–1272.

43. Balter M. Dinosaur metabolism neither hot nor cold, but just right. *Science* 2014; 344:1216–1217.

44. Rowe TB, Macrini TE, Luo ZX. Fossil evidence on origin of the mammalian brain. *Science* 2011; 332:955–957.

45. Alvarez LW, Alvarez W, Asaro F, Michel HV. Extraterrestrial cause for the Cretaceous-Tertiary extinction. *Science* 1980; 208:1095–1108.

46. Vellekoop J, Sluijs A, Smit J, Schouten S, Weijers JWH, Sinninghe Damste JS, Brinkuis H. Rapid short term cooling following the Chicxulub impact at the CretaceousPaleogene boundary. *PNAS* 2014; 111:7537–7541.

47. Brusatte SL, Butler RJ, Barrett PM et al. The extinction of the dinosaurs. *Biol Rev Camb Philos Soc.* 2014 Jul 28. doi: 10.1111/brv.12128.

48. Lin SC, van Keken PE. Multiple volcanic episodes of flood basalts caused by thermochemical mantle plumes. *Nature.* 2005; 436:250–2.

49. Benton MJ. How birds became birds. Sustained size reduction was essential for the origin of birds and avian flight. *Science* 2014; 345:508–509.

50. Lee MSY, Cau A, Naish D, Dyke GJ. Sustained miniaturization and anatomical innovation in the dinosaurian ancestors of birds. *Science* 2014; 345:562–566.

51. Springer MS, Murphy WJ, EizirikE, O'Brien SJ. Placental mammal diversification and the Cretaceous-Tertiary boundary. PNAS 2003; 100:1056–1061.

52. Gu G, Dickens GR, Bhatnagar G et al. Abundant Early Palaeogene marine gas hydrates despite warm deepocean temperatures. *Nature Geoscience* 2011; 4, 848–851 doi:10.1038/ngeo1301.

53. Adams K. Genomic Clues to the Ancestral Flowering Plant. *Science* 2013; 342: 1456–1457. doi:10.1126/science. 1248709.

54. Isbell LA, *The Fruit, the Tree and the Serpent* (Cambridge, Massachusetts: Harvard University Press, 2009).

55. Tudge C, Young J. *The Link. Uncovering Our Earliest Ancestor* (New York : Little Brown and Company, 2009).

56. Jones N. Battle to degas deadly lakes continues. *Nature* 2010; 466: 1033. doi: 10.1038/4661033a.

57. Rasmussen DT, Brown TM, Simons EL. The EoceneOligocene transition in continental Africa. In: Prothero DR, Berggren WA (eds). Eocene-Oligocene climatic and biotic evolution. (Princeton, New Jersey: Princeton University Press, 1992).

58. Milton K. Body weight, diet and home range area in primates. *Nature* 1976; 259; 459–462.

59. Lieberman DE. The story of the human body. Evolution, health and disease. (New York: Pantheon Books, 2013).

60. Vrba ES, Denton GH, Partridge TC, Burckle LH (eds). Paleoclimate and evolution. (New Haven: Yale University Press, 1995).

61. Schopf JW, Kudryavtsev AB, Walter MR et al. Sulfurcycling fossil bacteria from the 1.8-Ga Duck Creek Formation provide promising evidence of evolution's null hypothesis. *Proc Natl Acad Sci U S A.* 2015; 112: 2087–92.

62. Trauth MH, Maslin MA, Deino AL, Strecker MR, Bergner AG, Duehnforth M. High and low latitude forcing of the Plio-Pleistocene East African climate and human evolution. *Journal of Human Evolution* 2007; 53:475–486.

63. Schmieder F, von Dobonek T, Bleil U. The Mid-Pleistocene climate transition as documented in the deep South Atlantic Ocean: initiation, interim state and terminal event. *Earth and Planetary Science Letters* 2000; 179:539–549.

64. Gibbons A. Food for thought. Did the first cooked meals help fuel the dramatic evolutionary expansion of the human brain. *Science* 2007; 316:1558–1560.

65. Goodale, MA Milner AD. Separate visual pathways for perception and action. *Trends Neurosci* 1992; 15, 20–25. doi:10.1016/0166-2236(92)90344-8.

66. Holloway R, Broadfield D, Yan M. the Human Fossil Record. Volume Three: The Brain Endocasts: The Palaeoneurological Evidene. Hoboken John Wiley & Sons Inc., 2004.

67. Johnson-Frey SH. The neural bases of complex tool use in humans. *Trends Cogn. Sci.* 2004; 8; 71–78 (doi:10.1016/j.tics.2003.12.002).

68. Stout D, Toth N, Schick K, Chaminade T. Neural correlates of Early Stone Age toolmaking: technology, language and cognition in human evolution. *Phil. Trans. R. Soc. B* (2008) 363, 1939–1949. doi:10.1098/rstb.2008.0001.

69. Lewis JW. Cortical networks related to human use of tools. *Neuroscientist* 2006; 12:211231. doi:10.1177/1073858406288327.

70. Wynn and Coolidge. *The Rise of* Homo sapiens: *The Evolution of Modern Thinking* (New York: Wiley Blackwell, 2009).

71. Bruner E, De La Cuétara JM, Holloway R. A bivariate approach to the variation of the parietal curvature in the genus homo. *Anat Rec.* 2011; 294:1548–56. doi: 10.1002/ ar.21450.

72. Tulving E. Modernhumanversus Neanderthalevolutionary distinctiveness. *Current Anthropology* 2006; 47:597–622.

73. Bruner E. Geometric morphometrics and paleoneurology: Brain shape evolution the genus Homo, *Journal of Human Evolution* 2004; 47:279–303.

74. Bruner E, Manzi G, Arsuaga JL. Encephalization and allometric trajectories from Neanderthal and modern lineages. *Proceedings of the National Academy of Sciences* 2003; 100:15335–15340.

75. Evans PD, Gilbert SL, Mekel-Bobrov N. Microcephalin, a Gene Regulating Brain Size, Continues to Evolve Adaptively in Humans. *Science* 2005; 309:1717–1720.

76. Konopka G, Geschwind DH. Human brain evolution: harnessing the genomics (r)revolution to link genes, cognition, and behavior. *Neuron.* 2010; 68(2): 231–244.

77. Boeckx, C, Benitez-Burraco A. The shape of the human language-ready brain. *Frontiers in Psychology.* 2014; 5:1–23.

78. Mattick JS. The central role of RNA in human development and cognition. *FEBS Letters* 2011; 585:1600–1616.

79. Semendeferi K, Lu A, Schenker N, Damasio H. Humans and great apes share a large frontal cortex. *Nat Neurosci.* 2002; 5:272–276.

80. Schrott G. Micro RNAs at the synapse. *Nature Reviews Neuroscience* 2009; 10:842–849.

81. Baddeley AD. Implications of neuropsychological evidence for theories of normal memory. *Philos Trans R Soc Lond B Biol Sci.* 1982; 298:59–72.

82. Cummings JL. Frontal-subcortical circuits and human behavior. Arch Neurol. 1993; 50:873–80.

83. Coolidge FL, Wynn T. The rise of *Homo sapiens.* (Oxford, UK: Wiley Blackwell, 2009).

84. Read D, van der Leeuw S. Biology is only part of the story. In Renfrew C, Frith C, Malafouris L (eds). *The Sapient Mind* (Oxford: Oxford University Press, 2009).

85. Read D. Working memory: a cognitive limit to nonhuman primate recursive thinking prior to hominid evolution? *CogSci Proceedings* 2006:2674–2679.

86. Diamond A, Doar B. The performance of human infants on a measure of frontal cortex function, delayed response task. *Dev Psychobiol* 1989; 22:271–294.

87. Alp IE. Measuring the size of working memory in very young children: the imitation sorting task. *Int J Behav Dev* 1994; 17:125–141.

88. Chow TW, Cummings JL. Frontal subcortical circuits. In Miller B, Cummings JL (eds). *The Human Frontal Lobes* (New York: The Guilford Press, 2009).

89. Arbib M. From Mirror Neurons to Complex Imitation in the Evolution of Language and Tool Use. *Ann Rev Anthropol* 2011; 40:257–273.

90. Semendeferi K, Armstrong E, Schleicher A, Zilles K, Van Hoesen GW. Prefrontal cortex in humans and apes: a comparative study of area 10. *American Journal of Physical Anthrorpology* 2001; 114:224–241.

91. Semendeferi K, Armstrong E, Schleicher A, Zilles K, Van Hoesen GW. Limbic frontal cortex in hominoids: a comparative study of area 13. *American Journal of Physical Anthropology* 1998; 106:129–155.

92. Wynn T, Coolidge FL. The Implications of the Working Memory Model for the Evolution of Modern Cognition. *International Journal of Evolutionary Biology* 2011; 2011:741357. doi: 10.4061/2011/741357.

93. Tulving E. Episodic memory: From mind to brain. *Annual Review of Psychology* 2002; 53:1–25.

94. Shepard R. The genetic basis of human scientific knowledge. In: Characterizing Human Psychological Adaptations. Bock G, Cardew G (eds). Wiley & Sons, Chichester, 1997:4–13.

95. Coolidge FL, Wynn T. Working memory, its executive functions and the emergence of modern thinking. *Cambridge Archeological Journal* 2005; 15-5-26.

96. Coolidge FL, Wynn T. The Role of Episodic Memory. Memory and autonoetic thought in upper Paleolithic life. *PaleoAnthropology* 2008; 212–217.

97. Kemperman G, New Neurons for survival of the fittest. Nature Neuroscience Reviews 2012; 13:727–736

98. Suddendorf T, Corballis M. The evolution of foresight: What is mental time travel and is it unique to humans. *Behavioral and Brain Sciences* 2007; 30:299–313.

99. Jablonka E, Ginsburg S, Dor D. The co-evolution of language and emotions. *Phil. Trans. R. Soc. B* 2012; 367:2152–2159 doi:10.1098/rstb.2012.0117.

100. Koechlin E, Hyafil A. Anterior Prefrontal Function and the Limits of Human Decision Making. *Science* 2007; 318:594–598.

101. Burgess PW, Durmontheil I, Gilbert SJ. The gateway hypothesis of rostral prefrontal cortex (area 10) function. *Trends Cogn Sci* 2007; 11(7):290–298.

102. Hoffmann M, Bar-On R. Isolated frontopolar cortex lesion: a case study. *Cogn Behav Neurol.* 2012 Mar; 25(1):50–6. doi: 10.1097/WNN.0b013e318249a479.

103. Lewis-Williams D. The Mind in the Cave. (London : Thames and Hudson, 2002).

104. Laming-Emperaire A. Lascaux: Paintings and Engravings. Translation by Armstrong EF. (Barltome: Penguin Books 1959).

105. Stout D, Toth N, Schick K, Chaminade T. Neural correlates of Early Stone Age toolmaking: technology language and cognition in human evolution. *Phil Trans R Sco B* 2008; 363:1939–1949.

106. Johnson-Frey SH. The neural bases of complex tool use in humans. *Trends Cogn. Sci.* 2004; 8:71–78 (doi:10.1016/j.tics.2003.12.002).

107. Barham LS. Systematic pigment use in the Middle Pleistocene of South-Central Africa. *Current Anthropology* 2002; 43:181–190.

108. Renfrew C, Frith C, Malafouris L. *The Sapient Mind: Archeology Meets Neuroscience* (New York: Oxford University Press, 2009).

109. Arbib MA. From mirror neurons to complex imitation in the evolution of language and tool use. *Ann Rev Anthropol* 2011; 40:257–273.

110. Suddendorf T. Foresight and evolution of the human mind. *Science* 2006; 312:1006–1007. doi:10.1126/science 1129217.

111. Corballis MC. Mental time travel: a case for evolutionary continuity. *Trends Cogn Sci.* 2013; 17:5–6. doi: 10.1016/j.tics.2012.10.009.

112. Suddendorf T, Rose Addis D, Corballis MC. Mental time travel and the shaping of the human mind. *Phil. Trans. R. Soc. B* 2009; 364; 1317–1324. doi:10.1098/ rstb.2008.0301.

113. Lewis Williams D., *The Mind in the Cave* (London: Thames and Hudson, 2002).

114. Jablonka E, Ginsburg S, Dor D. The co-evolution of language and emotions. *Phil. Trans. R. Soc. B* 2012; 367:2152–2159.

115. Fitch TW., *The Evolution of Language* (Cambridge: Cambridge University Press, 2010).

116. Lieberman P. The Evolution of Human Speech. *Anthropology* 2007; 48:39–66.

117. Fleming SM, Dolan RJ. The neural basis of metacognitive ability. *Phil Trans R Soc B* 2012; 367:1338–1349.

118. Stanley SM, Ruddiman WF. Neogene Ice Age in the North Atlantic Region: Climatic Changes, Biotic Effects and Forcing Factors. In: Effects of Global Change on Life National Academy of Sciences 1995:118–133.

119. Stanley SM., *Children of the Ice Age* (New York: WH Freeman and Company, 1998).

120. Goldner A, Herold N, Huber M. Antarctic glaciation caused ocean circulation changes at the Eocene–Oligocene transition. *Nature* 2014; 511 (7511): 574 DOI: 10.1038/ nature13597.

121. Patriat P, Achache J. India-Eurasia collision chronology has implications for crustal shortening and driving mechanism of plates. *Nature* 1984; 311:615–621.

122. Cook CP, van de Flierdt T, Williams T et al. Dynamic behavior of the East Antarctic ice sheet during Pliocene warmth. *Nature Geoscience* 2013; DOI: 10.1038/ ngeo1889.

123. Hays JD, John Imbrie J, Shackleton NJ. Variations in the Earth's Orbit: Pacemaker of the Ice Ages. *Science* 1976; 194:1121–1132.

124. Kutterolf et al. When the Ice Melts, the Earth Spews Fire. *Science Daily* Dec. 19, 2012.

125. Kuhlbrodt, T, Griesel A, Montoya M, Levermann A, Hofmann M, Rahmstorf S. On the driving processes of the Atlantic meridional overturning circulation, *Rev. Geophysics* 2007; 45:RG2001. doi:10.1029/2004RG000166.

126. Rossby T. The North Atlantic Current and surrounding waters: At the crossroads. *Reviews of Geophysics* 1996; 34:463–481.

127. Sutton RT, Hodson DLR. Atlantic Ocean Forcing of North American and European Summer Climate. *Science* 2005; 309:115–118. Doi 10.1126/science.1109496.

128. Broecker WS. Thermohaline circulation, the Achilles' heel of our climate system: will man-made CO_2 upset the current balance? *Science* 1997 Nov 28; 278(5343):1582–8.

129. Stow D., *Vanished Ocean: How Tethys Reshaped the World* (Oxford: Oxford University Press, 2010).

130. Calvin WH., *A Brain for All Seasons* (Chicago: The University of Chicago Press, 2002).

131. Petit JR, Jouzel J, Raynaud D et al. Climate and atmospheric history of the past 420,000 years from the Vostok ice core, Antarctica. *Nature* 1999; 399:429–436.

132. Dansgaard, W, Johnson SJ, Clausen HB et al. "Evidence for general instability of past climate from a 250-kyr icecore record." *Nature* 1993; 364 (6434): 218–220.

133. Heinrich H. "Origin and consequences of cyclic ice rafting in the Northeast Atlantic Ocean during the past 130,000 years." *Quaternary Research* 1988; 29:142–152.

134. Bond G, Showers W, Cheseby M et al. A Pervasive Millennial-Scale Cycle in North Atlantic Holocene and Glacial Climates. *Science* 1997; 278:1257–1265.

135. Lisiecki LE, Raymo ME. *Paleoceanography* 2005; 20:1–17. DOI: 10.1029/2004PA001071.

136. deMenocal PB. The Plio-Pleistocene African Climate. *Science* 1995; 270:53–59.

137. Trauth M, Maslin MA et al. High and low latitude forcing of Plio-Pleistocene East African climate and human evolution. *J Hum Evol* 2007; 53:475–486.

138. Coulthard TJ, Ramirez JA, Barton N, Rogerson M, Brücher T. Were rivers flowing across the Sahara during the last interglacial? Implications for human migration through Africa. *PLoS ONE* 2013; 8(9): e74834.doi:10.1371/journal.pone.0074834.

139. Tolleson J. The case of the missing heat. *Nature* 2014; 505276–278 and Kosaka Y, Xie S-P. Recent global warming hiatus tied to equatorial Pacific surface cooling. *Nature* 2013; 501:403–407.

140. Bond G, Kromer B, Beer J et al. Persistent solar influence on North Atlantic Climate during the Holocene. *Science* 2001; 294:2130–2136.

141. Raymo ME, Ruddimen WF, Froelich PN. Influence of the late Cenozoic mountain building on ocean geochemical cycles. *Geology* 1988; 16:649–653.

142. Raymo ME, Ruddiman WF. Tectonic forcing of late Cenozoic climate. *Nature* 1992; 359:117–122 and Raymo ME. The Himalayas, organic carbon burial and climate in the Miocene. *Paleoceantography* 1994; 9:399–404.

143. Beaulieu E, Godderis Y, Donnadieu Y, Labat D Rolandt C. High sensitivity of the continental weathering carbon dioxide sink to future climate change. *Nature Climate Change* 2012; 2:346–349

144. Stow D., *Vanished Ocean: How Tethys Reshaped the World* (Oxford: Oxford University Press, 2010).

145. Cliver, EW, Svalgaard L., "The 1859 Solar–Terrestrial Disturbance and the Current Limits of Extreme Space Weather Activity." *Solar Physics* 2004; 224:407.
146. Feigin VL, Parmar PG, Barker-Collo S. et al. Geomagnetic storms can trigger stroke. Evidence from 6 large population based studies in Europe and Australasia. *Stroke* 2014; 45: 1639–1645.
147. Yeung JW. A hypothesis: Sunspot cycles may detect pandemic influenza A in 1700–2000 AD. *Med Hypotheses.* 2006; 67(5):1016–22.
148. Jozsa R, Halberg F, Cornélissen G et al. Chronomics, neuro-endocrine feed sideward and the recording and consulting of nowcasts-forecasts of geomagnetics. *Biomed Pharmacother.* 2005; 59 Suppl 1:S24–30.
149. Davis GE, Lowell WE. Solar cycles and their relationship to human disease and adaptability. *Med Hypotheses.* 2006; 67:447–461.
150. Merrill, RT, McElhinny MW, McFadden PL Phillip L. *The Magnetic Field of the Earth: Paleomagnetism, the Core, and the Deep Mantle* (London: Academic Press, 1998).
151. Mörner N-A. The Gothenburg Magnetic Excursion. *Quaternary Research* 1977; 7:413–427.
152. Noel M, Tarling DH. The Laschamp geomagnetic event. *Nature* 1975; 253:705–707.
153. Nowaczyk NR, Arz HW, Frank U, Kind J, Plessen B. Dynamics of the Laschamp geomagnetic excursion from Black Sea sediments. Earth and Planetary *Science Letters* 2012; 54:351–352 DOI:10.1016/j.epsl.2012.06.050.
154. Fan J1, Katz A, Randall L, Reece M. Dark-disk universe. *Phys Rev Lett.* 2013; 110(21):211302.
155. Randall L, Reece M. Dark matter as a trigger for periodic comet impacts. Reference: *Phys Rev Lett.* 2014 Apr 25; 112(16):161301.
156. Shultz S, Maslin M. Early Human Speciation, Brain Expansion and Dispersal Influenced by African Climate Pulses. *PLOS ONE* 2013; 8:1–7.
157. Coppens Y. East Side Story: the Origin of Humankind. *Scientific American,* May 1994:88–95.

158. Zimmerman M. The Nervous System in the Context of Information Theory. In Schmidt RF, Thews G (Eds). Human Physiology. Springer 1989: 166–173, Berlin.

159. Hassin RR, Uleman JS, Bargh JA., *The New Unconscious* (Oxford: Oxford University Press, 2005).

160. Libet B, Gleason CA, Wright EW, Pearl DK. Time of conscious intention to act in relation to onset of cerebral activity (readiness potential): the unconscious initiation of a freely voluntary act. *Brain* 1983; 106:623–642.

161. Attwell D, Laughlin SB. An energy budget for signaling in the grey matter of the brain. *J Cereb Blood Flow Metab.* 2001; 21:1133–45.

162. Squire LR, Berg D, Bloom FE, du Lac S, Ghosa A, Spitzer NC (eds). Fundamental Neuroscience 4th edition, 2012. Elsevier, Academic Press, New York, 2012:136–137.

163. Carey N., *The Epigenetics Revolution* (New York: Columbia University Press, 2012).

164. Douglas Fox D. "The Limits of Intelligence." *Scientific American* July 2011.

165. Van den Heuvel MP, Stam CJ, Kahn RS, Hulshoff Pol HE. Efficiency of functional brain networks and intellectual performance. *Journal of Neuroscience* 2009; 29:7619–7624.

166. Crossley NA, Mechelli A, Scott J, Carletti F, Fox PT, McGuire P, Bullmore ET. The hubs of the human connectome are generally implicated in the anatomy of brain disorders. *Brain* 2014; 137:2382–2395.

167. Liu X, Li G, Xiong S, Nan J, Li J et al. Hierarchical alteration of brain structural and functional networks in female migraine sufferers. *PLoS One* 2012; 7:e51250.

168. Buckner RL, Sepulchre J, Talukdar T et al. Cortical hubs revealed by intrinsic functional connectivity: mapping, assessment of stability and relation to Alzheimer's disease. *Journal of Neuroscience* 2009; 29:1860–1873.

169. Saxena S, Caroni P. Selective neuronal vulnerability in neurodegenerative disease: from stressor thresholds to degeneration. *Neuron* 2011; 71:35–48.

170. Cherniak C. The bounded brain: Toward quantitative neuroanatomy. *Journal of Cognitive Neuroscience* 1990; 2:58–66.

171. Berlyne DE. Uncertainty and epistemic curiosity. Br J Psychol. 1962; 53:27–34 and Leslie I. Curious. The desire to know and why your future depends on it. Basic Books, New York 2014.
172. Kringelbach MI, Vuust P, Geake J. The pleasure of reading Interdisciplinary *Science Reviews* 2008; 33:321–333.

2

Physical Exercise, Neurogenesis, Evolutionary Origins, and Implications for Brain Health

Global Health Challenges and the Pivotal Role of Exercise

The benefits of physical activity (PA) have been associated with a reduction of physical disease (coronary artery disease, obesity, colon cancer, breast cancer), neuropsychiatric disability (anxiety, depression), and improved cognition (attention, memory). Yet in the United States three quarters of adults fail to meet the rather lenient recommended 150 minutes of moderate exercise per week. Translating this inactivity amounts to seventy-five billion dollars in health cost in the year 2000.[1] In 2011, the US GDP was 10 trillion dollars, the amount spent on health care was 20%, yet estimates were that the majority (70%) of the diseases were preventable.[2] This confirmed earlier reports of a multinational study (52 countries) of thirty thousand elderly people that adopted a healthy lifestyle by incorporating fruits and vegetables in the diet, smoking cessation, avoiding excess alcohol, and adhering to a regular moderate exercise program, lowered heart disease by 50%.[3]

Physical Exercise Has Emerged as the Single Most Important Intervention for Primary Prevention of Alzheimer's Disease

The worldwide prevalence of Alzheimer's disease is predicted to increase from 30 million noted in 2010 to 106.2 million by 2050. Yet approximately one-third of cases can be attributed to seven modifiable risk factors, and this could potentially be translated into a reduction of Alzheimer's disease prevalence globally between 8.8–16.2 million individuals.[4] Of the seven risk factors, the most important modifiable one is inactivity and also the highest population attributable risk (table data for the United Kingdom).[5]

Table 2.1. Conditioning

Condition	Relative Risk	PAR (%)
Physical inactivity	1.82	21.8
Depression	1.65	8.3
Midlife hypertension	1.61	7.0
Midlife obesity	1.60	6.6
Smoking	1.59	10.6
Low educational attainment	1.59	12.2

Legends

PAR – population attributable risk. Taking into account the prevalence of the condition in the general population and combining it with the relative risk according to Levin's formula PAR = P × (RR-1)/ 1 + Px (RR-1).[6]

Evolutionary Overview

Our Exercise Heritage: We Are Born Runners Morphologically, Physiologically, and by Comparative Analysis Against Other Mammalian Runners

There is strong evidence that bipedalism and an athletic body form designed for endurance-type running preceded brain enlargement in humans.[7] The Laetoli footprints dated 3.6 million years ago, discovered in Tanzania, support bipedalism in australopithecine hominoids (figure 1.2.1).

Fig. 2.1. The Laetoli footprint trace fossils.
The oldest evidence for bipedalism denoting a heel strike, nondivergent big toe and distinct arch. Dated at 3.6 million years ago and discovered by Mary Leakey in Tanzania in 1978. Other features of this presumed *Astralopithecus afarensis* (Lucy) individual would have included a brain slightly bigger than a chimpanzee (~375–425 ml), a flared rib cage, curved fingers, horizontally rotated iliac blades, valgus knees and relatively larger semicircular canals.
Figure credit with permission: Donatius Kamamba, director of the Department of Antiquities and Museums, Tanzania and The Getty Conservation Institute (www.getty.edu).

Many of the specific adaptations in humans support the evolution of an endurance runner rather than walking although both are human features. *Endurance running* is loosely defined as "running several to dozens of kilometers at a time relying predominantly on aerobic metabolism." Among mammals, although humans are non-contestants in sprint-type distances, we compare very favorably in comparative analysis against prominent mammalian distance runners such as wolves, hyenas, wildebeest, and horses 8–10. In fact, trained distance runners can outperform conditioned horses over marathon and ultramarathon distances. Since 1980, although the annual British Man versus Horse Marathon (twenty-two miles) is usually won by the horse, less often by humans (2004 and 2007), the race is usually close.[11] Humans have developed energy-storing musculoskeletal leg components such as the relatively long and well-developed Achilles's tendons (human length 10 cm, chimpanzee length 1cm), the iliotibial tract, peroneus longus muscle, the longitudinal foot arch and plantar flexors, with energy-saving estimates of up to 50% during running.[12, 13] A fortuitous gene mutation of the ACTN3 gene may have contributed to the preponderance of slow-twitch muscle fibers that are required for endurance running in homo.[14] Our propensity to use fat as an energy source also speaks to our heritage as endurance runners.[15]

Table 2.2. Composite table of the musculoskeletal, metabolic, and cerebral adaptations of humans to running

Axial skeletal adaptations (adapted from Bramble and Lieberman)[16]
Relatively large and powerful gluteus maximus and erector spinae muscles
Narrow pelvis, waist, and thorax tall, narrow body morphology
Strong nuchal ligament for improved balance of head on shoulders
Head and pectoral girdle relatively decoupled
Low, wide shoulders Forearm shortening
Lumbar vertebral surface area relatively expanded
Iliac pillar relatively enlarged
Sacroiliac joint relatively stabilized

Appendicular skeletal adaptations
Long Achilles tendon Plantar arch Adducted hallux Short toes
Tuber calcaneus relatively enlarged Close packed calcaneocuboid
joint Relatively shorter femoral neck

Muscle adaptations
Slow-twitch fibers relatively emphasized

Metabolic adaptations
Fat metabolism
Ketone metabolism adaptation

Cerebrovascular
Cerebral venous circulation changes enabling improved blood cool-
ing Brain radiator theory[17]
More accessory foramina and expanded diploic veins[17]
Heat exchange between the veins and the carotid arteries in cavern-
ous sinus[18]

Cranial and cerebral adaptations
Enlarged radius of the anterior and posterior semicircular canals[19]
Mouth breathing and development of smaller snout[20]
Dentate gyrus with improved memory formation – critical to mov-
ing through a challenging environment[21]
Dopamine the predominant neurotransmitter of humans and cool-
ing effect[22]

The archeological record provides support for most of these
features to have first appeared in *Homo erectus* and some evidence
in *Homo habilis*. Comparisons are to chimpanzees and archeological comparisons to australopithecines. Carrier has proposed that
the endurance running evolved in early hominids for pursuing animals before the invention of spears, bow, and arrows in what has
been termed chase hunting or persistence hunting.[23] The hominids
had better heat tolerance, thanks to becoming relatively furless with
extensive skin sweating, our five to ten million sweat glands that cool
the blood and skin, enabling maximum sweat rates of two to four
liters per hour with 531 calories required to evaporate one liter of
water. This cools the skin by a similar amount.[24] In addition, the
upright posture with less surface area exposed to the sun, the lon-

ger and more slender limbs, and perhaps the cooling influence of a dopaminergic brain all played a role.[25] The chased quadruped succumbed to chase myopathy (heat-related muscle damage) and heat stroke before the human did. Because the most significant cerebral enlargement occurred after the appearance of *Homo*, it was bipedality and endurance running that set the stage for the markedly improved diet quality (meat, proteins, tubers) and subsequent brain growth and concomitant endurance running physique that we are equipped with today, accompanied by smaller guts—or meant to have![26]

Dopamine First Cooled Our Brains Then Became the Principal Neurotransmitter

In one of the largest cerebral networks, the frontal subcortical circuits, dopamine is the principal neurotransmitter.[22] How this came to be remains uncertain, but dopamine played a key role in the emergence of human intelligence. After paleoclimatological and the geological events that led to East Africa becoming relatively dry and arid, heat management and combating hyperthermia became a critical factor in survival of early hominoids such as *Australiopithecus africanus*. Dopamine lowers body temperature and perhaps played a significant role in early hominoids withstanding hyperthermia and enabling chase hunting and catching other mammals prone to chase myopathy (figure 2.2).[27]

Fig. 2.2. The concept of chase hunting and power scavenging.
Large African herbivors and carnivors were least active during the
midday heat. The hominin practice of chase hunting in the midday heat
exploited this niche opportunity as animals overheat before humans.
Artwork by Todd Soper, concept and design by author

Progressive dopamine expansion occurred within the cerebral
circuitry aided by calcium metabolism from prolonged aerobic activity and the increased dietary tyrosine (dopamine precursor) from
meat consumption in the period 2–3 mya.[28] There is also clinical
support for this theory as dopamine-blocking drugs (haloperidol,
risperidone, quetiapine) cause malignant hyperthermia (markedly
elevated body temperature) and neuroleptic malignant syndromes
(coma and encephalopathic states). Hence, it may be that dopamine
became accepted as the principal neurotransmitter in our evolving
brains and subsequently became a key neurotransmitter involved
with working memory and executive functioning.[22]

Power scavenging, or opportunistic scavenging, was a method early
hominins employed to obtain meat. This opportunistic strategy refers
to hominids being orientated in their pursuit of meat by the sight of
vultures flying over a distant animal carcass or seeking remains of kills
made by the large carnivores. This again underscores the importance of
long-distance and endurance running in our development (figure 2.3).[29]

**Fig. 2.3. Hominin cognitive evolution sequence:
Modern bodies first, then modern minds**

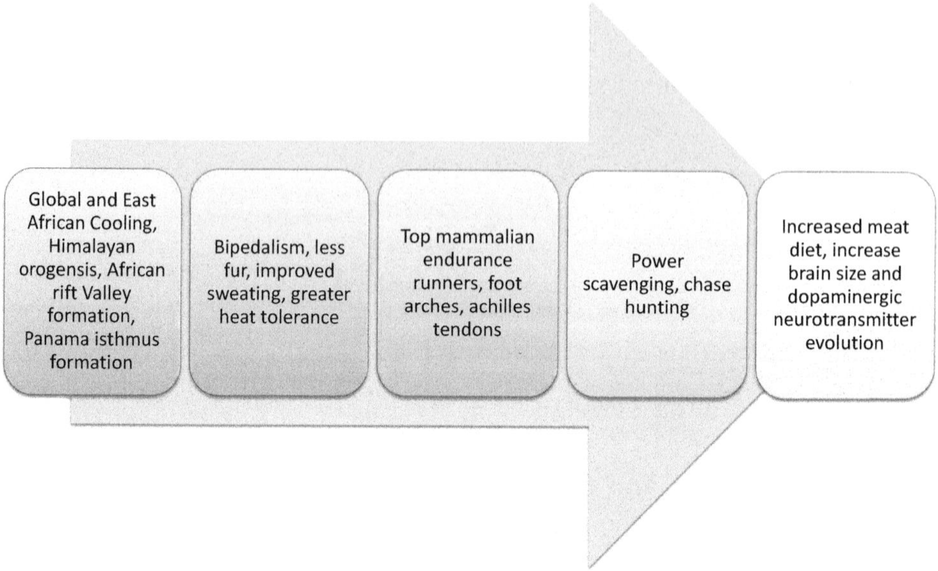

Global and East African Cooling, Himalayan orogensis, African rift Valley formation, Panama isthmus formation	Bipedalism, less fur, improved sweating, greater heat tolerance	Top mammalian endurance runners, foot arches, achilles tendons	Power scavenging, chase hunting	Increased meat diet, increase brain size and dopaminergic neurotransmitter evolution

A Number of Musculotendinous and Skeletal Features Made Human Running More Efficient

The foot arch reduces the energy cost of running by 17%, and the Achilles's tendon releases approximately 35% of the stored mechanical energy only during running, not walking. An enlarged gluteus maximus muscle relative to the apes further aided bipedal running, and stabilization of the neck and head while running was achieved through modification of the semicircular canals and a more robust nuchal ligament.[7]

During Hominin Evolution, Endurance Running Became Our Discerning Feature and This Was Subsequently Wired into the Brain's Hedonic Reward System (the Runner's High)

Endorphins and cannabinoids both feature in high-intensity exercise. The so-called runner's high refers to the subjective experience of a euphoric state after a mediumto long-distance running session. A positron emission tomography using an opioidergic ligand in ten athletes at rest and after two hours of endurance running (21.5 +/ km) revealed reductions in opioid receptors in prefrontal and limbic/ paralimbic cerebral regions. The rating of euphoria was significantly increased postrunning and inversely correlated with opioid binding in the following brain regions: orbitofrontal, anterior cingulate, bilateral insula, parainsular, and temporoparietal cortices. The data was interpreted by the researchers as supportive of the opioid theory of the runner's high.[30]

Corroborating findings have been documented from animal studies. It has been established that rats running on a treadmill increase hippocampal neurons. In a study to determine the opioid influence, brain sections from a group of running rats revealed a five-fold increase in hippocampal neurogenesis, which was attenuated by naltrexone, an opioid receptor antagonist. In voluntary running rats group, there was in addition a threefold elevation of hippocampal Metenkephalin-Arg-Phe contrasted with the nonrunning rats implying an increase in hippocampal opioid activity during running. These findings support an involvement of endogenous opioids in the regulation of hippocampal proliferation mediated through hypothalamic-pituitary-adrenal axis.[31]

Neurobiological and Basic Science

Endocannabinoids May Be Integral to the Runner's High in Humans and Other Mammals That Habitually Run

The endocannabinoid neurotransmitters are also expressed in the reward/hedonic circuitry and mediate reward by activating cannabinoid receptors after exercise. In a study of humans, dogs, and ferrets, exercise-induced endocannabinoid stimulation after high-intensity endurance running, but this effect was not seen with low-intensity activity such as walking. An increase in levels of anandamide and 2 arachidonoylglycerol (2-AG) were noted. This neurological reward circuitry may be the reason why mammals such as humans and dogs for example frequently partake in high-intensity endurance activity notwithstanding the demands in terms of exertion, energy usage, and potential risk. This effect was not seen in ferrets, which are regarded as noncursorials.[32, 33]

Table 2.3. Exercise-induced trophic factors that influence adult neurogenesis

1. BDNF - Brain-derived neurotrophic factor
2. IGF-I - Insulin-like growth factor I
3. VEGF - Vascular endothelial growth factor
4. BFGF2 - Basic fibroblast growth factor
5. EGF - Epidermal growth factor
6. Beta endorphin
7. Serotonin

Neurobiological Mechanisms of Physical Exercise Principally Affect Regulation of Growth Factors and Inflammation Attenuation

The proliferation of several growth factors in both the central and peripheral nervous system are triggered by physical exercise (table 2.3). A second major mechanism whereby PA reduces neurodegeneration and cognitive impairment is through the attenuation of inflammation.[34]

Animal Studies: Running Mice Grow New Brain Cells

Exercise studies conducted with mice running on a treadmill (forty-day periods) with evaluation of their hippocampal neurogenesis labeled by BrdU (5-bromodeoxyuridine) uptake were performed by Rhodes JS et al. During the initial exercise period, mice were injected with BrdU. Subsequent microtome sections through the dentate gyrus enabled counting of BrdU positive as an estimation of neurogenesis. Physical exercise (wheel running) increased BrdU positive cell number (significance established by two-way ANOVA, $F_{(1, 86)}$ = 505.1, $p < .0001$), whereas mice without access to wheels showed no significant increase.

A summary of the findings included the following:

1. A 56% increase in BDNF in hippocampus after forty days of wheel access

   A 20% increase in dentate gyrus volume after wheel access

2. Mice with wheels had 23% more granule neurons in granule layer of hippocampus
3. Spatial learning with access to running (figures 2.4 and 2.5)[35, 36]

Fig. 2.4. Hippocampal dentate gyrus neurogenesis in exercising mice.
Neurons depicted in green and new neurons in orange, in mice
exposed with no running wheel (A) compared to those with
a running wheel (B). The mean number of bromodeoxyurine
(BrdU) that labels dividing neurons in control and runner groups
(voluntary wheel runners) in (C). The distance run (over 10
days) and BrdU cell count in runners and controls (D).
Figure credit with permission: Rhodes JS, van Praag H, Jeffrey S
et al. Exercise increases hippocampal neurogenesis to high levels in
mice. Behavioral Neuroscience 2003; 117:1006–1016.

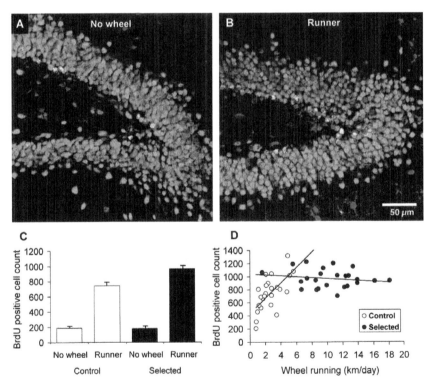

Fig. 2.5. Exercising (wheel running) mice and green fluorescent protein indicating new neurons in the hippocampus.

Figure credit with permission: van Praag, H, Schinder AF, Christie BR, Toni N, Palmer T, Gage FH. Functional neurogenesis in the adult hippocampus. Nature 2002; 415:1030–1034

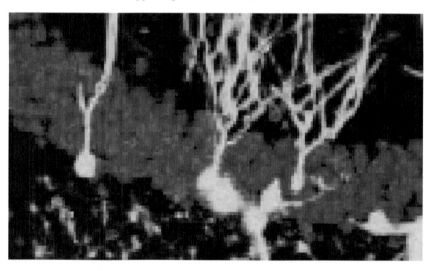

What Is Known About Neurogenesis in Animals in General?

Zebra fish have a relatively high number of neurogenic zones (sixteen regions), and within mammals there is much variation in neurogenesis. For example, the challenging environment of the red fox is thought to account for elevated neurogenesis. Mammals occupying relatively stable environmental niches are therefore considered to require lower levels of neurogenesis, and mammalian levels of hippocampal neurogenesis can be related to their flexibility and adaptability to their particular environment.[37]

Neurogenesis is known to occur in the hippocampus, which is an ancient component of the brain dating to the fish and amphibians. However, nonmammals do not have a dentate gyrus (DG), which therefore represents a more recent evolutionary addition, appearing after the monotremes. Overall the DG increase in size when tracked from the insectivores to humans is enlarged by a factor of 2.6 and the subcomponent CA1 by a factor of 6.6.[38]

What Is Known About Human Neurogenesis?

Three areas of neurogenesis have been under consideration, including the subgranular zone in the hippocampal dentate gyrus (associated with lifelong neurogenesis), the subventricular zone (which forms new interneurons destined for the olfactory bulb, which stops after childhood) and the striatum (which also forms interneurons, from the lateral ventricle wall).[39, 40]

Verifying neurogenesis had been a challenge in humans, but a magnetic resonance spectroscopy (MRS) method enabling imaging for the first time of neuronal progenitor cells in vivo was reported. Detection of the relatively low concentrations of neuronal progenitor cells in both live humans and rodent brains is therefore a promising technique in the evaluation of neurogenesis in neurological and psychiatric conditions.[41, 42]

Epidemiological Studies

Physical Activity Can Profoundly Reduce the Top Four Medical Illnesses

Regular exercise can reduce several categories of major illnesses by impressive margins. For example, dementia (50%), heart disease, stroke (35%), the risk of metabolic syndrome and type 2 diabetes mellitus (40%), overall mortality (30%) has been reported with moderate physical activity. In addition, improvements in weight management, sleep quality, mood and subjective energy occur.[43–45] The accumulating information in this regard has already led to primary care and general practitioner general guideline recommendations to include the "exercise prescription" as a vital part of the treatment regimen.[46]

Physical Activity Maintains Appropriate Weight and Lowers Hypertension

A well-conducted large study by Lee et al. showed that up to one hour moderate exercise per day maintains weight in the normal range in women.[47] Although the American Heart Association (AHA) guidelines recommend thirty minutes five days per week, several lines of evidence support more exercise than that, perhaps in the range of one to two hours five to six days per week. Thirteen prospective cohort studies involving 136,846 people, found that the relative risk (RR) of high and moderate physical activity was 0.81. There is an inverse dose response association between levels of PA and risk of hypertension.[48]

Improved Methods of Physical Activity Monitoring Continue to Show Similar Results

Higher levels of daily physical activity has been associated with a reduced Alzheimer's disease risk. More recent prospective cohort studies using sophisticated exercise tracking and using actigraphy to detect incident Alzheimer's disease—for example, from the rush memory and aging project—has also shown that adjusting for age, sex, and education, total daily physical activity was associated with a lower incident AD (hazard ratio = 0.477; 95% CI: 0.273–0.832) (Cox proportional hazards model).[49]

With Accumulating Clinical Trials, Eventually Meta-Analyses Emerge and Recent Ones Continue to Deliver the Same Message

The variance among published studies with respect to the relationship between physical activity and cognitive function relationship was recently addressed by a meta-analysis of prospective studies looking at the association between physical activity and cognitive decline in so-called normal people without dementia. An electronic literature search using the Cochrane library, MedLine, Embase, Google Scholar, and Web of Science enabled review of fifteen prospective studies (33,816 nondemented people) tracked for an average of one to twelve years. During follow-up, almost 10% (3,210 people) had cognitive decline, and the high-level physical activity group showed significant protection (~38%) with respect to cognitive decline (HR) 0.62, 95% (CI) 0.54–0.70; P < 0.00001). Even the low to moderate exercise group were protected to the tune of (~35%) against cognitive decline (HR 0.65, 95% CI 0.57–0.75; P < 0.00001). These results were interpreted as "a significant and consistent rotection for all levels of physical activity against the occurrence of cognitive decline."[50]

Physical Activity Decreases Rate of Cognitive Impairment and Dementia Onset

The Monongahela Valley Independent Elders Survey (MoVIES) was a population-based epidemiologic cohort study of cognitive impairment in dementia from 1987 to 2002. Subjects were aged sixty-five or older, and the original cohort was 1681.

Cognitive tests included MMSE, Trails A and B, CERAD 10 word list learning and delayed recall, story immediate recall, and delayed recall, initial letter fluency (P and S), category fluency (fruits and vegetables) fifteen-item CERAD version of the Boston Naming Test, CERAD constructional praxis and clock drawing. Among the high level exercise group, > 30 minutes per session, three times per week versus normal controls the rate of cognitive decline decreased by approximately 55%. In those with low levels of exercise, <30 minutes three times per week, the cognitive decline decreased rate by about 35%.[51, 52]

With aging the hippocampus shrinks, which is correlated with dementia as well as impaired memory. In a study examining aerobic exercise in 120 elderly people, it was found that the training increased the volume of their hippocampus overall by 2% (anterior aspect) with a clinical correlate of improved spatial memory. Not only did this reverse age-associated atrophy but also elevated serum BDNF, which is associated with neurogenesis, was noted.[53]

Physical Activity Protects Against Cognitive Decline: Meta-analyses Studies

In another meta-analysis of both randomized controlled trials and cross-sectional studies, examining aerobic exercise in healthy people showed improved cognitive scores, larger hippocampal volumes, and improved spatial memory. In addition improved connectivity by functional magnetic resonance was also documented after exercise periods that ranged from six to twelve months. This analysis concluded that benefits of physical exercise include a cerebral protective effect, attenuation of cognitive decline as well as decreasing small vessel cerebrovascular disease that leads to vascular cognitive impairment and vascular dementia. Physical exercise was rightly labeled a disease-modifying modality in aging and dementia.[54]

White Matter Changes on MRI Scans Frequently Signify Vascular Disease, Which Correlates with Memory Loss, Alzheimer's Dementia, Vascular Dementia; Predicts Decline in Mild Cognitive Impairment MCI; and Is Mitigated by Physical Exercise

Leukoaraiosis seen on MRI brain scans, also called white matter hyperintensities (WMH), usually indicate cerebrovascular small-vessel vascular disease.

Community-based research of 717 individuals using cognitive testing, MRI brain scans, and evaluation of cognitive reserve revealed that people with higher reserve had more leukoaraiosis implying improved capability of dealing with the pathology.[55]

Normal people that subsequently develop amnestic mild cognitive impairment were shown to have significant white matter signal reductions in parahippocampal gyrus, cingululm, precuneus, fornix as well as subcortical white matter changes. Diffusion tensor imaging studies using FA values found these to be predictive of conversion to amnestic MCI, which frequently develop Alzheimer's disease.[56]

White matter hyperintensity accumulation correlates with increasing small vessel disease, Alzheimer's disease and MCI. The increasing leukoaraoisis seen with increasing age are usually due to small vessel cerebrovascular disease but also suggest a link between Alzheimer pathology and white matter integrity.[57] The extent of leukoaraiosis seen on MRI is also predictive of more rapid decline in cognition in people already afflicted by mild cognitive impairment.[58] Impaired speed of information processing is affected (working memory) by white matter pathology components of the frontal sub cortical circuits, the frontal interhemispheric as well as thalamic fiber tracts. Cerebrovascular small vessel disease correlated with impaired processing speed.[59] In another study, looking at the effect of age and white matter disease with diffusion tensor imaging DTI a significant shortening of the white matter fiber bundle length in the anterior thalamic, radiation was noted for every one year of age increase over fifty years.[60] Finally in a meta-analysis, white matter lesions were shown to affect all cognitive domains adversely, but mostly severely affected were executive function and attention.[61]

Physical activity is related to the structural integrity of cerebral white matter. Physical activity and white matter integrity was examined in 440 people with small vessel cerebrovascular disease by DTI and revealed improved diffusivity (axial, radial, and mean diffusivity) in white matter areas. Impaired microstructural integrity is associated with reduced FA values.[62]

Cardiorespiratory Fitness and Cognition: Both Young and Old Stand to Benefit as well as Those Already Affected by Mild Cognitive Impairment

A positive association between cardiorespiratory fitness (CRF) and cognitive function was shown by the twenty-five-year CARDIA study. The methodology included a symptom limited treadmill exercise and VO_2 max measurements. Cognitive tests included tests for executive function (Stroop), psychomotor speed (RAVLT and DSST), and modified MMSE. The results after year 25 showed that in those > 55 years higher baseline CRF correlated with less diminution by the modified MMSE and improved cognitive tests performances for the Stroop and RAVLT tests.[63] A meta-analysis of eighteen studies in elderly patients showed fitness improvement after several months of physical exercise correlated significantly with psychomotor speed and several other cognitive domains but with the largest effect seen in the realm of executive function.[64]

Colcomb et al. subsequently revealed evidence of "brain building" in a number of brain regions, especially the frontal lobes, in response to a six-month aerobic exercise program in elderly people. The prefrontal and temporal cortices in particular were affected by the exercise, and these are the areas that most often deteriorate in the aging process. The preponderance of the executive areas involved are particularly noteworthy, as these relate to requisite personal and interpersonal capacities (figure 2.6).[65]

Fig. 2.6. Aerobic exercise increases brain gray matter volume (blue) and brain white matter, fiber tracts (yellow) in older adults involved in a six-month aerobic exercise program.
Results in blue and yellow refer to significant
differences, recorded compared to controls
Legend: ACC-anterior cingulate cortex, SMAsupplementary motor area, rIFG right inferior frontal gyrus, lSTL left superior temporal gyrus; AWM anterior white matter
Figure credit with permission: Colcomb SJ, Erickson KI, Scalf PE et al. Aerobic Exercise Training increases brain volume in aging humans. J Gerontology 2006; 61:1166–1170

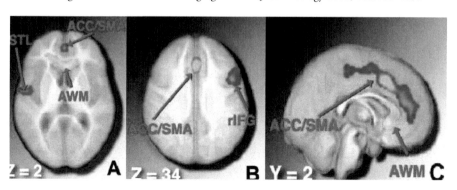

The mild cognitive impairment category of people also stands to benefit. In a study of study of thirty-three elderly people diagnosed with MCI, in whom the exercise was quantified by VO_2 peak (CRF surrogate) after six months, it was shown that an increasing VO_2 peak correlated with improved executive function, attention, multitasking and information processing performance.[66] Older patients also benefit, but activity measurement needs to be evaluated differently. Because physical activity includes both formal exercise as well as so-called nonexercise activity, actigraphy has been used to measure such activities. Continuous activity over a ten-day period was evaluated by actigraphy and cognitive evaluations in 716 elderly nondemented people as part of the prospective observation cohort study, the Rush memory and aging project. Tests after four years of monitoring showed that seventy-one had developed Alzheimer's disease, and that daily physical activity by actigraphy analysis was associated with a much reduced likelihood of developing AD with a hazard ratio of 0.477 (95 % confidence interval 0.273–0.832).[67]

Physical Activity Appears to Be a Promising Modality in Alleviating and Treating Depression and Anxiety

Animal Studies

All mammals have neurogenesis to varying degrees that give rise to both neurons as well as glial cells. No more than three sites have so far been verified in rats and humans, including the dentate gyrus of the hippocampus, the olfactory bulb, and the subventricular zone abutting the lateral ventricles. The number of neurons generated per day in the rat hippocampal dentate gyrus rats has been estimated to be approximately 9,000 per day.[68] New glial cells also grow in these two zones from precursor cells. Studies so far reveal that three environmental influences in mice support neurogenesis, including a learning-enriched environment, learning new tricks and physical exercise. After such stimuli, neurogenesis has been observed after three days but maximally by about one week. New neurons seem to take four to five weeks to become functional, which is the latency period typically seen for antidepressant therapy to work.[69] The adult neurogenesis hypothesis of major depressive disorder (MDD) is supported by brain volume studies indicating reduced hippocampal volume as well as by functional imaging (activity and blood flow studies) of low amygdala and prefrontal blood flow. Further support for this theory is suggested by an increase in adult neurogenesis after treatment for MDD with selective serotonin reuptake inhibitors.[70]

Effects of Exercise on Depression, Cognition, and Anxiety

In those with depression, both exercise and cognitive behavioral therapy have similar beneficial effects. Multiple epidemiological studies showed that exercise significantly improved depressive symptoms, the effects of which can persist for months (six and twenty-one months) after exercise therapy ceases. The beneficial effects of exercise effects also include cognitive improvement and an antianxiety effect. Activation of both the endocanniboid and opioid cerebral networks may be the neurobiological mechanism for the anxiolytic effects of exercise.[71] Physical activity boosts trimonoamines, and the antidepressant as effective as serotonergics appears to be as least as effective as serotonergics, which may be partly explained by enhanced neurogenesis. Antidepressants such as sertraline and fluoxetine are considered to have a neurogenesis effect.[72]

The neurobiology of molecular mediators of neurogenesis and the beneficial effects of exercise include increased levels of β-endorphins and serotonin (both promote DG neurogenesis) whereas VEGF and BDNF both enhance survival of new neurons.[73-75]

Small vessel disease (SVD), a type of cerebrovascular disease, causing stroke is typically associated with risk factors such as hypertension, and diabetes and may also be associated with depression. Traditionally depression has been attributed to the physical limitations and or disabilities related to stroke. However, in a study of one hundred patients with SVD using diffusion tensor imaging, it was shown that fractional anisotropy (FA) as a marker of white matter impairment correlated directly with depression as measured by the thirty-item Geriatric Depression Scale. Damage to the frontal subcortical circuits, which subserve a variety of executive and higher cortical functions, also regulate mood and consequently depressive symptoms result. One possible intervention is clearly exercise, which may mediate its beneficial effects through improved cerebrovascular health.[76]

Metabolic Effects of Physical Activity: Improved Lipid Profile and Glucose Levels

Physical activity facilitates muscle glucose uptake, a process that does not require insulin. High levels of insulin are associated with increased cancer risk such as of the colon and breast.[77] Physical exercise has an effect on small and large LDL molecules with a decrease in small LDL (bad) and an increase in the large LDL (good) molecule. This is important as the same overall LDL levels in different people translates into a different risk status.[78] Skeletal muscle function is improved via mitochondrial mechanisms that respond to protein peroxisome proliferator-activated receptor γ coactivator 1α (PGC-1α), which enhances lipid oxidation of muscle for improved sustained muscular activity.[79]

Improved Educational Outcome in Children's School Performance and Physical Activity

A Swedish study of a physical exercise intervention program and academic performance conducted according to a controlled and cross-sectional methodology was conducted to assess grade five students who achieved the national learning goals in Swedish national goals (mathematics, English, Swedish) compared to reference schools. A twofold increase in students in the exercise program achieved the national goals (all three subjects) compared to the reference schools.[80]

Physical Activity and Immune System: The J-Shaped Curve Relationship Between Exercise and Susceptibility to Infection

Exercise immunology searches yield over two thousand reports and the formation of the International Society of Exercise and Immunology (ISEI) in 1989 speaks to the importance of this field www.isei.dk/index.php. Moderate exercise, in comparison to a sedentary, state is associated with an overall decrease in the incidence of infection. Strenuous exercise on the other hand, especially if frequent (daily) or prolonged (for example, 1.5 hours or more) and relatively intense (55–75% of maximum oxygen uptake), has been associated with a transient depression of various immune function indicators. These include parameters such as lymphocyte proliferation, neutrophil respiratory burst, and major histocompatibility complex class II protein expression and monocyte antigen presentation expression. This immune depression has been measured to last three to twenty-four hours after exercise.[81] Exercise may also be protective against some types of neoplasms with one of the mechanisms mediated by enhanced antitumor immunity.[82]

The Immune System: Many Alterations Have Been Documented, but the Relationship to Benefit from Exercise Remains Uncertain

The beneficial effects of exercise may be a consequence to the alterations in various immune-related substances that affect leucocyte functions. These include plasma concentration increases of various substances that are known to influence leukocyte functions, including inflammatory cytokines.[83]

1. TNF-alpha
2. macrophage inflammatory protein-1
3. IL-1Beta
4. Cytokines, interleukins (IL), IL-6, IL-10, and IL-1receptor antagonist (IL-1ra)
5. Acute phase reactants, C-reactive protein (CRP)
6. Toll-like receptor (TLR) expression

Toll-like receptors are transmembrane proteins involved in the recognition of microbes. Strenuous exercise has been shown to decrease TLR 1, 2, 4 on monocytes for several hours.[84] They may represent one of the links between inactivity, inflammation, and chronic disease.[85, 86] The beneficial response to exercise may be due to an anti-inflammatory mediated via the cytokine pathway, involving IL-1 and IL-10. Both acute and chronic exercise alters the number and function of the innate immune system, including monocytes, neutrophils, and natural killer cells.[87]

Measurement of saliva IgA (mucosal immunity marker) have revealed that intense or prolonged exercise (as opposed to mild or moderate exercise) may decrease secretion of saliva IgA. A reduction of saliva IgA is associated with susceptibility to upper respiratory tract infection. A positive correlation between hippocampal IL-18 and GRO-KC levels and neurogenesis has also been reported in rats. Daily exercise improved cognition in these rats with hippocampal neurogenesis and neuroimmune cytokine signaling being the proposed mechanisms.[88]

Evolutionary Perspective: The Unique Role of the Hippocampal Dentate Gyrus

When the first amphibians (*Tiktaalik*) first ventured onto land, they encountered a new kind of environment and challenges that required not only a more flexible response but also an ability to call upon previous encounters for a more adaptable response. This has been reflected both in a progressive increase in cortical size from fish, through amphibians, reptiles, to mammals, but also the development of neurogenesis. In mammals, adult hippocampal neurogenesis in particular has been a defining feature. Even though the hippocampus is regarded as ancient part of the brain dating back to fish and reptiles, the dentate gyrus (DG) evolved more recently with specific adaptive responses seen particularly in mammals. The dentate gyrus has an extensive connectivity with other cortical areas making it a suitable structure to influence differing cortical regions especially in the context of new memory formation and neurogenesis in the DG. This mammalian feature is regarded as a major evolutionary attribute that allowed a more efficient and advantageous response to environmental challenges that ultimately translated into improved survival.[89]

Why Does Neurogenesis Occur in Response to Physical Exercise: Neurobiological Functions of the Dentate Gyrus

Venturing onto land and, much later in evolution, changing from an arboreal to a terrestrial environment (leaving the tree for the savanna) both resulted in more mobility and its consequent increase in likelihood of encounters with potential adversaries. The demand for more complex cognition and information processing in terms of units of time became necessary. Integrating new information and incorporating this with previously learned experiences was key and was provided by the hippocampus. From a neurobiological perspective, the terms "pattern separation" and "contextualization of information" are processes enabled by the hippocampus. Garthe A. et al. refer to *pattern separation* as the "ability to distinguish two items of information in time"—neurons are "time stamping" new information.[90] The adaptability consequent to adult hippocampal neurogenesis, however, comes at a price. In humans, deficient adult neurogenesis has been correlated with depression, decreased cognitive flexibility, and schizophrenia.[91]

There Is a Mismatch Between the Emerging Message and What People Do

Even though physical activity (PA) is associated with a reduction in so many medical conditions, including physical (coronary artery disease, colon cancer, breast cancer, obesity) disorders, mental (depression, anxiety) and cognitive (memory, attention), however, in the United States, 74% of adults do not meet guidelines for thirty minutes of moderate intensity physical exercise most days of the week. The cost effects of inactivity is associated with 2.4% of health care expenditure in 1995, seventy-six billion dollars of medical costs in 2000.[92]

Some Pertinent Physiological Aspects of Physical Exercise

Table 2.4. Terminology of physical activity measures

TEE—Total energy expenditure
TDEE—TEE over a twenty-four-hour period
PAL—Physical activity level (TEE/ BMR)
PAR—Physical activity ratio, energetic costs of individual activity
RMR—Resting metabolic rate
MET—Metabolic equivalent; a ratio of exercising metabolism to RMR

PAL is a method of describing energy expenditure as a consequence of physical activity and varies from 1.2 (bedbound), light activity range from 1.4–1.69, moderate 1.7–1.99, vigorous 2.0–2.4, and elite sportsmen may attain 4.5–5.0 to 5 (Tour de France).[93, 94]

The relationship between PAL and PAR is PAL = ΣPARi (Ti) /24 Where PARi is physical activity ratio of each activity "i" and Ti is time spent in hours in each activity "i."

Table 2.5. Some selected PAR activities in men (women)[95]

Sleeping 1.0 (1.0)
Standing 1.4 (1.5)
Walking 2.8 (3.0)
Weeding garden 3.3 (2.9)
Cycling (moderate speed) 5.6 (3.6)
Long distance running 6.3 (6.6)
Sprinting 8.2 (8.3)

MET, similar to PAR metabolic equivalents, is the ratio of exercising metabolism to RMR for specific activities. These are roughly equivalent to PAR's varying from light <3.0 METs, moderate 3.0–6.1 and vigorous >6.0[96]

A compendium containing 821 codes of specific activities has been published (2011) with measured MET values as an attempt at quantifiction of physical activity.[97]

Measuring Physical Activity

Doubly labeled water 18O and 2H
Heart Rate monitoring with flex point
Accelerometers (tri-axial type)
Time allocation interviews, questionnaires, diaries
Time allocation, behavioral observation

The major problem with accelerometers concerns those that are worn at the waist, which will not capture upper body movements.

Activity levels based on pedometer step counts per day:
Sedentary <5,000
Low activity 5,000–7,499
Somewhat active 7,500–9,999
Active 10,000–12,499
Highly active >12,500

Amount of Daily or Weekly Exercise: 150 Minutes or 420 Minutes?

Women who exercised for approximately sixty minutes per day of moderate intensity were successful in maintaining normal weight and gaining fewer than 2.3 kg over a thirteen-year study. Federal guidelines recommend over 150 minutes of exercise per week published in 2008 may therefore be insufficient.[98] In healthy, active individuals, a physical activity program of at least thirty minutes in duration for three sessions per week is associated with consistent improvements in health status.[99]

Exercise Intensity

Calculation of maximal heart rate for a particular age and gender can be calculated by a number of different formulas. One such formula is Millers: MHR = 217 (0.85 × age). Thereafter one can evaluate intensity of exercise according to the individual heart rate parameters set out by his formula:

> Low intensity up to 80% of maximal heart rate
> Medium intensity 80–85% of maximal heart rate
> High intensity 85–90% of maximal heart rate
> Maximal 90–100% with buildup of lactic acid (anaerobic)[100]

VO$_2$ Max

Volume of oxygen uptake maximum (VO$_2$ max) is widely accepted as a measure of aerobic endurance and athletic cardiovascular fitness. Hypothetically, the more oxygen the body can use during intense exercise, the more ATP can be produced. VO$_2$ max is measured in the laboratory and recorded in units of ml of oxygen per minute per kg of body weight. Values for the average untrained man are 35–40 mL/kg/min and woman 27–31 mL/kg/min.[101] These values decrease with age and can be improved with training. The highest recorded values in humans have been in endurance sports such as one of the Tour de France winners (Miguel Indurain) VO$_2$ max 88.0 and Norwegian cross-country skier Bjørn Dæhlie 96. These values pale in comparison to our fellow mammalian cursorials (good running animals) such as the cheetah at 130, Siberian dogs involved in the Iditarod marathon at 240, and the best of all, the North American pronghorn antelope 300.[102] One may wonder why the latter have such superlative credentials. Some ten thousand years ago there were cheetahs chasing them in North America, who have since become extinct whereas the pronghorn antelope live on with this pedigree of a 300 VO$_2$ max as a reminder of the distant past coaching.

Table 2.6. Measuring VO max[104, 105]

Fick equation

$VO_2 max = Q \times (CaO_2 - CvO_2)$

Uth – Sorensen – Overgaard Pedersen estimation

$VO_2 max = 15 HRmax/HRrest$ Legend

Qcardiac output, CaO_2—arterial oxygen, CvO_2 – venous oxygen content

HRmax/HRrest—An estimate of VO_2 max, using maximum and resting heart rates

A Danish study of runners training aerobically (100 km per week at 60–80% of their VO_2 max) compared to a group training more anerobically (only 50 km per week but with many faster interval sessions) showed a VO_2 improvement only in the latter group. Hence, the tenet for high intensity as opposed to high-volume training for improving VO_2 max. However, the top speed attained during a test may be a better predictor of performance than VO_2 max itself. This factors in what is called running economy, which includes the oxygen consumption of running at a particular speed which includes body leanness, calf circumference, leg stiffness, step length, orthotics, such as running shoes, which may worsen efficiency, and barefoot training, which may improve efficiency.[106]

The Concept of vVO₂ Max

The velocity at maximal oxygen uptake (vVO₂max) is the peak running pace that an athlete can maintain for an average of about six minutes at which maximal oxygen uptake is reached. For elite distance runners this may be a four-minute mile pace or less or a speed of 24 km/hour or more. This is defined as the minimum running speed that elicits the VO_2 max in a runner or other sport. Those with good running economy for example would use less oxygen to run at a specified speed in comparison to a runner with less efficient running economy. Hence, vVO₂ max is dependent on VO_2 max as well as running economy. The duration of time for which a runner can maintain their vVO₂ max is called the tlimvVO₂ max and the average time for endurance type runners is six minutes (range 4–10 minutes). By incorporating frequent running sessions at vVO_2 max as part of their training, a runner thereby improves both running economy as well as neuromuscular control.[107]

Determining and Using vVO_2 Max During Training

After a warm-up, run at maximal pace on the track for six minutes and measure the distance travelled in meters. This distance is divided by 3,600 to yield a vVO_2 result, recorded in meters per second. Research by Billat has suggested that one weekly session at vVO_2 max is successful for improving vVO_2 max in experienced athletes. He pioneered the so-called 30-30 workouts (30 sec maximal running exertion followed by 30 sec at 50% VO2 max). One progresses one month later to 60–60 workouts and then to 5 × 180 second sessions yielding the Billat formula: 30-60-180 second intervals at vVO max.[108–110]

Lactate Threshold

The lactate threshold (or anaerobic threshold, AT) refers to the exercise intensity in a particular individual and sport where lactic acid begins to accumulate in the blood, rather than being removed. It is very useful for determining exercise intensity in endurance-type sports, and interval training can increase this capacity, during which the LT is temporarily exceeded. It is measured by taking blood samples during a treadmill test and resting values are around 1 mM and a typical LT is 4 mM.[111]

Biochemistry

Glycolysis provides pyruvate (via the Krebs cycle) for immediate energy required by muscular activity. Carbohydrates are the most important energy source for high-intensity exercise. Intense or stenuous physical activity causes a buildup of pyruvate as well as lactate (via lactate hydrogenase). Lactate can move from the muscles to the liver where it can be metabolized into glucose as well as synthesis of glycogen. Glycogen is the most important form of carbohydrate storage in the body. The ability of lactate to be converted back into pyruvate during exercise makes it an important source of immediate energy for muscles. Lactate can also be converted into glycogen (which is used for immediate energy). Lactate is a much more immediate energy source as it is not dependent on insulin (as is glucose) and therefore can be transported into muscles, as well as other organs (especially the heart) for energy much more quickly. Lactate is rapidly removed from the bloodstream, not so for glucose, which is transported away more slowly by insulin and so keeps the insulin levels low. One of the effects of high insulin levels is the transport of glucose into adipose (fat) tissue with obesity as a consequence.[112]

Training

Every athlete or runner has a specific lactate threshold at which blood lactate levels continue to build up and the speed at which this occurs is one of the best indicators of endurance activity.[113] The role of lactic acid—rather than impede muscle contractility, it may function as a key fuel for muscles and may improve rather than retard performance.[14,115]

Polypill or Polyintervention?

A considerable number of publications have debated the feasibility of a polypill (such as aspirin, statin, and antihypertensive agent) for the prevention of cardiovascular disease. However, a much more sensible alternative, from an evolutionary point of view, and effective alternative, is physical exercise. PE has many other beneficial effects such as improved cognition, depression, weight reduction, and energy levels, a vastly diminished side effect profile and extremely low cost by comparison.[116]

The Exercise Prescription Is a Top Priority

A methodical approach will need to be followed for implementing physical activity. Many people have musculoskeletal impairments, imbalance, and cardiac compromise. The following are suggested:

Screening

An evaluation of musculoskeletal and cardiac status is important prior to embarking on an exercise program. Depending on the pre-morbid status and concomitant medical illnesses, a physiotherapy consultation for assessment of balance, coordination, musculoskel-etal ability and a cardiovascular assessment that includes an ECG, rhythm strip and cardiac stress testing is recommended.

Types of Exercise

This may vary from monitoring nonexercise activity only measured by triaxial actigraphy to vVO_2 max and lactate threshold in compet-itive athletes and those who are able to participate in high-intensity aerobic exercises.

Exercise prescription should include the following:

1. Aerobic (becoming fit running, cycling, swimming, kayaking)
2. Anaerobic (improve fitness interval training sessions)
3. Strength training (many benefits including hypertension and weight reduction)
4. Yoga (flexibility, stretching, correcting muscle imbalance due to specific sports) [117, 118]

Some Particularly Noteworthy Sports:
Swimming, Kayaking, and Fencing

Swimming

Swimming is beneficial not only from a cardiorespiratory point of view, but it also has direct cognitive value. The study by About-Dest et al. used eight different tests to evaluate executive function in the swimming and control groups.

According to their study, there were indicators of possible direct effects on augmenting cognitive reserve in addition to the cardio-vascular and cerebrovascular benefits on brain function, derived from physical exercise.[119] Aquatherapy, as a related water-based activ-ity, refers to pool activities not necessarily including swimming.

Supervised by an aquatic therapist in a heated pool, it is particularly suited to those with compromised joints, poststroke weakness, musculoskeletal, spinal or imbalance conditions.

Kayaking

Despite our species being described as born runners, not everyone is suited to running or cycling for that matter because of various musculokeletal, balance, or plain preference issues. In addition road-sharing with cars presents a potential hazard especially for cycling. In this regard, kayaking or kayak therapy has some unique advantages:

1. Maximal aerobic potential, comparable to running and swimming
2. Can be done in tandem, which facilitates learning and safety
3. Exercise in natural environment (nature therapy)
4. Gravity-related injuries not an issue
5. Safety (no roads, no falls, no collisions)
6. High BMI not as compromising as running, cycling
7. Presbyopia and presbyacusis not compromising
8. Various subdisciplines (river, lake, ocean, one-, two-, or four-person craft)

Kayaking also combines both aerobic and anaerobic components. VO_2 max measurements for high-level competitive kayakers are generally high with readings by van Someren and Oliver for example at 58 ml/kg/min comparable to swimming at 58.4 ml/kg/min.[120] Lower body activities such as running, cycling, and Nordic skiing may range in values up to the seventies and higher. The smaller muscle mass involved with paddling as opposed to running or cycling has to be factored in. Upper and lower body activities may need their own tables.[121] Billat et al. reviewed exhaustion times for kayakers and found these to be higher than cyclists for example. However, heart rates and blood lactate levels were similar among these endurance sports with the exception of swimmers who tended to generate lower heart rates as well as lower lactate levels.[122]

Physical Exercise in Combination with Cognitive Challenge

There is evidence from rodent studies that physical exercise combined with cognitive challenges may have the most benefit. Whereas physical exercise induces neurogenesis, mostly in the hippocampus, simultaneous involvement with cognitive challenges was associated with survival of the newly formed neurons. These so-called physical and mental (MAP) training tasks, therefore, led to neurogenesis and cell survival (figure 2.7).[123]

Fig. 2.7. Mental and physical (MAP) training in combination is more effective than one or the other.

The ability in being able to balance on the accelerating rotarod (labeled physical skill learning) yielded the largest number of surviving cells.

Figure credit with permission: Curlik DM, Shors TJ. Training your brain: Do mental and physical (MAP) training enhance cognition through the process of neurogenesis in the hippocampus? Neuropharmacology. 2013 Jan; 64:506–14.

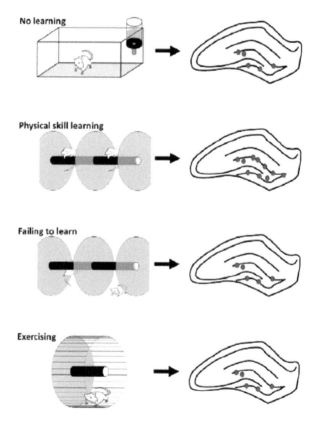

If applicable to humans, this would have relevance to a number of sporting activities that combine both.

Fencing

Fencing combines physical exercise, cognitive challenges, and most likely emotive attributes. Modern sport fencing presents a relatively unique combination of affronts that tax both physical and mental swiftness, simultaneously, as well possible emotional intelligence control. The constant movement of engagement, with lightning-speed decision making, often referred to as physical chess, also taxes the emotional component by constantly invading the extrapersonal space, or transgressing into the peripersonal space of the opponent. The peripersonal space is the space around us that can be reached by our own limbs, or body centered, and restricted to the space around the body within approximately 70 cm. These are subserved by the neural circuitry, predominantly of the posterior brain regions (post central and supramarginal gyri of the parietal lobe). Tool or object use can modify this peripersonal space.[124] The discovery and use of metals and, subsequently, swords had major implications for the way people interacted during those eras. Face-to-face social interaction takes place in the interpersonal space. This can be infringed upon by an object such as use of a sword, which can invade the extrapersonal space. Our extrapersonal space is subserved by different neuronal circuitry that involves predominantly anterior brain regions (right dorsolateral prefrontal, ventral premotor cortex, BA6, anterior and ventral medial frontal gyrus, superior and middle temporal lobe gyrus), overlapping considerably with many of the regions of the emotional brain circuitry.[125] The sword allows extension into the extrapersonal space (or invasion of the interpersonal space), forcing a connection between the two contestants. The skills required to vanquish the opponent necessitates an adeptness of movement from the feet to the head, together with the utmost focus of attention of the arm, hand, and sword tip with the right emotional valence. At the same time the constant challenge of the opponent's moves require evasion. [126] A human study using MRI based cerebral blood volume (CBV) measurements revealed hippocampal dentate gyrus (DG) blood volume increases in response to physical exercise. The DG blood volume increases correlated positively with both cognitive and cardiopulmonary function. This exercise-induced neurogenesis effect on the DG is particularly noteworthy in view of the DG being implicated in neurological diseases such as dementia, memory disorders, and schizophrenia. This study was based on the findings that exercise induces both neurogenesis (new neurons) as well as angiogenesis (new blood vessel formation) and that the increased CBV noted by MRI scanning represents a real time correlate of neurogenesis. [127]

Monitoring Devices

Actigraphy devices (Nike fitbit, Withings Pulse Monitor)

GPS systems (allow speed, distance, heart rate, cadence locality monitoring)

GPS with VO_2 max estimation (Garmin 620 the first with VO_2 estimation)

Monitor Progress

Electronic charting from actigraphy and GPS units—day to day, week to week, or monthly progress—can easily be monitored either in terms of overall activity, number of steps taken per day. The more advanced GPS devices allow demonstration of speed, distance travelled, average heart rate, heart rate zone, and VO_2 max measurements. In addition, the benefit of the particular exercise it measures, also called training effect, which measures the impact (maintaining it or level of improvement) of the particular exercise on the current aerobic fitness of the individual. The GPS Garmin 620 in addition to estimating VO_2 max grades the training effect on a scale of 1 to 5:

1 – Minor
2 – Maintaining
3 – Improving
4 – Highly improving
5 – Overreaching

Reconciliation

As with drug prescriptions, a reconciliation of activity per week, month, or other period can be relatively easily performed by downloading the electronic information from these monitors, whether actigraphy or GPS-based systems.

References

1. Hillman CH, Erickson KI, Kramer AF. Be Smart exercise your heart: exercise effects on brain and cognition. *Nature Neuroscience Reviews* 2008; 9:58–65.
2. Russo P. Population health. In health care delivery in the United States. Eds: Kovner AR, Knickman Jr. New York, Springer 2011:85–102.
3. Yusuf S et al. Effect of potentially modifiable risk factors associated with myocardial infarction in 52 countries. The Interheart Study. *Lancet* 2004; 364:937–952.
4. Brookmeyer R, Johnson E, Ziegler-Graham K, Arrighi HM. Forcasting the global burden of Alzheimer's disease. *Alzheimers Dement* 2007; 3:186–191.
5. Norton S, Matthews FE, Barnes DE, Yaffe E, Brayne C. Potential for primary prevention of Alzheimer's disease: an analysis of population based data. *Lancet Neurology* 2014; 13:788–7794.
6. Levin ML. The occurrence of cancer in man. *Acta Unio Int Contra Cancrum* 1953; 9:531–541.
7. Bramble DM, Lieberman DE. Endurance running and the evolution of Homo. *Nature* 2004; 432:345–352.
8. Garland T Jr. The relation between maximal running speed and body mass in terrestrial mammals. *J Zool* 1983; 199:157–170.
9. Bramble DM, Carrier DR. Running and breathing in mammals. *Science* 1983; 219:251–256.
10. Minetti AE. Physiology: efficiency of equine express postal systems. *Nature* 2003; 426:785–786.
11. http://news.bbc.co.uk/2/hi/uk_news/wales/mid_/6737619. stm. Two men beat horses in marathon. BBC Saturday, 9 June 2007.
12. Alexander RM. Energy saving mechanisms in walking and running. *J Exp Biol* 1991; 160:55–69.
13. Ker RF, Bennett MB, Bibby SR, Kester RC, Alexander RM. The spring in the arch of the human foot. *Nature* 1987; 325:147–149.
14. Yang N et al. ACTN3 genotype is associated with human elite athletic performance. *Am J Hum Genet* 2003; 73:627–631.

15. Horvath PJ, Eagen CK, Fisher NM, Leddy JJ, Pendergast DR. The effects of varying dietary fat on performance and metabolism in trained male and female runners. *J Am Coll Nutr.* 2000 Feb; 19(1):52–60.

16. Bramble DM, Lieberman DE. Endurance running and the evolution of Homo. *Nature.* 2004; 432:345–52.

17. Falk D. Brain evolution of Homo: the radiator theory. *Behav Brain Sci* 1990; 13:333–381 Carrier DR. The energetic paradox of human running and hominid evolution. *Curr Anthropol* 1984; 25:483–495.

18. Cabanac M, Caputa M. Natural selective cooling of the human brain: evidence for its occurrence and magnitude. *J Physiol Lond* 1979; 286:255–264.

19. Spoor F, Wood B, Zonnefeld F. Implications of early hominid labyrinthine morphology for evolution of human bipedal locomotion. *Nature* 1994; 369:645–648.

20. Niinimaa V, Cole P, Mintz S, Shephard RJ. The switching point from nasal to oronasal breathing. *Resp Physiol* 1981; 42:61–71.

21. Kemperman G, New Neurons for survival of the fittest. Nature Neuroscience Reviews 2012; 13:727–736.

22. Previc FH. Dopamine and the origin of human intelligence. *Brain and Cognition* 1999; 41:299–350.

23. Carrier DR. The energetic paradox of human running and hominid evolution. *Current Anthropology* 1984; 25:483–495.

24. Lieberman DE. The story of the human body. Pantheon Books, New York 2013.

25. Previc FH. Dopamine and the origin of human intelligence. *Brain and Cognition* 1999; 41:299–350

26. Latimer B, Lovejoy CO. The calcaneus of *Australopithecus afarensis* and its implications for evolution of bipedality. Am J Phys Anthropol 1989; 78:369–386.

27. Bortz WM II. Physical exercise as an evolutionary force. *Journal of Human Evolution* 1985; 14:145–155 and Carrier DR. The energetic paradox of human running and hominid evolution. Current Anthropology 1984; 25:483–495.

28. Leonard WR, Robertson MS. Comparative primate energetics and hominid evolution. *American Journal of Physical Anthropology* 1997; 102:265–281

29. Speth JD. Early hominid hunting and scavenging: the role of meat as an energy source. *Journal of Human Evolution* 1998; 18:329–343.

30. Boecker H, Sprenger T, Spilker ME, Henriksen G, Koppenhoefer M, Wagner KJ, Valet M, Berthele A, Tolle TR. The runner's high: opioidergic mechanisms in the human brain. *Cereb Cortex.* 2008; 18:2523–31.

31. Persson AI, Naylor AS, Jonsdottir IH, Nyberg F, Eriksson PS, Thorlin T. Differential regulation of hippocampal progenitor proliferation by opioid receptor antagonists in running and non-running spontaneously hypertensive rats. *Eur J Neurosci.* 2004 Apr; 19(7):1847–55.

32. A. Raichlen DA, Foster AD, Gerdeman G, Seillier A, Giuffrida, Wired to run: exercise induced endocannabinoid signaling in humans and cursorial mammals with implications for the 'runner's high'. *J Exp Biol* 2013; 215:1331–1336.

33. Panksepp, J, Knutson, B. and Brurgdorf, J. The role of brain emotional systems in additions: a neuroevolutionary perspective and new "self-report" animal model. *Addiction* 2002; 97:459–469.

34. Cotman CW, Berchtold NC, Christie LA. Exercise builds brain health: key roles of growth factor cascades and inflammation. *Trends in Neuroscience* 2007; 30-464–472.

35. Rhodes JS et al. Exercise increases hippocampal neuogenesis to high levels in mice. *Behavioral Neuroscience* 2003; 117:1006–1016.

36. Van Praag H. Neurogenesis and exercise: past and future directions. *Neuromolecular Medicine* 2008; 10(2):128-40.

37. Grandel H, Kaslin J, Ganz J, Wenzel I, Brand M. Neural stem cells and neurogenesis in the adult zebrafish brain: origin, proliferation dynamics, migration and cell fate. *Dev Biol* 2006; 295:263–277.

38. Amrein I, Lipp HP. Adult hippocampal neurogenesis of mammals: evolution and life history. *Biol Lett* 2009; 5:141–144.

39. Ernst A, Alkass K, Bernard S, Salehpour M, Perl S, Tisdale J, Possnert G, Druid H, Frisen J. Neurogenesis in the striatum of the adult human brain. *Cell* 2014; 156:1072–1083.

40. Kazanis I. The subependymal zone neurogenic niche: a beating heart at the center of the brain. *Brain* 2009; 132:2909–2921.

41. Manganas LN, Zhang X, Li Y, Hazel RD, Smith SD, Wagshul ME, Henn F, Benveniste H, Djuric PM, Enikolopov G, Maletic-Savatic M. Magnetic resonance spectroscopy identifies neural progenitor cells in the live human brain. *Science* 2007; 318(5852):980–5.

42. Uda M, Ishido M, Kami K, Masuhara M. Effects of chronic treadmill running on neurogenesis in the dentate gyrus of the hippocampus of adult rat. *Brain Res* 2006; 1104:64–72.

43. Naci H, Ioannidis JPA. Comparative effectiveness of exercise and drug interventions on mortality outcomes: metaepidemiological study. *BMJ* 2013; 347 doi: http:// dx.doi.org/10.1136/ bmj.f5577.

44. Milton K, Macniven R, Bauman A. Review of the epidemiological evidence for physical activity and health from low and middle-income countries. *Glob Public Health.* 2014; 9:369–81.

45. Faselis C, Doumas M, Pittaras A et al. Exercise capacity and all-cause mortality in male veterans with hypertension aged >70 years. *Hypertension.* 2014; 64(1):30–5.

46. Pugh DT. Time to encourage patients to take more exercise. *Practitioner* 2012; 256:25–28.

47. Lee IM, Djousse L, Sesso HD, Wangl L, Buring JE. Physical activity and weight gain prevention. *JAMA* 2010; 303:1173–1179.

48. Huai P, Xun H, Reilly KH, Wang Y, Ma W, Xi B. Physical activity and risk of hypertension. A meta analysis of prospective cohort studies. *Hypertension* 2013; 62:1021–6.

49. Buchman AS, Boyle PA, Yu L, Shah RC, Wilson RS, Bennett DA. Total daily physical activity and the risk of AD and cognitive decline in older adults. *Neurology.* 2012; 78(17):1323–9. doi: 10.1212/ WNL.0b013e3182535d35.

50. Sofi F, Valecchi D, Bacci D, Abbate R, Gensini GF, Casini A, Macchi C. Physical activity and risk of cognitive decline: a meta-analysis of prospective studies. *J Intern Med.* 2011; 269:107–17.doi:10.1111/j.1365–2796.2010.02281.

51. Lytle ME, Vander Bilt J, Pandav RS, Doge HH, 12 Ganuli M. Exercise Level and Cognitive Decline. The MoVIES project. *Alzheimer Dis Assoc Disorders* 2004; 18:57–64.

52. Dodge HH, Wang CN, Chang CCH, Gangul M. Terminal decline and practice effects in older adult without dementia. The MoVIES project. *Neurology* 2011; 77:722–730.

53. Erickson KI, Voss MW, Prakash RS et al. Exercise training increases size of hippocampus and improves memory. *Proc Natl Acad Sci U S A*. 2011; 108(7):3017–22.

54. Ahlskog JE, Geda YE, Graff-Radford NR, Petersen RC. Physical exercise as a preventive or disease-modifying treatment of dementia and brain aging. *Mayo Clin Proc*. 2011; 86(9):876–84.

55. Brickman AM, Siedlecki KL, Muraskin J, Manly JJ, Luchsinger JA, Yeung LK, Brown TR, Decarli C, Stern Y. White matter hyperintensities and cognition: Testing the reserve hypothesis. *Neurobiol Aging*. 2011 32(9):1588–98.

56. Zhuang L, Sachdev PS, Tollor JN, Kochan NA, Reppermund S, Brodaty H, Wen W. Microstructural white matter changes in cognitively normal individuals at risk of amnestic MCI. *Neurology* 2012; 79:748–754.

57. Erten-Lyons D, Woltjer R, Kaye J, Mattek N, Dodge HH, Green S, Tran H, Howieson DB, Wild K, Silbert LC. Neuropathologic basis of white matter hyperintensity accumulation with advanced age. *Neurology*. 2013; 81(11):977–83.

58. Tosto G, Zimmerman ME, Carmichael OT, Brickman AM. Predicting aggressive decline in mild cognitive impairment. The importance of white matter hyperintensities. *JAMA Neurology* 2014; 71:872–877.

59. Duering M et al. Strategic white matter tracts for processing speed deficits in age related small vessel disease. *Neurology* 2014; 82:1946–1950.

60. Baker LM, Laidlaw DH, Conturo TE et al. White matter changes with age utilizing quantitative diffusion MRI. *Neurology* 2014; 83:247–252.

61. Kloppenborg RP, Nederkoorn PJ, Geerlings MI, van den Berg E. Presence and progression of white matter hyperintensities and cognition. *Neurology* 2014; 82:2127–2138.

62. Gons RA, Tuladhar AM, de Laat KF, van Norden AG, van Dijk EJ, Norris DG, Zwiers MP, de Leeuw FE. Physical activity is related to the structural integrity of cerebral white matter. *Neurology* 2013; 81(11):971–6.

63. Zhu N, Jacobs DR, Schreiner PJ, Yaffe K, Bryan N, Launer LJ, Whitmer RA Sidney S, Demerath E, Thomas W, Bouchard C, He K, Reis J, Sternfeld B. Cardiorespiratory fitness and cognitive function in middle age. The CARDIA study. *Neurology* 2014; 82:1339–1346.

64. Colcomb S, Kramer AF. Fitness effects on the cognitive function of older adults: a meta-analytic study. *Psychol Sci* 2003; 14:125–130.

65. Colcomb SJ, Erickson KI, Scalf PE et al. Aerobic Exercise Training increases bran volume in aging humans. *J Gerontology* 2006; 61:1166–1170.

66. Baker LD, Frank LL, Foster-Shubert K et al. Effects of aerobic exercise on mild cognitive impairment: a controlled trial. *Arch Neurol* 2010; 67:71–79.

67. Buchman AS, Boyle PA, Yu L, Shah RC, Wilson RS, Bennett DA. Total daily physical activity and the risk of AD and cognitive decline in older adults. *Neurology.* 2012; 78(17):1323–9.

68. Cameron HA, McKay RD. Adult neurogenesis produces a large pool of new granule cells in the dentate gyrus. *J Comp Neurol* 2001; 435:406–17.

69. Ernst C, Olson A, Pinel JP, Lam RW, Christie BR. Antidepressant effects of exercise: Evidence for an adult neurogenesis hypothesis? *J Psychiatry Neurosci* 2006; 31:84–92.

70. Ernst C, Olson A, Pinel JP, Lam RW, Christie BR. Antidepressant effects of exercise: Evidence for an adult neurogenesis hypothesis? *J Psychiatry Neurosci* 2006; 31:84–92.

71. Thomas RM, Hotsenpiller G, Peterson DA. Acute psychological stress reduces cell survival in adult hippocampal neurogenesis without altering proliferation. *J Neuroscience* 2007; 27:2734–2743.

72. Hoffman BM, Babyak MA, Craighead WE, Sherwood A, Doraiswamy PM, Coons MJ, Blumenthal JA. Exercise and pharmacotherapy in patients with major depression: one-year follow-up of the SMILE study. *Psychosom Med.* 2011; 73(2):127–33.

73. Sparling PB, Giuffrida A, Piomelli D et al. Exercise activates the endocannibinoid system. *Neuroreport* 2003; 14:2209–2211

74. Dishman RK, O'Connor PJ. Lessons in exercise neurobiology: The case of endorphins. *Mental Health and Physical Activity* 2009; 2:4–9.

75. Van Praag H. Neurogenesis and Exercise: Past and future directions. *Neuromol Med.* DOI 10.1007/ s12017008-8028-z.

76. Brookes RL, Herbert V, Lawrence AJ, Morris RG, Markus HS. Depression in small vessel disease relates to white matter ultrastructural damage, not disability. *Neurology* 2014; 83:1417–1423

77. Dalzill C, Nigam A, Juneau M, Guilbeault V, Latour E, Mauriège P, Gayda M. Intensive lifestyle intervention improves cardiometabolic and exercise parameters in metabolically healthy obese and metabolically unhealthy obese individuals. *Can J Cardiol.* 2014 Apr; 30(4):434–40.

78. Dutheil F, Walther G, Chapier R et al. Atherogenic subfractions of lipoproteins in the treatment of metabolic syndrome by physical activity and diet the RESOLVE Trial. *Lipids Health Dis.* 2014; 13:112. doi: 10.1186/1476-511X-13-112.

79. Summermatter S1, Baum O, Santos G, Hoppeler H, Handschin C. Peroxisome proliferator-activated receptor {gamma} coactivator 1{alpha} (PGC-1{alpha}) promotes skeletal muscle lipid refueling in vivo by activating de novo lipogenesis and the pentose phosphate pathway. *J Biol Chem.* 2010; 285(43):32793–800.

80. Käll LB1, Nilsson M, Lindén T. The impact of a physical activity intervention program on academic achievement in a Swedish elementary school setting. *J Sch Health.* 2014; 84:473–80

81. Gleeson M. Immune function in sport and exercise. *J Appl Physiology* 2007; 103:693–699.

82. Walsh NP, Gleeson M, Shephard RJ, Gleeson M, Woods JA, Bishop NC, Fleshner M, Green C, Pedersen BK, Hoffman-Goetz L, Rogers CJ, Northoff H, Abbasi A, Simon P. Position statement. Part one: Immune function and exercise. *Exerc Immunol Rev.* 2011; 17:6–63.

83. Nieman DC. Exercise, infection and immunity. *Int J Sports Med* 1994; 15: S131–S141.

84. Gleeson M, McFarlin BK, Flynn MG. Exercise and Tolllike receptors. *Exerc Immunol Rev* 2006; 12: 34–53.

85. Stewart LK, Flynn MG, Campbell WW, Craig BA, Robinson JP, McFarlin BK, Timmerman KL, Coen PM, Felker J, Talbert E. Influence of exercise training and age on CD14+ cell-surface expression. *Brain Behav Immun* 2005; 19:389–397.

86. Lancaster GI, Halson SL, Khan Q, Drysdale P, Jeukendrup AE, Drayson MT, Gleeson M. The physiological regulation of toll-like receptor expression in humans. *J Physiol* 2005; 563; 945–955.

87. Walsh NP, Gleeson M, Shephard RJ, Gleeson M, Woods JA, Bishop NC, Fleshner M, Green C, Pedersen BK, Hoffman-Goetz L, Rogers CJ, Northoff H, Abbasi A, Simon P. Position statement. Part one: Immune function and exercise. *Exerc Immunol Rev.* 2011; 17:6–63.

88. Speisman RB, Kumar A, Rani A, Foster TC, Ormerod BK. Daily exercise improves memory, stimulates hippocampal neurogenesis and modulates immune and neuroimmune cytokines in aging rats. *Brain Behav Immun.* 2013; 28:25–43. doi: 10.1016/j.bbi.2012.09.01.

89. Kemperman G. Why new neurons? Possible functions for adult hippocampal neurogenesis. *J Neurosci* 2002; 22:635–638

90. Garthe A, Bher J, Kemperman J. Adult generated hippocampal neurons allow the flexible use of spatially precise learning strategies. *PLoS ONE* 2009; 4:e5464.

91. Braun SN, Jessberger S. Adult neurogenesis and its role in neuropsychiatric disease, brain repair and normal brain function. *Neuropathol Appl Neurobiol* 2014; 40:3–12.

92. Hillman CH, Erickson KI, Kramer AF. Be Smart exercise your heart: exercise effects on brain and cognition. *Nature Neuroscience Reviews* 2008; 9:58–65.

93. Westerterp KR, Saris WH, van Es M ten Hoor F. Use of doubly labeled water technique in humans during heavy sustained exercise. *J Appl Physiol* 1986; 61:2162–2167.

94. Black AE, Coward WA, Cole TJ, Prentice AM. Human energy expenditure in affluent societies: an analysis of 574 doubly labeled water measurements. *Eur J Clin Nutr* 1996; 50:72–92.

95. FAO/WHO/UNU 2004. Human energy requirements. Report of a joint FAO/WHO/UNU expert consultation. Rome: Food

and Agricultural Organization, United Nations University and World Health Organization.

96. Haskell WL, Lee IM, Pate RR et al. Physical activity and public health: updated recommendation for adults from the American College of Sports Medicine and the American Heart Association. *Circulation* 2007; 116:1081–1093.

97. Ainsworth BE, Haskell WL, Herrmann SD, Meckes N, Bassett DR Jr, Tudor-Locke C, Greer JL, Vezina J, WhittGlover MC, Leon AS. 2011 Compendium of Physical Activities: a second update of codes and MET values. *Med Sci Sports Exerc.* 2011; 43:1575–81.

98. Lee I-M, Djousse` L, Sesso HD, Wang L, Buring JE. Physical Activity and Weight Gain Prevention. *JAMA* 2010; 303:1173–1179.

99. Foulds HJ1, Bredin SS, Charlesworth SA, Ivey AC, Warburton DE. Exercise volume and intensity: a dose-response relationship with health benefits. *Eur J Appl Physiol.* 2014; 114(8):1563–71.

100. Miller WC, Wallace JP, Eggert KE. Predicting max HR. *Med Sci Sports* Exerc.1993; 25(9):1077–81.

101. Guyton A, Hall, JE. Textbook of Medical Physiology, 12th Ed: 1035–1036, Saunders Elsevier, 2011, Philadelphia.

102. Dlugosz, EM, Chappell MA, Meek T. H. et al. Phylogenetic analysis of mammalian maximal oxygen consumption during exercise. *Journal of Experimental Biology* 2013; 216:4712–4721.

103. Dunn R. The Wild Life of our Bodies. Predators, parasites and partners that shape who we are today. Harper Collins, 2011, New York.

104. Cuschieri J, Rivers, EP, Donnino, MW et al. Central venous-arterial carbon dioxide difference as an indicator of cardiac index. *Intensive Care Medicine* 2005; 31: 818–22.

105. Uth N, Sørensen H, Overgaard K, Pedersen PK. Estimation of VO2max from the ratio between HRmax and HRrest the Heart Rate Ratio Method. *Eur J Appl Physiol.* 2004; 91:111–5.

106. Anderson O. Running Science. Human Kinetics. Champaign, Illinois 2013.

107. Anderson O. Things were so easy until vVO2 and then tlimvVO2 had to come along. *Running Research News* 1999; 15:1–5.

108. Billat LV, Koralsztein JP. Significance of the velocity at VO2 max and time to exhaustion at this velocity. *Sports Medicine* 1996; 22:90–198.

109. Billat LV. Interval training for performance: a scientific and empirical practice. Special recommendations for middleand long-distance running. Part I: aerobic interval training. *Sports Med.* 2001; 31(1):13–31. Review.

110. Billat LV. Interval training for performance: a scientific and empirical practice. Special recommendations for middleand long-distance running. Part II: anerobic interval training. *Sports Med.* 2001; 31(1): 75–90. Review.

111. Beneke R, Leithäuser RM, Ochentel O. Blood lactate diagnostics in exercise testing and training. *Int J Sports Physiol Perform.* 2011 Mar; 6(1):8–24.

112. Astrand P et al. Disposal of lactate during and after strenuous exercise in humans. *Journal of Applied Physiology* 1986; 61:338–343.

113. Jacobs I. Blood lactate: Implications for training and sports performance. *Sports Medicine* 1986; 3:10–25.

114. Cairns SP. Lactic acid and exercise performance: culprit or friend? *Sports Medicine* 2006; 36:279–291.

115. De Paoli FV, Ørtenblad N, Pedersen TH, Jørgensen R, Nielsen OB. Lactate per se improves the excitability of depolarized rat skeletal muscle by reducing the CL conductance. *Journal of Physiology* 2010; 588:4785–94.

116. Fiuza-Luces C1, Garatachea N, Berger NA, Lucia, Exerciseis thereal polypill. *Physiology* (Bethesda).2013; 28(5):330–58.

117. Carlson DJ, Dieberg G, Hess NC, Millar PJ, Smart NA. Isometric exercise training for blood pressure management: a systematic review and meta-analysis. *Mayo Clin Proc.* 2014; 89(3):327–34.

118. Paoli A, Moro T, Bianco A. Lift weights to fight overweight. *Clin Physiol Funct Imaging.* 2014 Feb. 24. doi: 10.1111/cpf.12136.

119. About-Dest A, Albinet CT, Boucard G, Audiffren M. Swimming as a positive moderator of cognitive aging improving 3 out of 4 measures of executive functioning in an older population, compared to a sedentary control group: A cross sectional study

with a multitask approach. *Journal of Aging Research* 2012; ID 273185:1–2. Doi:10.1155/2012/273185.

120. van Someren KA, Oliver JE. The efficacy of ergometry determined heart rates of flatwater kayak training. International *Journal of Sports Medicine* 2001; 23:28–32.

121. Michael JS, Rooney KB, Smith R. The metabolic demands of kayaking: A review. *Journal of Sports Science and Medicine* 2008; 7:1–7.

122. Billat V, Faina M, Sardella F et al. A comparison of time to exhaustion at VO2 max in elite cyclists, kayak paddlers, swimmers and runners. *Ergonomics* 1996; 39:267–277.

123. Curlik DM, Shors TJ. Training your brain: Do mental and physical (MAP) training enhance cognition through the process of neurogenesis in the hippocampus? *Neuropharmacology.* 2013 Jan; 64:506–14.

124. Holmes NP, Spence C. The body schema and the multisensory representations of peripersonal space. *Cogn Process* 2004; 5:94–105.

125. Committeri G, Ptizalis S, Galati G et al. Neural basis of personal and extrapersonal neglect in humans. Brain 2007; 130:431–441 and Pessoa L. On the relationship between emotion and cognition. *Nature Reviews Neuroscience* 2008; 9:148–158.

126. Gosden C. Social ontologies. In: Renfrew C, Frith C, Malafouris L (eds). The Sapient Mind. Archeology meets neuroscience. Oxford University Press, Oxford, 2009.

127. Pereira AC, Huddleston E, Brickman AM et al. An in vivo correlate of exercise-induced neurogenesis in the adult dentate gyrus. *PNAS* 2007; 104:5638–5643

Brain Foods: Evolutionary Insights into Nutrition and Advantageous Biocultural Changes

Food Ingestion Is Vital for Nutrition, Disease Prevention, Mood, and Cognition

Fig. 3.1. Complex systems

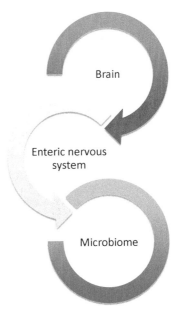

The ingestion of the type, quantity, and combinations of foods can lead to improved memory, cognition, stave off cardiovascular disease and dementia, improve athletic prowess, lessen recurrent viral infections, and have antidepressant effects.[1] There is an extensive anatomical and neurochemical communication network between our brain, the enteric (gut) nervous system, and the microbome (bugs in our gut) that are interdependent on each other (figure 3.1).[2]

The microbiome itself constitutes a so-called complex system in its own right with 200 trillion (2×10^{14}) organisms resident, and there is currently intense research into the ramifications and factors that constitute the concept of the psychobiome or the bug contribution to our brain functioning, processing, and mental health.[3] The gut bacteria weigh about the same as our brain does (~3 pounds), and we have approximately two hundred times more gut bacteria than all of our own cells combined. Numerical interest aside, far-reaching clinical applications have already been realized with the advent of fecal transplantations (a simple procedure from a healthy human to a sick one) that may be lifesaving in infections, such as *Clostridium difficile* that have been resistant to antibiotics, are testimony to their importance and effectiveness.[4] Neuropsychiatric diseases, including depression, anxiety, bipolar disease, schizophrenia, and their relation to the status of the microbiome are presently an area of very active investigation.[5]

Some of the Challenges

Both the type and quantity of food we should be eating as well as the dietary effects of health have proved difficult to measure, resulting in a plenitude of books, Web sites, and opinions on food and health. Despite the barrage of information available, considerable insights may be gleaned from a number of basic and clinical science disciplines, most notably the archeological record. The latter has yielded a preponderance of information from bones and teeth, which fossilize, whereas, plants and meats do not and are therefore relatively underrepresented. In addition, the inherent problems associated with measuring dietary intake by food questionnaires, for example, and the inability to conduct a randomized, controlled blinded trial with food substances make this a particularly challenging area of research. Furthermore, publication and citation biases are a major problem. Publication bias can be resolved to some extent by meta-analyses using a statistical procedure of funnel plots that appear as asymmetric plots. One trend of citation bias concerns the outcomes of drug-related studies that may be getting more publicity than lifestyle intervention studies.[6] For example, the Lyon Heart Study reported a dramatic reduction of between 50 and 70% lower recurrent atherosclerotic-related heart disease, including heart attacks, angina, cardiac death, and stroke among those in the Mediterranean diet arm.[7]

Furthermore, studies using single interventions with vitamins—for example, vitamin B group, E, C—have all failed their primary endpoints for stroke and Alzheimer's dementia recently evaluated in major multinational trials exemplified by the VITATOPS study and vitamin E for Alzheimer's dementia and mild cognitive impairment trials.[8, 9] The probable explanation for these failures is that we are dealing with complex systems. Even more unpropitious, a meta-analysis of vitamin E in stroke revealed a worse outcome with a 22% increase in intracerebral hemorrhage.[10] Interestingly, studies that have used food combinations, such as the Mediterranean diets, have been spectacularly successful with respect to their primary end points.[11]

There Are Extensive Communication Systems Between the Gut and the Brain: Overview of Relevant Neuroanatomy and Neurophysiology

The brain and gastrointestinal tract are intimately and extensively connected by three major systems (figure 3.2).

Fig. 3.2. Multiple connections exist to transmit effects from the gut, feeding, and food on cognition

Adapted from: Gomez Pinilla F. Brain Foods: the effects of nutrients on brain function. Nature Reviews Neuroscience 2008; 7:568–578.

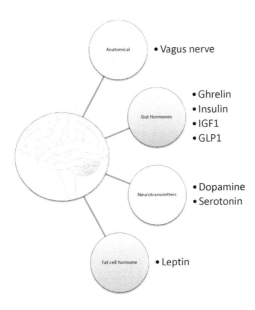

143

These include neural anatomical (central, autonomic, peripheral, and enteric nervous systems), neurotransmitter (table 3.1), and hormonal mechanisms (table 3.2). In addition, the hormone, leptin communicates directly from fat cells to the brain. The enteric (gut) nervous system and brain have many similarities with respect to neurotransmitters and cellular architecture;

Table 3.1. The enteric nervous system (ENS): Anatomical and physiological brain gut statistics[12–14]

Brain	Enteric nervous system
• Neurons (85 billion)	Neurons (500 million)
• Glial cells - cerebral	Glial cells - enteric
• Neurotransmitters ~100	Neurotransmitters ~40
• Serotonin - produces ~5%	Serotonin - produces ~95%
• Dopamine - produces ~50%	Dopamine - produces ~50%
• Barrier – blood brain barrier	Barrier – intestinal epithelial monolayer

Table 3.2. Hormonal communication channels between the brain and gut

Hormone Functions	Origin	Cognition effect
Leptin reduces appetite	adipose	increases BDNF, synaptic plasticity in hippocampus
Ghrelinappetite stimulant	stomach	increases synapses, dendritic spines, memory LTP
GLP1 stimulates pancreas insulin	intestine	improve associative, memory, rats spatiial
IGF 1 stimulated by exercise	liver, muscle	improves learning and memory
Insulin stimulated by digestion	pancreas	increase synaptic activity, cognitive processing

The Vagus Nerve Is a Major Two-Way Information Highway Connecting the Brain and Gut

Some insights into the neurophysiology of the vagus has been gleaned from nerve stimulation studies first used for seizure prophylaxis.[15] Vagal nerve stimulation in humans enhances memory,[16] and in animal studies, vagal nerve stimulation increases mRNAs for nerve growth factors such as brain-derived neurotrophic factor (BDNF) and fibroblast growth factor 2 (FGF2) in rat hippocampus. Furthermore, increase in noradrenaline in the prefrontal cortex and the dorsal motor nucleus of the vagus nerve retrogradely transports BDNF and other neurotrophins. This represents a form of sensorimotor signaling from the viscera to the brain.[17–19]

Neurochemistry: Because of the Brain's Relatively Large Energy Consumption, the Transfer of Energy from Nutrients to Neurons Developed to Be Integral to Brain Function

There is a close link between BDNF-mediated synaptic plasticity and energy metabolism (figure 3.3).

Fig. 3.3. Cognition, energy homeostasis, and the BDNF link.
Excess energy intake results in reactive oxygen species (ROS), and if the buffering capacity is exceeded, this will cause impaired synaptic plasticity and cognition. Epigenetic mechanisms such as the SIRT1 (silent information regulator) reduces ROS, modifies chromatin by histone deacetylase and also affect cognition
Figure credit with permission from: Gomez-Pinilla F. Brain Foods: the effects of nutrients on brain function. Nature Reviews Neuroscience 2008; 9:568–578.

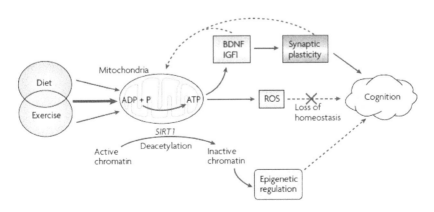

BDNF is an example of a central molecule closely related to energy metabolism and synaptic plasticity and not surprisingly is prolific in brain areas associated with cognitive (hippocampus) and metabolic regulation (hypothalamus). In the hypothalamus, for example, melanocortin 4 receptor involved in energy balance control regulates expression of BDNF.[20, 21]

IGF-1 Is Involved in Several Key Roles in This Regard

BDNF exerts its effects via IGF-1 receptors, which are expressed predominantly in the hippocampus and influences nerve growth, neurotransmitter synthesis, release, and synaptic plasticity.[22]

Food-Derived Signals (Energy Metabolism) Are Translated into Brain Plasticity (Synaptic Plasticity, Cognition) via the mTOR (Mammalian Target of Rapamycin) and Akt Activation Pathways

Akt (or protein kinase B) is a protein kinase that plays a key role in many different cellular processes such as glucose metabolism, apoptosis, and cell proliferation. Similar to BDNF, IGF-1 shares pathways such as the Akt signaling system, and docosahexanoic acid (DHA) stimulates neuronal plasticity through the Akt pathway. Omega-3 FA influence synaptic plasticity and cognition and Akt activation and mTOR pathway translate food derived signals (energy metabolism) into brain plasticity such as increased synaptic plasticity and cognition.[23, 24] Accruing evidence from clinical studies point to an association between abnormal metabolism such as diabetes mellitus II, metabolic syndrome, and psychiatric disorders, with the clinical implication that food intake control is a rational strategy for neurological and neuropsychiatric diseases (table BDNF and neuropsychiatric disease). This is already evident in trials such as seizure treatment with a ketogenic diet as well as depression, schizophrenia, and attention-deficit hyperactivity disorder.[25]

The Brain-Gut Interaction Has Effects on the Brain and Mind and Implicated in Neuropsychiatric Disease

In addition to the vagal nerve effects and direct neurotransmitter effects, several other potential mechanisms are implicated. These include hormonal (cortisol), immune-mediated (cytokines), tryptophan metabolism (a precursor to serotonin), and bacterial metabolic related effects. Bacterial fermentation of complex carbohydrates may release short chain fatty acids (SCFA), which have neuroactive effects[26, 27] (figure 3.4).

Fig. 3.4. The brain-microbial-gut communication systems.
This is bidirectional and includes neural, endocrine, immune, neurotransmitter, short-chain fatty acids (neuroactive and processed by gut bacteria), and tryptophan metabolism.
Figure credit with permission: Crynan JF, Dina TG. Mind-altering microorganisms: the impact of the gut microbiota on brain and behaviour. Nature Reviews Neuroscience 2012; 13:701–712.

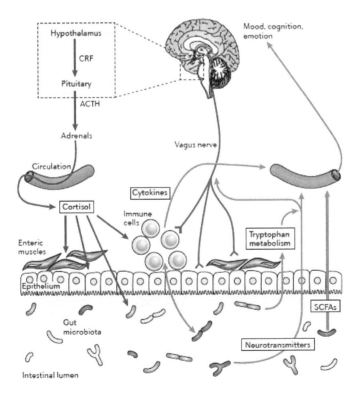

Table 3.3. BDNF and neuropsychiatric disease[28-30]

Clinical Studies

- Low BDNF levels are associated with DM-II and impaired glucose metabolism.
- BDNF is reduced in the hippocampus and in serum of schizophrenic patients.
- BDNF levels are reduced in the plasma of patients with major depression.
- Chronic administration of antidepressants elevates hippocampal BDNF levels.
- In depression, treatments such as pharmacotherapy and physical exercise involve the action of BDNF.

Animal Studies

- Genetic deletion of the TrkB receptor in the forebrain produces schizophrenic-like behavior in mice.

Neurophysiology: Healthy Living Requires the Intake of Six Major Food Components Aided by Six Different Taste Senses

Macronutrients—of which the major components are fats, proteins, carbohydrates—may be differentiated from micronutrients, which include many different minerals, fat, and water-soluble vitamins and water. There are currently six different known taste senses, common to all animals that are augmented by our sense of smell (olfaction). The different taste senses include salt, sweet, umami (savory, amino acids detection), fat detection, sour, and bitter. The first four are linked to the dopaminergic system and hence prone to addiction underlying the concept of hyperpalatable foods with sugar, salt, fat excesses in foods. The latter, sour, for detection of acids, may indicate that the food is spoiled; and bitter helps discriminate potentially beneficial from toxic substances. In 2012 a sixth sense, for fat detection, was proposed.[31]

Table 3. 4. The six different taste senses Tastant Taste Receptor Type   Function

Tastant	Taste Receptor Type	Function
Sugar	Sweetness, all mammals	high density/energy food
Fat	Fat detection receptor	high density/energy food
Protein	Umami (savory, MSG)	high density/energy food
Salt	Salty	critical electrolyte, all animals
Acid	sour	H+ detection, food decomposition
Toxin	bitterness	Toxin detection

Legend
MSG – monosodium glutamate
H+ – protons signifying acid detection

Addiction to foods, especially fats, salt, sugar, is mediated by the dopaminergic reward system, an example of ancient evolutionary circuitry that facilitates the acquisition of these, essential to life (figure 3.5).

Fig. 3.5. The principal dopaminergic systems: mesocortical, mesolimbic, nigrostriatal, tuberinfundibular, unnamed

Abbreviations: PAG – periacqueductal gray matter, M – mesencephalon, LPBN – lateral parabrachial nucleus Supporting reference: Cropley VL, Fujita M, Innis RB, Nathan PJ. Molecular imaging of the dopaminergic system and its assocation with human cognitive function. Biol Psychiatry 2006; 59:898–907.

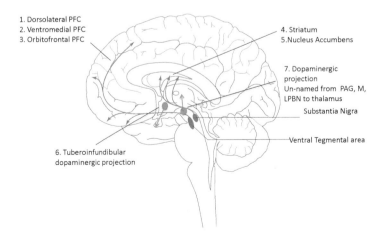

1. Dorsolateral PFC
2. Ventromedial PFC
3. Orbitofrontal PFC

4. Striatum
5. Nucleus Accumbens

7. Dopaminergic projection Un-named from PAG, M, LPBN to thalamus

Substantia Nigra

Ventral Tegmental area

6. Tuberoinfundibular dopaminergic projection

Several neurochemical dopaminergic pathways in the brain with the mesolimbic system mediate reward and addiction. Processed foods and fast foods exploit these "addictions" that evolved in our evolutionary past to preserve us. Today these important biological drives are capitalized on in the making of so-called hyperpalatable foods. The ramifications are overeating and obesity, which is well researched and enunciated in David Kessler's book *The End of Overeating*.[32]

Overeating and obesity may be regarded as an addiction, and consideration was given to labeling it as such for the DSM-V criteria. The striatum of obese individuals reveals relatively lower levels of the dopamine D2 receptor, which is similar to opiate, alcohol, cocaine, methamphetamine addiction. A drug, rimonabant (inhibits the cannabinoid 1 receptor), developed for curbing appetite in obese people was tested and shown to have side effects of severe depression and suicide and not marketed.[33]

What Should We Be Eating? Current Guidelines from the World Health Organization and Institute of Medicine

Table 3.5. Macronutrient requirements: Recommendations by the WHO and IOM daily compared to estimated Paleolithic diet in daily kcal %[34-37]

Macronutrient	WHO/IOM (g/kg/d)	Paleolithic (g/kg/d)
Protein	10–30 (0.7–1.0 g/kg/d)	25–30% (2.5–3.5)
Carbohydrates	45–65 (130 g)	45–50%
Fats (total)	20–35	20–25%
- SFA	10	6
- TFA	7–8	~5

Fats (PUFA) ratio	WHO/IOM	Paleolithic
n-6:n-3	~10:1	4:1-1:1

Abbreviations: SFA – saturated fatty acids, PUFA – polyunsaturated acids, TFA – transfatty acids (ruminant and industrial)

Some additional notes to the above are pertinent. Transfatty acid recommendations by the WHO and IOM are less than 1 g/day, and in Paleolithic times these would have been absent. With respect to carbohydrates, the proportion of fruit and vegetable intake of Paleolithic was 45–50% of daily energy in line with present-day recommendations but different to the 23% of the American diet, which is mostly in the form of refined sugars and grain flours.[38] Regarding fiber, in the Paleolithic diet this is estimated at > 100 g/day and present adult American consumption ranges from 20–30g/day.[39]

To simplify, the major macronutrients—protein, fats, and carbohydrate proportions—can be approximated to 1/6, 2/6, and 3/6. However, our ancestors often had a predominantly meat and fat diet, and present-day hunter-gatherer (HG) groups have been observed in good health with predominant fibrous carbohydrate diet and many combinations in between these extremes, without obvious ill health. Postagricultural communities, on the other hand, were generally less healthy, had more illnesses (rickets, scurvy beriberi, pellagra), and were shorter in stature than hunter-gatherer societies.[40] This was in part due to the micronutrient deficiencies that are still present with us today and are best summarized in the table.

Table 3.6. Micronutrient requirements: Paleolithic intake estimated from contemporary and recent hunter-gatherer populations compared to current US intakes (adapted from Eaton SB et al.)[41]

Nutrient	Paleolithic intake	US-RDA	US intake (average)
Vitamins mg/d			
Riboflavin	6.49	1.3–17	1.34–2.08
Folate	0.357	0.18–0.2	0.149–0.205
Thiamine	3.91	1.1–1.5	1.08–1.75
Vitamin A	17.2	4.8–6.0	7.02–8.48
Vitamin C (mg)	604	60	77–109
Vitamin E (mg)	33	8–10	7–10
Minerals mg/d			
Calcium	1,956	800–1,200	750
Magnesium	700	350	250

Potassium	10,500	3,500	2,500
Zinc	43	12–15	5–14
Fiber (grams)	50–104	25–35	10

Micronutrient Deficiencies

There are many reasons for possible micronutrient deficiencies, including chronic medication use, chronic illness, aging, excessive physical activity, and discretionary habits (smoking, alcohol, substance abuse). Some specific examples of medications inducing micronutrient deficiencies are noted in the table.

Table 3.7. Some common medications causing micronutrient deficiencies

Medication	Deficiency
Antacids	B_{12}, folate, calcium, iron, vitamin D, zinc
Statin drugs	Coenzyme Q
Antidepressants	Vitamin B_2, coenzyme Q
Antibiotics	Vitamin K, vitamin B group, magnesium, calcium, zinc
Anti-seizure agents	Vitamin B group, D, K, calcium, zinc, copper, selenium
Anti-hypertensives	Vitamin B group, C, coenzyme Q, calcium, magnesium, zinc
Anti-diabetics	B_{12}, folate, Coenzyme Q
Anti-inflammatories	Vitamin B group, D, C, calcium, magnesium, chromium, zinc

A wide variety of syndromes result from micronutrient deficiencies that depending on the specific nutrient may include immune deficiency, fatigue, depression, cardiovascular disease, anemia, osteoporosis, sleep disturbances, cognitive impairment, and increased cancer risk.[42]

There Is the Potential of Micronutrient Deficiencies on a Global Scale as a Consequence of Elevated CO_2

In particular, iron and zinc deficiencies may be a consequence of rising CO_2 levels as they are dependent on C3 grains and legumes for their supply, with two billion people estimated to be deficient globally. Elevated CO_2 concentrations that are predicted to occur in the coming decades may exacerbate this situation.[43]

Table 3.8. Micronutrient subtypes

Vitamins
Vit A

B group
B_1 (thiamine)
B_2 (riboflavin)
B_3 (niacin)
B_5 (pantothenate)
B_6 (pyridoxine)
B_7 (biotin)
B_8 (inositol)
B_9 (folate)
B_{12} (cobalamin)

Vit C
Vit D_3
Vit E
Vit K_2

Minerals
Magnesium, calcium, manganese,
selenium, zinc, copper, chromium, iron

Metabolites
Carnitine, Choline, Inositol

Other antioxidants
Coenzyme Q-10
Alpha lipoic acid
Cysteine Glutathione
Oleic acid
Essential amino acids

Evolutionary Perspectives: Humans Improved Their Diet Quality Between 1–3 Mya

Overall among mammals, the basal metabolic rate (BMR) of larger mammals is proportionally lower than smaller mammals, defined by the Kleiber relationship BMR = 70 × weight.[44] Considering primates, with their brains being relatively larger as a group, more energy is channeled to their brains with humans averaging 20–25%; primates in general, 8–10% and mammal species studied to date, 3–5%.[45]

Diet quality improvement by hominins was accomplished by several factors, including the use of mechanical processing of meat, bone, fibrous tubers by stone tool use and chemical processing with increased nutrient yield by fire and cooking. Overall diet quality increased through meat and tubers (starch) consumption.[46] These changes did not occur in isolation. At the same time the use of fire facilitated the all-important tree-to-ground transition for improved sleep quality with consequent improvements in memory, dreaming, creativity, and also promotion of sociality. Diet quality may be characterized as nutrient dense that has been ranked as 100 (100% foliage intake) to 350 (100% faunivory intake) by Sailer et al. Small primates tend to have a higher diet density consuming insects and gums whereas the largest primate, the gorilla, consumes a diet that is approximately 85% folivorous, with some frugivorous components.[47] Further examination of the primates as a group has revealed that there is a negative relationship between body weight and diet quality when plotted logarithmically indicating a decreasing diet quality (DQ) with increasing body size (correlation coefficient r = -0.66), known as the Jarman-Bell relationship.[48] As can be seen from the figure, humans have a much higher DQ than is expected for their body size (figure 3.6).

Fig. 3.6. Diet quality versus log body weight for 72 primates and 5 human hunter-gatherer groups

Figure credit with permission: Leonard WR. Human Nutritional Evolution. In: Stinson S, Bogin B, O'Rourke D (eds). Human biology. Wiley Blackwell, Hoboken NJ, 2012 and Leonard WR, Robertson ML. Evolutionary perspectives on human nutrition: the influence of brain and body size on diet and metabolism. Am J Hum Biol 1994; 6:77–88.

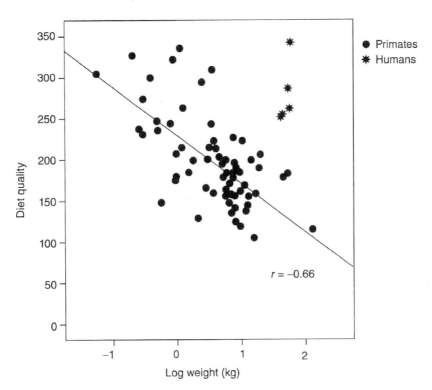

A High-Quality Diet Is Required for the Energy Demands of Our Large Brains

For primates, the relationship of brain weight in grams to BMR in kcal/day conforms to a straight line relationship plotted logarithmically (brain weight in grams = 0.37 BMR 0.97, r = 0.98), but humans are outliers with their brains requiring two to three times more energy compared to primates. Diet quality in primates (in z-scores) plotted against brain size (in z-scores) reveals a positive relationship (r = 0.63) with humans again as outliers in this representation (figure 3.7).

Fig. 3.7. Primate species: Relative Brain size and relative diet quality
Figure credit with permission: Leonard WR. Human Nutritional Evolution. In:
Stinson S, Bogin B, O'Rourke D (eds). Human Biology. Wiley Blackwell, Hoboken
NJ, 2012 and Leonard WR, Snodgrass JJ, Robertson ML. Effects of brain evolution
on human nutrition and metabolism. Ann Rev Nutr 2007; 27:311–327.

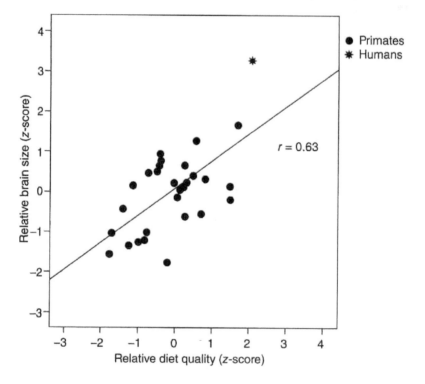

The interpretation is that within the primate group, larger
brains require a higher-quality diet. Humans have the largest brains,
the highest-quality diets, and smaller guts (small intestine, colon),
which have become relatively smaller and so differ from other large
primates (gorillas, orangutans) whose guts have become larger to aid
extraction of nutrients from large amounts of low-quality foods such
as leaves and stems.[49]

Dietary Flexibility Was a Defining Feature of Human Evolution: The Dual Diet Strategy

Review of the archeological record suggests that dietary flexibility together with early cooperative groups in a continuously changing environment was a pivotal adaptation. Enhanced dietary quality was an achievement by human ancestors by what has been termed a dual dietary strategy. This involved utilizing animal sources to supply essential nutrients and plant-based foods to satisfy energy demands. Using underground storage organs, for example, which are rich in energy but lacking in nutrients, was one of the strategies deployed.[50]

As Plant-Eating Mammals Develop a Greater Body Size, Their Dietary Quality Decreases

This is in contrast to the carnivorous animals. For example, large extant apes such as the gorilla and orangutan, with their primarily plant-based diet, have a large body mass, which is associated with less sociality and mobility. In contradistinction the hominin line had lower gut volume; dentition changes with smaller teeth, masticatory muscles, and jaws; and increase in brain size.[51]

What Should We Be Eating? Some Insights from Comparative Studies of Present-Day and Recent Hunter-Gatherer Groups

Although clinical, epidemiological, and animal studies in nutrition and basic science normally guide recommendations, in the realm of nutrition, science this is particularly challenging. The reasons include inherent inaccuracy of measuring dietary intake by food questionnaire and the technical difficulty with conducting a randomized, controlled, blinded trial with food substances. Hence, our best guidelines are considered to be from close scrutiny of what our ancestors ate, notably preagricultural although changes in the last ten thousand years (10 ky) need to be considered too especially in regard to lactose tolerance and amylase genetics.

Perhaps it is no surprise that present-day hunter-gatherer HG and pastoralists maintain normal body mass index BMI. Modern

Western-type diets are mostly associated with abnormally high BMIs (figure 3.8). [52]

Fig. 3.8. Mean BMI (kg/m2) from subsistence level populations and industrialized nations from WHO Global Infobase 2005.

Data for men, women are similar.

Figure credit with permission: Leonard WR. Human Nutritional Evolution. In: Stinson S, Bogin B, O'Rourke D (eds). Human biology. Wiley Blackwell, Hoboken NJ, 2012 and Katzmarzyk PR, Leonard WR. Climatic influences on human body size and proportions: ecological adaptations and secular trends. Am J Phys Anthropol 1998; 106:483–503.

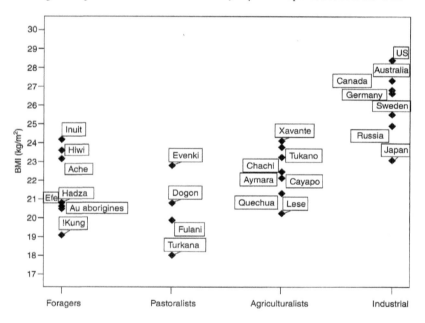

Examples of Adaptability to Macronutrients Around the World: Amylase, Maize, Lactase, and Fava Beans

Australopithecine Tuber Diet, Increased Starch Consumption, and Salivary Amylase

Although starch formed a significant component of the Paleolithic diet, with the advent of agricultural societies, this became even more important. For example, today starch accounts for about ~50% carbohydrate fraction of the average American diet. Among different populations, the number of copies of the salivary amylase gene

(AMY1) is variable but, in an important study by Perry, showed that salivary amylase concentration correlates well with the amylase gene copy number that leads to an increase in saliva amylase concentration and improved digestion of dietary starches. For example, the amylase copies are higher in starch-eating societies such as the Hadza, Europeans, and Americans compared to those societies traditionally eating low quantities of starch (African Mbuti foragers, Siberian Yakut). The implications are that a strong selection for the AMY1 locus occurred, with humans also displaying three times as many copies of the AMY 1 copies compared to chimpanzees. This kind of selection suggests the evolution of diets different from other primates.[53] This was probably due to increased consumption of tubers and other underground storage organs (USOs) during the australopithecine evolution, with the overall increased starch consumption with respect to the forest-dwelling apes.[54]

Agriculture Further Increased Starch Consumption, Which Can Have a Number of Antinutrient Effects

Subsequent to agriculture, some human populations relied for most of their dietary calories on carbohydrates such as indigenous South American populations and maize consumption. Maize consumption is associated with a relative deficiency of vitamin B_3 (niacin) and amino acids (lysine, tryptophan) due to an unfavorable leucine (excess) to isoleucine ratio, the former, which antagonizes the conversion of tryptophan to niacin. Through their innovative adaptation, deficiency of both components was largely negated by the processing of corn with alkaline ash, lime and lye by.[55, 56] In Africa and India where maize is an important crop, such practices are not known, and there is consequently widespread malnutrition due to pellagra (vitamin B_3 or niacin deficiency). With the introduction of maize into Africa by earlier European explorers, it became widespread and a staple crop in many regions. There is a strong correlation in Africa with maize consumption and pellagra. The cultural knowledge of alkali processing that was known to Mesoamericans was not transferred to either Europeans or Africans. Katz formulated his lock-and-key hypothesis based on the maize nutrition deficiency and alkali processing model enunciating the important relationship between toxins and antinutrients occurring in some foods (lock) and culturally transmitted knowledge regarding food processing in countering these. Although crops can be easily exported to other societies, the cultural food processing knowledge is much less likely to be transferred (key).[57] This cultural activity of treating maize with alkali can be considered a chemical processing as an adaptation for improving the diet quality of foods, following earlier mechanical and fire processing techniques by hominins.

The relatively high glycoalkaloids that occur in some varieties of potatoes impart both a bitter taste as well as being poisonous. Potatoes and other starch organs form the staple diet of the Peruvian Quenchua, who derive 40–61% of their calories from these complex carbohydrates and maintain low serum cholesterol levels and normal blood pressures.[58, 59] A method of alternate nighttime freezing and daytime heat treatment and drying in the sun improves caloric density as well as countering the alkaloid content.[60]

Lactase Persistence and Milk Consumption

Lactose is the sugar present in milk that is digested in the microvilli by lactase-enzyme-yielding glucose and galactose. In humans this activity declines before reaching adulthood, which is true for most mammals. Selection for the retention of lactase persistence has occurred independently during evolution in parts of Africa and Europe who have retained high intestinal lactase levels with lactose tolerance into adulthood in the last 10 ky in those with dairy herds.[61]

Fava Beans, Malaria, and G-6PD Deficiency

Fava beans have been an important food source in the Mediterranean region since the agricultural revolution about ~10 kya. Fava bean toxicity was well-known and was subsequently shown in more recent times that this occurs in those with glucose-6-phosphate dehydrogenase (G-6PD) deficiency causing hemolytic anemia. The incidence of malaria has been correlated with G-6PD gene deficiency (a common genetic disorder globally), which is protective against malaria. An interesting biocultural balance between these factors evolved in these societies whereby the selection for the gene deficiency, nutritional use of fava beans and resistance to malaria coevolved.[62]

The Original Nervous System: The Enteric Nervous System and the Importance of the Mind-Altering Microbiome

The enteric nervous system evolved before the central nervous system. The close anatomical and neurochemical links between the two have been noted in table 1. Taking the microbiome into account then seems most important. For example, the microbiome of anxious mice differs from that of normal mice and transplantation of anxious mice microbiota into normal mice makes the normal mice anxious. Gut microbiota affect brain neurophysiology and neurochemistry by way of immune activation, proinflammatory and anti-inflammatory cytokine effects, production of neurotransmitters that include GABA, serotonin, noradrenaline, dopamine, and acetycholine by different microbes. This microbiome brain interaction may provide options for modulating brain functioning in both health and disease.[63]

The enteric nervous system ENS is the original nervous system that evolved 500 mya in the first vertebrates. This became more complex as vertebrates evolved and probably gave rise to the brain itself, which can work independently or in conjunction with the brain. Importantly, the majority of information from the gut to the brain does not come into conscious awareness, and it has been estimated that approximately 90% of signals traversing the vagus nerve originate from the ENS and not from the brain.[64, 65] All are complex systems and their interaction even more so. No wonder many of our diet and food-related trials have turned out remarkable failures (dietary fat and heart disease) and in some instances even worsened our health or the outcome measure (routine vitamin supplementation). It is worth purveying some of the known anatomical and physiological data concerning these systems (tables 3.1 and 3.2).

What Should We Be Eating? Insights from Archeological Record, Present-Day Hunter-Gatherer Societies, and Cellular Metabolism

Not only the omnivorous diet, but also in association with the ability to use fire led to the improved nutritional and energy yields from foods especially meat and USOs. It's no surprise, therefore, that humans are capable of thriving on a particularly wide range of diets. Hence, we are able to wear many hats when it comes to food ingestion, including the following:

> Faunivory—insectivory, carnivory, pescatarian
>   (seafood) Frugivory (fruits)
> Foliovory (leaves, other plant parts including tubers, vegetables)
> Graminivory (grasses, sages, and their seeds)
> Gumnivory (gums and saps)
> Nuts
> Honey

This is consistent with the so-called Paleo diet, ancestral diet, and the Mediterranean diet, accepting that the latter includes a significant proportion of various grains in the diet. The amount and types of grain consumption is the subject of some controversy, especially with respect to its relation to gluten enteropathy, celiac disease, and the long list of purported medical conditions that may or may not be associated with gluten enteropathy.

The Defining Feature of the Human Diet Is Its Flexibility

At the most basic level, this flexibility is reflected in the cellular biochemistry with the key intermediary metabolic components being glucose and ATP (adenosine triphosphate), the universal energy molecule. There is an interchangeability of macronutrients as energy sources as this process of transformation can utilize carbohydrates, fats, and proteins as well as alcohol to supply energy for ATP. This is the ultimate basis for dietary flexibility in humans. The tricarboxylic acid (TCA) cycle is central to this premise. The TCA cycle enables interchange of the three basic macronutrients from one form into another.

The Hadza: A Living Example of What Our Diets Should Be Today

The Hadza hunter-gatherer tribe in Tanzania have a varied diet that encompasses all the above. They are perhaps the most representative of our past diets in that they are living in East Africa where we emerged some 6–8 mya. Nothing much has changed in the way they live now compared to the past, and we are able to study them directly today. Nor has the all-important topography or climate changed significantly. Furthermore, they have no evidence of cardiac disease or cancer in the current study. Although many die at a young age (injuries, infections), living into the seventies and eighties is common, and the most commonly cited cause of death among older men is falling out of trees collecting honey and not cardiovascular disease as it is in Western civilizations.[66]

High Fat and Protein Diets Are Consistent with Healthy Living and Barely Detectable Coronary Artery Disease

The Masai in Kenya subsist on a diet almost exclusively on meat and a high intake of milk. Their cholesterol levels are generally low, and they rarely have detectable coronary heart disease.[67, 68] A wide range of proportions of fat, protein, and carbohydrates are consistent with healthy living as evidenced by scrutiny of living hunter-gatherer traditional societies. For example, extremes of fat ingestion are exemplified by the Inuit—96% animal food, with negligible carbohydrate content. Extremes of carbohydrate ingestion of 81% and only 11% animal food are exemplified by the agriculuralist society, the Tukanoan from Colombia.[69–71]

Higher Carbohydrate Diets Are Certainly Consistent with Healthy Living as well as Unsurpassed Olympic Performances

Peak athletic performances for distance races (800 m to marathons) are consistently won by runners from the Kenyan Kalenjin tribe of about three million people. The Kalenjin tribe makes up about 70% of elite Kenyan athletes and consistently win races from 800 m to marathon events, much more so than any other country. In

2003, Africans (mostly Kenyans and Ethiopians) had won 102 of 120 slots in the various distance races.[72, 73] They are pastoralists, and consequently their diet includes milk and meat but also a significant amount of complex carbohydrates (71 %; 8.7 g/kg body weight per d), low in fat (15 %), but relatively high in total protein (13 %; 1.6 g/kg body weight per d), above the daily intake recommended by the World Health Organization. The carbohydrate intake is derived predominantly from vegetable, maize, and kidney beans.[74] Studies into their phenomenal success has included findings of lifestyle activities in childhood town and village boy study, perhaps altitude and perhaps diet.[75] Extensive genetic studies of Kenyan and Ethiopian runners specifically for a number of genes (ACE, PPAE delta gene, PFCP, ACTN3, IGF1 protein) and training methods have not found any differences compared to athletes from other countries.[76]

The diet of our ancestors has changed many times. Tracing all the way back to the ancestral mammals who were insectivores, after which primates reverted to folivory type/vegetable ingestion and at the same time their body mass increased. The advent of the angiosperm plant revolution, which began 130 mya and continued during the Miocene era (24–5 mya) was associated with fruits becoming the predominant diet for primates. Hominins, however, had a mixed diet with the fossil dental record and masticatory muscles indicating faunivory (animal) and folivory vegetable consumption.[77] Cro-Magnons in Europe (30 kya), however, had a predominantly meat diet. A shift occurred again with the advent of agriculture about 10 kya, with vegetables making up ~90% of the diet resulting in shorter stature and relative malnourishment compared to the Cro-Magnons who were also much taller by ~6 inches.[78] The American Paleoindians likewise hunted large animals such as bison (10 kya), and when they reverted to agriculture with minimal meat diet, they became shorter and manifested with skeletal abnormalities typical of poor nutrition.[79] Subsequent to farming, several further adverse nutritional eras have followed; the industrial, the commercialized food production commencing in the 1950s and refined foods including the high-fructose corn syrup (HFCS) era.

Both Ancestral Diet Reconstructions and Study of PresentDay Hunter-Gatherer Diets Are Our Best Standard of Reference of What Should Constitute Our Diets

Hunter-gatherer societies (including the Hadza, Kung, Kade, San, Philippine Tasaday) who derive 50–80% of their food by weight from plants and 20–50% from animal sources and Arctic Eskimos who eat less than 10% plant food have been thoroughly studied. From the archeological records we know that Cro-Magnons (40–10 kya) had relatively massive bones implying plentiful calcium intake and fiber from fruits and vegetables. Their estimated 35% meat diet has been calculated to contain only one-sixth of the sodium of a typical Western diet today with the vitamin levels, iron, folate, and protein far exceeding the typical Western diet intake. Estimates of the relatively high meat diet included much higher cholesterol content that our current limits and less total fat but a higher ratio of PUFA to saturated fat than does our modern diet.[80–81]

What Has Happened? Macronutrient Deterioration in Industrialized Society

It's not so much the proportions but the quality of the macronutrients that may be at fault. The three major culprits causing Western-type chronic diseases and obesity include the following:

Sugar—added sugars and refined sugars in place of complex sugars

Fats—influence of transfats (not saturated fats or cholesterol, which are important nutrients) and the ratio of n-3/n-6 PUFA changing from 1:1 or 1:3 to 1: 10 to 1:20

Salt—excess intake, primarily because of ease of availability and its hyperpalatable effects

Overview of Macronutrients

Energy Yield

The varying proportions of carbon, hydrogen, and oxygen atoms determine the amount of food energy per mass or energy density.

Fats	9 kcal/gram
Proteins	4 kcal/gram
Carbohydrates	4 kcal/gram

Counting calories, however, needs to be interpreted in the setting of the hologenome (host and microbiome). For example, ingesting whole grains, vegetables, and nuts use up more energy in the digestive process in comparison to processed foods. Two dominant bacterial phyla, Firmicutes and Bacteroidetes, form the dominant populations in human intestines with the former predominating in obese people, facilitating improved extraction of nutrients. This provides yet another reason for eating natural, fibrous, nonprocessed foods.[82]

Protein

We require not only 0.7–1.0 g/kg/day (Paleolithic humans were accustomed to 2.5–3.5 g/kg/day) of protein but also nine essential amino acids (valine, threonine, leucine, histidine, phenylalanine, tryptophan, methionine, isoleucine, lysine) from the diet that we cannot synthesize endogenously. Excess consumption is harmful. Protein metabolism is limited by the human liver metabolism of amino acid metabolism to about 300 g/day (range 200–365) as well as the kidney's limit in processing urea, the by-product of protein catabolism. An excess of protein leads to vomiting, diarrhea, and coma. A type of protein poisoning termed rabbit starvation refers to a type of encephalopathy associated with hyperammoninemia due to protein excess. This syndrome was first described in early American explorers that subsisted on eating predominantly small mammals such as rabbits, which had meager fat deposits, during the winter months with resultant high protein and minimal fat intake leading to this syndrome.[83] Meat intake was high during most of hominid evolution. A requirement appears to be fat or carbohydrate to avoid this syndrome. An example illustrating this point comes from observation of the Gauchos in the South American Pampas who may eat beef for several weeks to months at a time, but consume such with a considerable amount of fat, an observation first made by Charles Darwin.[84]

Protein Quality Is Important. Proteins Derived from Predominantly Plant-Based Diets Are Deficient in Some of the Essential Amino Acids.

The WHO has developed an amino acid score that discloses the percentage of essential amino acids that are lacking in plant-based foods such as lysine, methionine, tryptophan, threonine, and cysteine. Animal-derived proteins such as beef, eggs, and milk all provide an amino acid score of 100%, whereas plant-based foods vary from rice (86%), kidney beans (84%), maize (58%), and wheat (57%).[85]

Fats: The Importance of Fat in Our Diets—the Evidence

We are currently living in a state of both excess (transfats and perhaps certain saturated fats) and deficiency of other fats (omega-3 fatty acids). Saturated fats based on prehistoric HG intake estimates of 25–50% of total daily energy intake were provided by meat and animal organ consumption. This is in contradistinction to current intakes, estimated at 30–40% of daily energy intake of many Western societies, which derive mainly from marbled (fatty) meats, processed meats, dairy products, margarine, and a variety of toxic, manufactured transfats that appear in baked goods and pastries.

Polyunsaturated fats: Both omega-3 and omega-6 fatty acids need to be acquired through the diet as we cannot manufacture them; hence, they are termed essential fats. The ratio is important, optimally 1:2 up to 1:4 range whereas current estimates of a typical Western diet are in the range of 1:15–17.[86]

Classification of Fats

Fig. 3.9. A classification of fats

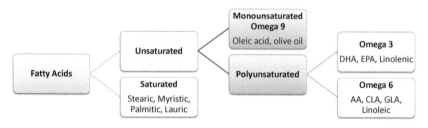

The Critically Important Fats and Their Derivatives in Our Bodies: Cholesterol, Eiscosanoids, Prostaglandins, Thromboxanes, Leukotrienes

Cholesterol Is an Essential Component of All Cell Membranes

Cholesterol modulates membrane fluidity and is involved in intracellular transport, nerve conduction, and cell signaling. Cholesterol is the precursor for vitamin D and steroid hormones synthesis (progesterone, estrogens, and testosterone) as well adrenal steroids cortisol and aldosterone. Critical to all animal life, cells synthesize their own cholesterol involving many steps, with the initial step beginning with the intracellular enzyme HMG-CoA reductase (inhibited by statin drugs).[87]

Eicosanoids Are Fat-Derived, Critical Molecules for Survival

The eicosanoids (E) are signaling molecules derived from omega-3 and omega-6 fats as oxygenation products of PUFA long chain fatty acids, ubiquitous among animals as well as occurring in several plants (oxylipins, jasmonates). They comprise a large family of compounds that have a wide variety of biological activity and are highly potent. The most abundant E precursor is arachidonic acid (AA) (twenty carbon fatty acid, four double bonds), which is synthesized by one of three phospholipase A2 enzymes. The prostaglandins family includes both thromboxane and prostacyclin (together called prostanoids) and are derived from PGH2 (figure 3.10).

Fig. 3.10. Arachidonic acid metabolism

Abbreviation EET: Epoxyeicosatrienoic acids

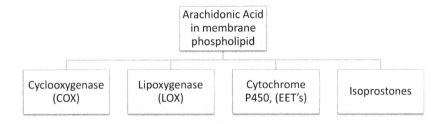

Products of the Cyclo Oxgenase /Arachidonate Series That Are Clinically Important

For example, TXA 2 promotes platelet aggregation and vasoconstriction, which is opposed by PGI2, both important in stroke and myocardial infarction. PGE is involved in modulation of neurotransmitter release, an inflammatory mediator in the brain, and PGE2 and PGF2 alpha are used to induce labor. Lantanoprost (PGF2 alpha derivatives) are used for open-angle glaucoma treatment (figures 3.11 and 3.12).[87]

Fig. 3.11. Arachidonic acid cyclooxygenase cascade

Clinical uses: labor induction, glaucoma treatment, platelet aggregation inhibition, patent ductus arteriosus closureAbbreviations: AA – arachidonic acid, PGH2 – prostaglandin H2, TXA – thromboxane A2, PGI – prostacyclin 2, PGF2 prostraglandin F2, PGE2 prostraglandin E2, PGD2 prostraglandin D2.

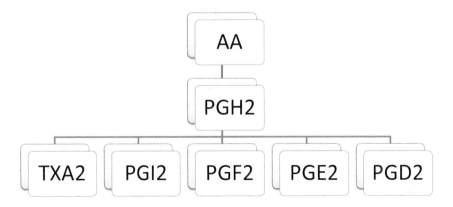

Fig. 3.12. Arachidonic acid cyclooxygenase cascade functions.
Adapted from: Brady ST, Siegel GJ, Albers RW, Price DL. Basic
Neurochemistry, 8th edition. Elsevier Academic Press, New York 2012.

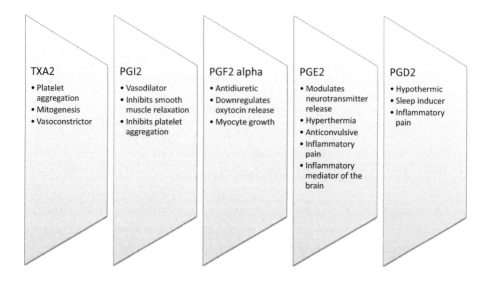

Products of Lipoxygenase Series

Arachidonic acid by metabolism by lipoxygenase (LOX) leads to the
hydroperoxyeicosatetranoic acids (HPETEs), which in turn are converted to leukotriene and hydroxy derivatives (HETEs) (figure 3.13).

Fig. 13.13. Arachidonic acid lipoxygenase pathway
Adapted from: Brady ST, Siegel GJ, Albers RW, Price DL. Basic
Neurochemistry, 8th edition. Elsevier Academic Press, New York 2012.
Abbreviations: HPETE hydroperoxyeicosatetraenoic acids, HETE
hydroxyeicosatetraenoic acids, LTA4 – leukotriene A4, B4, C4, D4, E4.

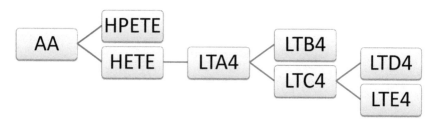

For example, leukotrienes in leucocytes and mast cells are of great interest as these are associated with the pathogenesis and also treatment options in cardiovascular disease, asthma, and anaphylactic shock (figure 3.14).[88]

Fig. 3.14. Arachidonic acid lipoxygenase leukotriene functions: Leukotrienes are predominantly generated in leucocytes, some are generated in endothelial cells.

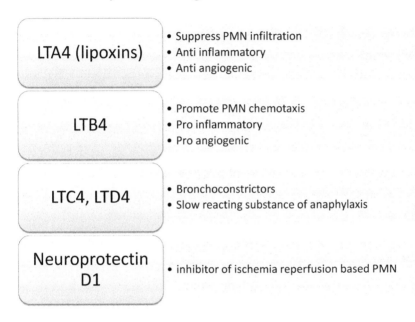

LTA4 (lipoxins)
- Suppress PMN infiltration
- Anti inflammatory
- Anti angiogenic

LTB4
- Promote PMN chemotaxis
- Pro inflammatory
- Pro angiogenic

LTC4, LTD4
- Bronchoconstrictors
- Slow reacting substance of anaphylaxis

Neuroprotectin D1
- inhibitor of ischemia reperfusion based PMN

Epidemiology: There Is No Association Between Saturated Fat Intake and Coronary Heart Disease or Cerebrovascular Disease

Evidence from the largest meta-analysis performed to date with twenty-seven randomized trials and forty-five observational studies in over 600,000 people performed on three continents concluded that there was no evidence that lowering saturated fats promoted heart health and that the saturated fat heart hypothesis should be refuted. In addition, the analysis did not find support for the current cardiovascular guidelines that recommend high consumption of polyunsaturated fatty acids and low saturated fat consumption.[89]

In a 2010 meta-analysis of twenty-two prospective studies of coronary heart disease (CHD n = 15) and stroke (n = 8), in 347,747 people followed between five and twenty-three years, there was no association between saturated fat being associated with either coronary or cerebrovascular disease. This review included almost all major, prospective studies published to date including the Framingham Study, Coronary Heart Disease Study, Honolulu Heart Study, Caerphilly Study, Israeli Ischemic Heart Disease Study, Health Professionals Follow Up Study, Lipid Research Clinics Study, Alpha Tocopherol Beta Carotene Study, Health and Lifestyle Survey, Malmo Diet and Cancer Study, Nurses Health Study, Baltimore Longitudinal Study of Aging, Strong Heart Study, and Adult Health Study. Importantly, the strengths included the large numbers of subjects, the prospective nature, and use of the random effects model for analysis. However, the weaknesses certainly were the dietary histories and nutrient assessments. In addition there was a strong suggestion of publication bias favoring studies with significant results as indicated by the funnel plot of studies. The overall risk ratio for association of saturated fat with CHD or CVD was 1.00 (0.89, 1.11, p = 0.95).

In addition the question of the ratio of saturated fats to polyunsaturated fats as well as the amount of transfats counted with saturated fats are both important factors that we know of today and that this meta-analysis was unable to decipher.[90]

Why was this message ignored for decades? Two landmark comments, thirty-six years apart, had come to the same conclusion. In 1977 in a leading article in the *New England Journal of Medicine*, George Mann MD, DsC, wrote a current concepts article concerning the lack of evidence for a low-fat diet in cardiovascular disease entitled "Diet-Heart: End of an Era."[91] Again in 1991 George V. Mann, MD, as a senior researcher and one-time director of the Framingham Heart Study, commented,

> The diet heart hypothesis suggests that high intake of fat and cholesterol causes heart disease has been repeatedly shown to be wrong and yet for complicated reasons of pride, profit and prejudice, the hypothesis continues to be exploited by scientists, fund raising enterprises, food companies and even governmental agencies. The

public is being deceived by the greatest health scam of the century.[92]

In 2013 an editorial entitled "Saturated Fat Is Not the Major Issue: Let's Bust the Myth of Its Role in Heart Disease" was published in the *British Medical Journal* outlining the many factors whereby saturated fats are actually protective and reduced saturated fat increases cardiovascular risk. Low cholesterol is associated with both increased cardiovascular and importantly also noncardiac mortality.[93] Saturated fats were first reviled as a consequence of Angel Key's seven countries study in 1970, with the implication of correlation between total cholesterol and coronary heart disease.[94] One of the reasons that may explain these contradictory findings is that the reduction of saturated fats affects large (type A) LDL although it is the small dense (type B) particles that are implicated in coronary artery disease and related to carbohydrate intake.[95] Consuming milk, for example, has a cholesterol lowering effect, which contains vitamin A, vitamin D, and trans palmitoleic acid that have a protective effect on coronary disease, lower triglycerides, CRP as well as having antihypertensive effects. Clinical studies have revealed that people with myocardial infarction mostly have the metabolic syndrome (approximately two-thirds), and furthermore, mostly have normal cholesterol levels (in 75%).[96] In the same year, a study of daily egg consumption was shown not to be associated with either coronary heart disease or stroke risk.[97] A comparison of lowering carbohydrates or lowering fats with the outcome being coronary heart disease risk factors indicated that lowering carbohydrates was more effective.[98]

Atherosclerotic Lesions Are Best Explained by the Hemodynamic Theory, First Proposed by Texon in 1957

Atherosclerosis lesions do not occur randomly in the cerebrovascular or cardiovascular vessels but in predictable locations in areas of diminished lateral pressure as a result of blood flow pressure effects secondary to vessel branching, bifurcation, and tapering. Atherosclerotic lesions may also occur in relatively straight vessels (such as the basilar artery) due to serpentine flow (flow along a straight vessel tends to become wavy in segmental zones with areas diminished lateral pressure). These localized decreases in static pressure translate into a type of suction action, exposing endothelium, which causes reactive thickening resulting by the endothelial cells and fibroblasts. Subsequent progressive changes include deposition of cellular collagen, lipid deposition, calcification, and finally thrombus formation and ulceration of plaque that may then embolize an atherosclerotic plaque with embolization.[99, 100] The predilection of atherosclerotic lesions in the cervicocephalic vascular tree strongly supports this theory with plaques preferentially at curvature sites (carotid siphon) as well as in relatively straight vessels such as the basilar artery, due to serpentine flow (figure 3.15).

Fig. 3.15. Predilection of atherogenic sites in the cerebrovascular tree. Darker colors indicate most frequent sites, lighter colors, less frequent involvement.
Figure adapted from: Mohr JP, Henning M. Carotid Artery Disease. In Mohr JP, Wolf PA, Grotta JC, Moskowitz MA, Mayberg Mr, von Kummer R (eds). Stroke. Pathophysiology, diagnosis and management 5th ed. Elsevier Saunders, Philadelphia 2011.

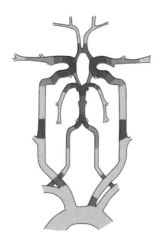

Ancient Egyptian and Peruvian Mummies Had Atherosclerosis Too

Researchers from the Horus study team documented atherosclerotic lesions in seventy-six Egyptian mummies and sixty-one Mesoamerican mummies that extend back over three thousand years, clearly negating the notion of atherosclerosis being a modern disease. Autopsy studies in ancient Egyptians have documented extensive parasitic infections most notably with bilharziasis, malaria, and *Trichinella spiralis*. Chronic inflammation due to the infectious load in the past may have been the main factor in promoting atherosclerosis whereas nowadays it has been replaced by lifestyle and dietary factors, auto-immune diseases, and human immunodeficiency disease.[101]

Vestiges of Our Body: Paleo-Archeological and Extant Evidence for the Importance of Fats. The Most Important Are Our Relative Fatness and Our Large Brains Compared to All Other Primates.

A number of observations from archeology, clinical sciences, and epidemiological studies reflect the roles of fats in human evolution:

1. Humans are relatively fat and undermuscled compared to other primates, and our infants are the fattest of all infants. [102]

2. Humans are uniquely capable of storing larger amounts of fat compared to other mammals and primates. The fat-brain trade-off hypothesis (as opposed to the gut-brain trade-off) suggests that body fat and brain size are both complementary strategies for warding off starvation. Fat stores fulfill the role of a physiological buffer against starvation and at the same time are not metabolically expensive. In mammals there is a negative correlation between brain size and fats stores, which is not the case in humans. In humans the combination of these two strategies are combined perhaps as a result of more efficient bipedal locomotor evolution. Humans are therefore unusual among mammals and primates in having both large brains and large fat storage. The development of this dual strategy is interpreted as being particularly advantageous in warding off starvation during the cooling and aridity that characterized hominin evolution in East Africa in the last three to four million years.[103]

3. The cognitive buffer hypothesis posits that a primary reason for large brain size is in developing behavioral

responses that, overall, will improve the outcome with respect to environmental challenges.[104]

4. Contemporary clinical trials: The lack of evidence for the diet-heart hypothesis in curtailing fats with evidence of harm (violence) when limiting fat intake.[90]

5. Evidence of benefit of ketogenic diet (ketosis > 5 nM), ketogenic diets and crossing the 5% metabolism line associated with improved cardiac contractility in rats of ~ 25% with ketones. In addition ketogenic have been correlated with improved athletic performance on high fat diet as well as successful treatment of refractory epilepsy.[105–107]

The Pivotal Role of Docosahexanoic Acid DHA: Animal and Clinical Study Insights

Available only through the diet, polyunsaturated fatty acids (PUFA), in particular, the n-3 PUFA, constitute approximately 30% of cell membranes. Animal studies have shown that deficiency of PUFA in rodents results in impaired learning and memory and in human studies deficiency correlates with neuropsychiatric disorder, dementia, attention-deficit disorder, depression, bipolar, and schizophrenia.[108–110] DHA elevates hippocampal BDNF, enhances cognition by facilitating synaptic plasticity, synaptic membrane fluidity, and stimulates mitochondrial function by reducing oxidative stress.[111, 112] In an Australian and Indonesian study, supplementation of PUFA (DHA 88 mg per day and eicosopentanoic acid EPA 22 mg per day) in schoolchildren was correlated with higher scores in learning, memory, and verbal intelligence scores.[113] Conversely, high transfats and saturated fat diets adversely affect cognition.[114] The role of DHA in neurodegenerative diseases, including amyotrophic lateral sclerosis (ALS), has recently been highlighted by the study of Fitzgerald et al. In 995 people with ALS, a relatively increased DHA intake was associated with reduced risk of ALS with a relative risk of 0.66 (95% CI: 0.53–0.81).[115]

DHA: Evolutionary Insights from Early LifeForms, Primitive Mammals, and Primates

DHA has been around for a long time. For about three-fourths of the history of life on Earth (the initial 2.5 billion years), blue-green algae dominated the early oceans and, by photosynthetic metabolism, produced carbohydrates, proteins, and lipids that were rich in n-3 fatty acids.

The Great Oxygen Event

Today oxygen makes up 21% of the atmosphere but this fraction used to be 0.001% of today's levels until the advent of the great oxygen event (GOE) 2.4–2.1 billion years ago (bya). However, oxygenation of the deep ocean lagged by about 2 by behind the atmosphere, and animal life forms had to wait for a second oxygenation event (the Neoproterozoic oxidation event).[116]

Both Arachidonic Acid (AA) for Vascular System Development and Decosahexanoic Acid (DHA) for Neural Development Availability Were Pivotal Factors in the Evolution of the Brain

Oxidative metabolism eventually appeared about 600 mya, and since then, animal neural and visual systems evolved in a docosahexanoic (n-3 fatty acids) abundant environment as these are produced by oxidative metabolism. The predominance of n-3 fatty acids in the early oceans translated into a requirement for fish and reptile species to obtain n-3 FA for their reproduction, which remained until the end of the Cretaceous period at about 65 mya, the time of dinosaur extinction, after which ferns, cycads, and angiosperms appeared, which stored lipids (during germination) as oils rich in n-6 fatty acids. The evolution of the placenta may have enabled enlargement of mammalian brain size with respect to antecedent egg laying amphibians, reptiles, and fish. A placenta may be regarded as a vascular system with a high requirement for n-6 FAs, especially arachidonic acid (AA). With both AA and DHA being major constituents of the brain, the evolvement of the n-6 FAs may have provided a key biochemical link for vascular development and subsequent evolution of the placenta and the relatively larger brains of mammals.[117]

With Climate Change and an Increase in Grasslands, African Herbivores Became Larger, but Their Relative Brain Size Decreased

With the evolution of larger bodies among African savanna animals, their relative brain size decreased in a logarithmic manner. There was an oblation of brain size rather than DHA, with the consequence of a relatively DHA poor biosphere for hominin brain evolution.[118] Furthermore, the more readily available n-3 docosapentanoic acid (n-3 DPA) was not used for the brain growth in place of DHA. One explanation might be that the emerging modern *Homo sapiens* evolved in the lacustrine (lake) environments in the East African Rift Valley at the same time that australopithecines inhabited more forested regions. Both Rift Valley lakeshore sites and fossils from the Southern African Cape coast are regarded as the earliest modern human fossils at 120–60 kya.[119, 120] This provided strong evidence for the consumption of seafood dating to the time of rapid cerebral expansion.[121, 122] These findings imply that our brain enlargement occurred because of adequate long chain PUFAs in the diet due to coastal and lacustrine exploitation as we evolved. Both present-day primates use of 16 and 18 carbon PUFA (from vegetarian resources) and likely, too, the australopithecines, explains their much smaller brain capacity as a consequence of their land-based diet, hence their evolutionary stasis for ~2 million years. The exploitation of lacustrine and coastal foods correlates well with the rapid and relatively recent cerebral expansion to ~1,500 grams.[123] The vascular component too was important, and because of the vascular system's high requirement for AA, its availability for further vascular development set the stage for the evolution of the large human brain.[124]

The Preference and Specificity for Docosahexanoic Acid (DHA) in Nature Is Profound

The n-3 docosapentaenoic acid (DPA) precursor was the major n-3 metabolite in savanna mammals. Despite this, neither n-3 or n-6

DPA was used for the function of the neuronal synapse of photoreceptor. Hence, large land mammals in whom DPA is the dominant n-3 metabolite, their neuronal membranes nevertheless still retain a DHA-rich composition observed in other species. The slight difference between the DHA (six double bonds) and DPA (five double bonds) molecules is very important for neural membrane functioning. This is despite the more readily available DPA, which is also less prone to oxidation.[125] DHA has been selected for membrane building since early evolutionary times, and it is postulated at present that this may be important for integral membrane protein interaction or electrical properties that influence neuronal signaling.[126]

DHA and Modern Times

Multinational studies show that marine fats, in particular, DHA, are cardioprotective, protective for the cerebrovascular systems as well as being neuroprotective.[127–129] A minimeta-analysis of neuropsychological benefit of n-3 FAs in randomized double-blind placebo-controlled studies of mild cognitive impairment and Alzheimer's disease patients revealed benefit for attention and processing speed in the mild cognitive impairment patients.[130]

The ratio of omega-6 to omega-3 is considered to have been between 1 and 2 in our ancestral diets, yet in the United States of America nowadays it is estimated to be 17. Different populations around the world may have more beneficial rations though.

Table 3.9. Omega-6 to omega-3 ratios in various populations (Modified from Simopoulos AP)[131]

Population type	Omega-6 to omega-3 ratio (approximated)
Coastal fishing	<1
Hunter gatherer	2–3
Greece (1900s)	2
Japan (current)	4
Northern Europe (current)	15
USA (current)	17

The global preponderance of neuropsychiatric diseases deserves special mention and in particular teenage children and the high incidence of conditions such as attention-deficit hyperactivity disorder ADHD and autism are areas of increasing concern. Lipid-deficient diets have long been implicated, and the first report of a randomized controlled trial of omega-3 FA in ADHD revealed efficacy in the emotion-processing domain in these children.[132] The profound mismatch of today's Western-type diet with the so-called primordial diet are probably influencing our biology prior to conception, during child and adolescent development as well as contributing to the most prevalent diseases today including cardio-cerebrovascular disease, cancer, dementia, and neuropsychiatric disease, particularly depression (figure 3.16).

Fig. 3.16. Fish consumption and major depression
Figure credit with permission: Gomez-Pinilla F. Brain Foods: the effects of nutrients on brain function. Nature Reviews Neuroscience 2008; 9:568–578,

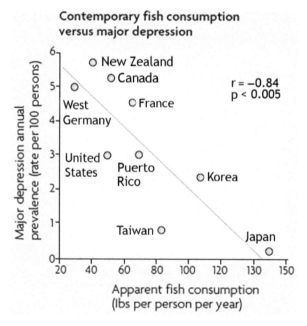

There is an urgent need to reexamine our biological nutritional needs and bring food production closer in alignment with these.[133]

At a regional level, the marked increase in cerebral disorders of many kinds, most notably dementia stroke and neuropsychiatric disease has been prioritized by the European Union with current cost estimates of €386 billion for the twenty-five member states (2004 prices). Previously the focus was on cardiovascular, proteins, and calorie consumption, during the last century. Brain disorders now require urgent attention as well as a reappraisal of the food processing and supply.[134]

There Has Been a Decrease in Healthy Fats and an Increase in Unhealthy Fat Consumption Compounded by a Marked Increase in Refined Sugars Intake

Overall as a species we have markedly increased our fat intake (saturated fats, linoleic acid, and transfats) in the last one hundred years, and at the same time we have decreased n-3 FA (alpha linoleic acid, or ALA, PUFA which includes eicosapentanoic acid and DHA).

The parent fatty acids, linoleic acid (LA), and alpha linoleic acids (ALA) cannot be synthesized by humans but can be converted into their long chain metabolites (>20 carbon, >3 double bonds). AA and DHA, both abundant in the retina and brain, are important components of structural lipids and mediate membrane properties such as fluidity, flexibility, and permeability. DHA is critical for the adequate functioning of vision-related proteins (rhodopsin) and neurotransmission (synaptic receptors). Arachidonic acid, eicosapentanoic acid, and dihomogamma linolenic acid (DGLA) derived from membrane phospholipids are also precursors of eicosanoids, which are potent regulatory hormones that mediate inflammation, platelet aggregation, and control of blood pressure.[135]

Comparative analysis with primates indicates we consume more PUFA and saturated fats. Humans have strong preferences for lipid-rich foods, and we seek out foods with a high DQ. The definition of the DQ index is defined as the following:

$DQ = s + 2(r) + 3.5 (a)$

s—indicates percentage of diet from plant parts (stems, leaves)

r—indicates percentage of diet derived from fruits, nectar, or flowers

a—indicates percentage of diet from animal components

The range varies from 100–350 where 100 represents 100% folivory and 350 represents 100% carnivory or sole ingestion of animal parts.

The ability to detect energy-rich foods to accommodate the demands of brain metabolism that comprises of 20–25% (of resting energy needs) in humans, compared to 8–10% in the primates and 3–5% mammals.[136] Chimpanzees and gorillas, on the other hand, have high CHO and low fat diets, as well as larger total gut and colon volumes.[137, 138] Our gastrointestinal tract (GIT) is more similar to the carnivore group, reflecting our high fat and meat diet. Evolutionary genetic analysis has yielded further insights with meat-adaptive genes. For example, the appearance of the unique E3 allele (apolipoprotein E locus) in hominins, which does not occur in chimps or gorillas, allowed our ancestors the exploitation of meat diets. Apo E regulates the uptake of cholesterol and lipids in the body and confers reduced cardiovascular risk with consumption of high fat diets.[139, 140]

Paleolithic Nutrition Reveals a Progressive Change in Diets from Insectivory (Ancestral Mammals) to Frugivory (Primates) Then Meat and Tuber Diets (Hominids)

As the primates expanded, more fruitand vegetable-type foods were ingested, and body size increased for most species.[141] Tectonic and paleoclimatic factors precipitated the main impetus for early hominids to change their nutrition, which altered from tropical woodland to tropical savanna (primary productivity).[142] Despite tropical savanna producing only half as much plant energy per year as tropical woodlands (4,050 versus 7,200 kcal/m²/year), the proliferation of herbivores (secondary productivity) converts to an approximately tripling of the productivity to that of in the savanna (10.1 versus 3.6 kcal/m²/year).[143] Savanna expansion limited the foods such as tubers but increased the herbivore populations at a time that the archeological record reveals the first stone tools. The emergence of *Homo erectus* at this time was therefore provided with the all-important long chain PUFAs (DHA and AA) for brain evolution and growth. DHA and AA availability constrained the evolution of larger brain sizes in most mammalian species except humans and dolphins.[144]

During Hominin Evolution, We Were Probably Fishing More Than Hunting

African savanna plant foods—such as tubers, nuts—contain small amounts of DHA and AA whereas herbivores provide more significant amounts. However, aquatic species supply the most. Hence, the major increase in hominid brain size is considered to be related to the systematic use of aquatic (marine, riverine, lacustrian) resources,[145] and humans evolved with omega-6 to omega-3 fatty acids diet ratio averaging 1:1 in contrast to the 10:1 to 20–25:1 ratio of current Western diets. DHA constitutes approximately 40% of the brain membrane phospholipid.[146]

Dietary omega-3 fatty acids have a noteworthy effect on neural gene expression, which likely endowed an advantage in the hominid line. However, the dearth of DHA in the land food chain supports the premise that a lacustrine or marine environment was most important, with a diet rich in DHA together with the accompanying micronutrients (iodine, zinc, copper, manganese, and selenium), also important in brain development, which counter peroxidation. Of note in this regard is the observation that, universally, terrestrial mammalian brains became relatively smaller with increasing body size.[147]

DHA Availability Appears to Have Been a Strong Determining Factor in Brain Size and Probably Connectivity

In those mammals (rats, mice) with relatively minimal body growth, synthesis of DHA by dietary intake or from plant-derived alpha linolenic acid usually suffices, allowing for brain to body weight ratio of >2%. In terrestrial mammals, with increasing body size, however, the rate limitation of DHA synthesis becomes more important, leading to a relative shrinking of brain size. Conversely, a good supply of preformed DHA available in the marine environment probably accounts for the dolphin's brain weight of 1,800 grams, markedly different when compared to a similar-size animal by weight (zebra) with a brain weight average to 360 grams.[148] The developing rat brain incorporates preformed DHA at a much greater rate than DHA synthesized from alpha linolenic acid.[149] whereas humans are only able to convert about 1% from alpha linolenic acid to DHA.[150] Presumably because of the high DHA diet available to dolphins and humans during evolution, their brain size increased whereas all other mammalian species show a logarithmic decrease in brain size with increased body mass.[151] DHA and its unique neural cell signaling capabilities and synaptic evolution are regarded as building blocks of symbolic thinking and cultural evolution that followed and surpassed biological evolution. We probably evolved closer to an aquatic environment than a semirid savanna with all its associated predator perils, at a time we had to also cope with increasingly more dependent offspring.[152]

There is evidence that intense exposure to the marine food environment (and underground storage organs) was restricted to a few hundred or a few thousand surviving hominids at the tip of Southern Africa during a particularly severe cold and arid spell during marine isotope stage 6, 195–123 kya. Soon thereafter, in an evolutionary time frame, the earliest signs of executive function and culture emerged.[153–154]

Why Is DHA So Special? It Alters the Physical Properties of Membranes, Speeding Up Vesicle Processing, and Is a Lipoxin Precursor with Anti-Inflammatory Properties

With the original source of DHA being marine algae, DHA is accordingly concentrated in fish and marine oils. Mammals do not have the specific enzymes required for the synthesis of the precursors for omega 3 FA, alpha-linolenic acid (ALA), which the photosynthetic cells of algae and higher plants have. Furthermore, endogenous synthesis of DHA from ALA in humans is limited, and the relatively high omega-6 fatty acids in current Western diets also displaces DHA from membrane phospholipids. In addition to the unique structural cellular membrane features, DHA is the precursor for resolvins and protectins. Collectively called lipoxins, their anti-inflammatory effect, occurs via reduction of interleukin-6, TNF-α and VEGF.[155]

DHA enables particular physical membrane properties, specifically the increasing the lateral motion of lipids and proteins within the membrane as well as impeding the rate of diffusion of charged molecules across the membrane. This is not, however, exclusive to omega-3 FA, as both saturated and monounsaturated fatty acids are now also recognized as signaling molecules.[156]

Within the brain, polyunsaturated fatty acids (PUFAs) not only guide structural aspects but also functional ones of neurons, endothelial cells, and glial cells. Palmitic and stearic acid are the main saturated fatty acids, oleic acid the main monounsaturated, and DHA and arachidonic acid the main PUFA in the brain.

Table 3.10. Long-chain fatty acid classification, carbon atom number, and double bonds

Fatty acid	Carbon atoms	Double bonds
Saturated		
Palmitic acid	16	0
Stearic acid	18	0
Monounsaturated		
Oleic acid	18	1
Polyunsaturated acids		
Alpha linolenic acid (ALA)	18	3
Eicosapentanoic acid (EPA)	20	5
Docosapentanoic acid (DPA n-3)	22	5
Docosahexaenoic acid (DHA)	22	6
Linoleic acid (LNA)	18	2
Docosapentanoic acid (DPA n-6)	22	5
Arachidonic acid (ARA)	20	4

(Modified from Bazinet RP, Laye S)[157]

Overall, PUFAs regulate synaptic activity, activate receptors, including endocannabinoid receptors (retrograde CB1signaling), promote neuronal survival and neurogenesis (synaptamide), synaptogenesis, have potent anti-inflammatory effects, and involved in regulation of brain glucose uptake.[157] Polyunsaturated phospholipids in the membranes speed up synaptic vesicle processing. Polyunsaturated phospholipids are abundant in the brain, and many epidemiological studies have implicated their deficiency in a wide variety of disorders of mental health and cognition. The phospholipid component is integral to most membranes of cells comprising of monounsaturated and saturated acyl chains. However, synaptic vesicle membranes are different with the phospholipid component mostly (~80%) containing polyunsaturated acyl chains. In an electron microscopy study, Pinot et al. studied the proteins dynamin and endophilin. Their results indicated that dynamin, for example, hydrolyzed GTP 7.5 times faster on liposomes containing polyunsaturated in comparison to the monounsaturated phospholipids. The plasma membranes with polyunsaturated phospholipids become more flexible, facilitating deformation required by endocytosis. In addition, the rate of endocytosis is escalated as well as the recycling of vesicles. In summary, the polyunsaturated phospholipid, controlled by dynamin and endophilin, expedited endocytosis.[158]

Even though DHA, n-3 DPA and n-6 DPA are differentiated by only one double bond, the latter two compounds are easier to synthesize and also oxidize less easily. In addition, the n-3 DPA and n-6 DPA did not replace DHA during six hundred million years of evolution in the context of profound genomic changes in that same extensive time period. Although AA is also abundant in the brain, it is much more easily synthesized from terrestrial rather than aquatic sources. This extraordinary conservation with respect to DHA prompted Michael Crawford to expound that "DHA was actually dictating to DNA rather than the more conventional view of evolution occurring the other way around." This is also consistent with Darwin's "conditions of existence." Together with natural selection, conditions of existence are considered the two forces of evolution. Darwin termed the former pangenes and regarded these as the more significant of the two. Since his deliberations, these have been discovered in the form of reverse transcriptases and the science of epigenetics.[159, 160]

Humans have high bandwidth synaptic communication

Synaptic conveyance is at the center of neuronal function, processing and information storage in the brain. Synaptic transmission, its associated plasticity and the impact on neuronal firing form the brain's cardinal computational building blocks. Compared to rodents, humans have a much higher information exchange at the level of pyramidal neurons, exceeding that of mice by a factor of 4–9 times. There is little doubt that DHA plays a unique and special role at the synaptic level.[161]

Table 3.11. DHA beneficial effects[162]

- Speeds up synaptic vesicle processing
- Unique electrical properties improving neuronal signaling
- Acceleration of lateral motion of lipids and proteins in the membrane
- Impedes rate of diffusion of charged molecules across membrane
- Enable supramolecular chemistry with six dimensions
- Precursor for resolvins and protectins with anti-inflammatory action

Ketones Are Regarded as Superfuels and Have Been Effective in Treating a Number of Neurological Conditions including Epilepsy, Traumatic Brain Injury, and Neurodegenerative Diseases (Alzheimer's Disease, Parkinson's Disease)

Although glucose is the major fuel for the human brain, during times of starvation, the brain adapts to the use of ketones, including beta hydroxybutyrate (ßOHB), acetoacetate, and acetone as its principal energy source. In protracted starvation, ketones provide 60–70% of the energy requirements of the brain.[163]

ßOHB is the predominant ketone during starvation, taking over from glucose as the principal brain energy source, and decreases the need for glucose synthesis by the liver and kidney and so avoids use of muscle-derived amino acids. As a consequence, an average human, instead of surviving a few weeks of starvation, is capable of surviving two to three months. ßOHB is considered superfuel because it produces ATP more efficiently than fatty acids or glucose.[164] Ketones supply 50% resting energy requirements for most body tissues, and about 70% for the brain. Normal levels of ßOHB and acetoacetate are below 0.1 millimoles, but during starvation these increase to 5–8 millimole, acetoacetate 1–2 millimoles, and acetone 1–2 millimoles.[165] Astrocytes have a key role regulating cerebral energy metabolism as they are able to produce ketone bodies from leucine and fatty acids.[166]

Table 3.12. Mechanisms whereby ketones exert their effects (principally beta hydroxybutyrate)[167–172]

- Are more energy efficient than glucose
- Stimulate mitochondrial biogenesis
- Increase acetyl CoA sixteenfold
- Protective against glutamate-mediated apoptosis (reactive oxidant species decreased)
- Enhance glutamate to GABA conversion, enabling GABAmediated inhibition
- Ketone metabolism can improve cerebral blood flow

Ketones Were an Important Human Evolutionary Starvation Adaptation

A ketoacid level of 5–8 mM during starvation appears to be unique to humans. For example, mammals with brains consuming less than 5% of basal metabolism have no need for ketosis because of the ability of their glycerol supplied by adipose tissue triglyceride to maintain adequate gluconeogenesis for the brain's requirement.[170] Early hominoids adapted to a higher than 5% basal brain metabolism because of relatively rapid punctuated nature of evolutionary changes. Beta hydroxybutyrate would have been an essential requirement to support survival during catastrophic famines encountered by the many relatively sudden global cooling events with increased aridity.[173]

Clinical Uses

The ketogenic diet is a high-fat diet with a tripling of the calories of fat to about 90% instead of the usually recommended 35%. People achieve this by consuming a high intake of dairy products, cheese, cream and butter for example. Some have difficulty to adhering to this regimen, but refractory seizure patients (drug failures) may achieve a 50% remission with this diet and up to 10% become seizure free.[174] The mechanisms of the ketogenic diet in epilepsy treatment remain uncertain, but one possibility is the epigenetic alteration of epilepsy gene expression that was discovered in rat studies with one group having a higher rate of methylation affecting DNA in comparison to the group on a ketogenic diet.[175] Early clinical and animal studies are promising for the use in neurodegenerative diseases such as Alzheimer's and Parkinson's disease as well as traumatic brain injury.[176]

Carbohydrates

Table 3.13. Classification of sugars

Simple sugars
Glucose
Fructose
Galactose

Complex sugars (disaccharides)
Sucrose (glucose and fructose)
Lactose (glucose and galactose)

Starches or polysaccharides
(helical amylose and branched amylopectin units)
Produced by most plants to store energy; maize, potatoes, wheat, rice

Carbohydrates and Primate Evolution

Our penchant for sweet things could be dated to primate evolutionary times in the Miocene period (23–5 mya) and the angiosperm (fruit, flowers) proliferation. Ripening fruit becomes more colorful and sweeter and may explain primate fondness for sugar. Seeds are bitter, and this aids in dispersal. The importance of frugivory in the primate diet is exemplified by the spider monkey and howler monkey that exist today in South and Central American tropical regions.

Both live in similar tropical regions and have a similar body size, but they have different dietary habits. At 107 grams (3.8 oz), the spider monkey brain is twice the size of a howler monkey brain of equivalent body size. This has been attributed to the spider monkeys' complex social system and their frugivorous diets, which consist primarily of ripe fruit from a wide variety (over 150 species) of plants. This requires the monkeys to remember when and where fruit can be found.[137–177]

Carbohydrates and Hominin Evolutionary Insights

Dietary components have varied markedly in the course of human evolution. The archeological records indicate periods of almost wholly fat and meat diets of some of the australopithecines (2–4 mya), the Neanderthals (200–30 kya), to subsistence on underground storage organs (USOs) as a major component (robust australopithecines). An adaptation to root vegetables may have started several million years back. It has been suggested that the early hominids became dependent on underground storage organs as fallback foods from about six million years ago.[178] In this respect, starches may have been used as an emergency food, as well as a transitional food at times of adversity. The high-quality foods, such as fruits and meat, both represent challenges; hence, we evolved eating whole-food carbohydrates. There are several traditional cultures with high carbohydrate intake and no obvious neurological disease. Laden and Wrangham have provided a number of supporting arguments for USOs as fallback foods and an important factor in human evolution and in understanding our current dietary needs. These were available all year round and therefore more reliable than obtaining fruit and meat. The evidence for this includes dentition, masticatory changes from great apes, nature of dentition of australopithecines, including the presence of both gracile and robust forms, expansion of USO-rich habits in the late Miocene, and the cooccurrence of hominid fossils with root eating rodents.[178]

Dentition Data Points More to USO Adaptation and Not Foliovory or Carnivory

Enamel is the hardest substance in our bodies and consequently is relatively better preserved in the fossil record, providing unique insights to the development and evolution of our diets. The dentition of early hominids was not adapted for meat eating[179] lacking the sharp and concave configuration, blade-like teeth, but adapted to a range of foods, including leaves, fruit, and hard objects such as nuts, seeds, and buds. The megadontia quotient is defined as "observed area of the mandibular last premolar and first two molars divided by the area predicted from body weight."[180] On this scale P boisei has the highest at 2.7, P robustus 2.2, A africanus 2.0, *Homo habilis* 1.9 and *Homo erectus*, *Homo sapiens* and Pan troglodytes all record 0.9.[181] The megadontia quotient implies that the Australopithecine species had chewing surfaces that were significantly larger than present-day African apes. Massive masticatory (chewing) muscles were also evident, particularly in *Australopithecus robustus.*[182]

The dentition of *Australopithecus paranthropus* was notable for very little evidence of a shearing quotient (relative shear potential of molar teeth) configuration,[183] which is needed for leaf eating or foliovory, implying this was not a significant part of their diet.[184, 185] The thicker enamel as opposed to thinner enamel with a higher shearing quotient, characteristic of australopithecines, is exemplified best by Paranthropus.[186, 187]

Cooking and Fire

There is supportive archeological evidence as early as 1.9 mya from the fossil record, including the reduction of digestive effort provided by smaller teeth, increased available energy from food, evidenced by the larger female body mass in *Homo erectus* (figure 3.17). It is surmised that this led to pair bonding and that cooking was partly responsible for the evolution of the early human social system.[188, 189]

Fig. 3.17. Brain size (cc): Australopithecus (~450),
Homo erectus (~850), Homo sapiens (~1300) Figure credit
adapted from: Gibbons A. Food for thought. Did the first cooked
meals help fuel the dramatic evolutionary expansion
of the human brain. Science 2007; 316:1558–1560.

- Bipedalism
- Endurance running
- Meat/fish diet
- Underground storage organ consumption
- Smaller gut
- Cooking

The Refined Sugar Epidemic, Diabetes Mellitus II, and Metabolic Syndrome

Marked fluctuations in food availability on a seasonal basis or over longer periods of time favored what has been termed the thrifty genotype, facilitating an insulin response to aid glucose storage at times of ample nutrition. Furthermore, the diets high in protein and fats and relatively low carbohydrates enhanced gluconeogenesis. The modern, high-glucose diet, often with refined simple carbohydrates, in the setting of a steady, abundant food, with higher levels of fats, the previously adaptive genotype, contributed to the emergence of diabetes with excess insulin production.[190] With adverse nutrition, a not infrequent event in our evolutionary past, nowadays in the presence of adult overnutrition, we risk the development of diabetes mellitus and the metabolic syndrome.[191] In particular, nowadays, both the quantity and quality (glycemic index, associated fiber) of carbohydrates is important leading to metabolic syndrome, obesity, diabetes mellitus, and hypertension.

Obesity Is Increasing Dramatically Worldwide and Is Associated with Increased Mortality and Disease in Practically Every Organ System

Methods of assessing body fat and obesity include underwater weighing, air displacement plethysmography ADP skinfold, bioelectrical impedance BIA, and BMI with the latter the most commonly used and give defining categories to what is overweight, obese, and underweight. Body mass index has become an acceptable but by no means accurate surrogate for body fat.

Table 3.14. The BMI categories from severe undernutrition (<16) to extreme obesity (> 40)[192]

BMI	Nutritional status
>40	Extreme obesity
>30	Obesity
25.0–29.9	Overweight
18.5–24.9	Normal
17.0–18.4	Mild undernutrition
16.0–16.9	Moderate undernutrition
<16.0	Severe undernutrition

More than one-third (~100 million) of people in the USA are obese, and WHO global obesity estimates 1.6 billion are either overweight or obese.[193, 194] The Framingham Heart Study data revealed a 1% increase risk of death per pound weight increase (thirty- to forty-two-year category) that rose to 2% in the fifty- and sixty-year age category.[195, 196]

Other than increased mortality, overweight and obesity are associated with an extensive comorbidity list. This includes hypertension, diabetes, cardiovascular disease, stroke, hyperlipidemia, gout, arthritis, colelithiasis, nonalcoholic fatty liver disease, gastroesophageal reflux disease, Barrett's esophagus as well as cancers of the breast, endometrium, ovaries, prostate, esophagus, and colon.[197]

Obesity Is a Complex Health Problem That Has Many Causes but a Major one Is Overuse of Refined Sugars Dating Back to the 1980s

Refined sugar sweetened drinks have increased by about 60% since the 1970s.[198, 199] High fructose corn syrup (HFCS) was invented in 1957 as a cheaper sweetening agent, and there may be a correlation between HFCS consumption and obesity, as approximately threefourths of packaged foods in the United States, for example, has added sugar.[200] Consumption of soft drinks has increased fivefold since 1950. Meta-analyses indicate sugar-sweetened beverages (SSB) are correlated with cardiovascular disease, diabetes, and the metabolic syndrome. For example, drinking just two SSB drinks per day (16 oz each) over a six-month period led to the metabolic syndrome and fatty liver disease. Randomized controlled trials in children and adults lasting six months to two years have shown that lowering the intake of soft drinks reduced weight gain.[201–203]

Overall energy overconsumption, however, needs to remain the primary focus in combating the obesity epidemic rather than singling out HFCS and refined sugars.[204] Other important factors implicated in obesity include vegetable oil increase (30% since 1970s) and transfatty acid consumption.[205]

In a Spanish study of sugar-sweetened drinks in children and adolescents, more than four soft drinks per week was associated with over threefold risk in obesity (OR 3.46), and each additional intake of a soft drink associated with a 69% increase in obesity incidence.[206] The stroke and soda association is particularly prominent. Even one SSB per day was a risk for stroke. In the Nurses Health Study involving, a prospective cohort study followed for twenty-eight years (1980–2008), the pooled RR of total stroke for >1 serving of sugar-sweetened soda/day, compared with none, was 1.16 (95% CI: 1.00, 1.34).[207] Very simply, use of soft drinks versus none at all was associated with increased vascular events by almost 50% in the Northern Manhattan Stroke Study. This study controlled for all the other risk factors such as hypertension, hyperlipidemia, diabetes, cardiac disease, and metabolic syndrome. The hazard ratio (HR) was 1.43 (95% CI = 1.06–1.94).[208]

Table 3.15. Adverse effects soft drink, both diet and regular[209-212]

Stroke
Obesity
Metabolic syndrome
Nephrotoxicity
Dental caries

Although a relationship has been documented between refined sugar consumption and obesity in the USA, this does not hold for all countries. The so-called Australian paradox for example has noted the opposite, at least since the 1980s where a decreased in nutritive sweeteners including high fructose corn syrup of about 16% between 1980 and 2003 at a time when the overall obesity prevalence increased threefold.[213]

Aside from the obesity, diabetes mellitus II, and cardiovascular association, acne vulgaris is also linked to refined sugar consumption[214] as well as the most common liver disease worldwide, nonalcoholic fatty liver disease (NAFLD), which is regarded as the liver component of the metabolic syndrome in association with diabetes and cardiovascular disease. Fructose, being a lipogenic carbohydrate, increases insulin resistance as well as having microbiome-altering effects that are considered important in the obesity process.[215] There is also concern about the bisphenol contained in soft drink cans and mold inhibitors bisphenol A (BPA)—endocrine inhibitor, which lines the cans, that causes CAD, reproductive organ damage, and obesity.[216] The pathophysiological mechanisms whereby artificial sweeteners such as saccharin, aspartame, and sucrolose induce or contribute to obesity may be through alteration of the microbiome, or gut bacteria. In an elegant study performed at the Weizmann Institute of Science in Rehovot, Israel, mice that were fed one of the sweeteners for eleven weeks developed glucose intolerance. Interestingly this glucose intolerance effect was abolished by administering antibiotics. Furthermore, fecal transplantation of those mice with glucose intolerance and artificial sweetener use caused mice with sterile intestines to develop glucose intolerance. The overall conclusion of the study was that artificial sweetener used in this study, saccharin, was altering the mice microbiome in an adverse manner.[217, 218]

Refined Sugar Production from Cane Has Been Known for Several Thousand Years but Experienced Two Major Upsurges

Known since early civilizations about two thousand years ago, it was scarce during medieval times and relatively expensive.[219] The first was the spread of cane production in the Caribbean was during the eighteenth century, and during this time, consumption in England increased fivefold from 1710 to 1770.[220] The second major surge in refined sugar intake, at least in the USA, was during 1970s after the introduction of high fructose corn syrup, discovered in 1957, and because of taxation of sucrose importation in the USA, HFCS was approximately 30% cheaper at the time and introduced in the 1970s.[221] By the 1980s an obesity epidemic was under way with the rate of obesity in the USA suddenly increasing markedly, affecting all races, men, women, children, and adults. For example, the average weight of young women (aged twenty to twenty-nine) increased from 128 pounds (1960) to 157 (2000).[222]

SSBs deliver calories without the accompanying satiation effect because fructose (~65% of sugar in SSB) does not activate leptin, leaving one still *hungry*. Furthermore, unlike glucose, fructose is not regulated by insulin and increases ghrelin, leading to overeating.[223,224] Current recommendations by the American Heart Association are that free sugar comprise of no more than five teaspoons (one teaspoon of sugar contains four grams) per day (80 calories or twenty grams) for women and up to nine teaspoons per day (144 calories or thirty-six grams) for an adult man. The average SSB contains ~8 teaspoons (128 calories, thirty-two grams).[225]

Complex Carbohydrates and Grains: Are They Beneficial, Harmful, or Both?

The agricultural revolution may have been precipitated by a number of factors, including a diminution of wild game in certain regions due to climate changes as well as possible overhunting with extinction of a number of large herbivores consequent to the last ice. It remains uncertain to what extent human genetic expression has adapted to major dietary to the foods (grains, corn, soy, legumes, wheat) associated with the agricultural revolution that took place about 10 kya.

Some investigators consider that a long list of adverse health conditions can be linked to grains including autoimmune disease, allergies, celiac disease, epilepsy, cerebellar ataxia, dementia, autism, and schizophrenia. Furthermore, legumes, which are particularly rich in starch (60%), contain a number antinutrients with a consequence of mineral deficiencies. Both grains and legumes contain phytic acid, which also binds with deficiencies in calcium, magnesium, iron, and zinc.[226] Goitrogens (thyroid-inhibiting substances) found in certain grains such as millet have been linked to autoimmune disease and thyroid disease.[227] Furthermore, some researchers have postulated a possible addictive factor to grains due to exorphins. These are opioid peptides derived from grains such as wheat that have a similar structure to endogenous opioids.[228]

The archeological record has provided evidence of a deterioration in health as shown by a decline in human stature, bone density, dental development, increase in birth defects, malnutrition, and several examples of degenerative diseases.[229]

Celiac disease is characterized by villous atrophy of the small intestine, which leads to malabsorption of nutrients and increased immuno-responsiveness to gluten that occurs in genetically predisposed people. Gluten is a generic term that includes reference to proteins contained in wheat (gliadins), rye (secalins), barley (hordeins), and hybrid cereals (triticale). It is one form of gluten sensitivity and part of a spectrum of disorders that includes celiac disease. People with celiac disease or gluten enteropathy have higher risk of death, cancer, and cardiovascular disease.[230] Celiac disease is one of the most common lifelong disorders in Europe and the USA and can lead to white matter lesions.[231] The inflammatory response involved by the gluten exposure also activates the brain's microglia, and a brain-based inflammatory response occurs. Gluten increases levels of an enzyme called zonulin, which controls intestinal permeability and allow undigested proteins to become absorbed through selectively permeable barriers, which it does by disassembling the intercellular tight junctions, and cause immunological reactions to foods.[232] Gluten sensitivity may present solely with neurological, a form of extra-intestinal, presentation without enteropathy. A wide range of neurological syndromes have been associated with gluten sensitivity.[233, 234]

The Science Regarding Gluten-Related Illness Remains Uncertain

Avoiding gluten has been popularized recently with claims that up to one in a hundred people may have a sensitivity to one or more grain-related proteins, mostly gliadin and glutenin with numerous associated syndromes and up to 22.5% of people with gluten sensitivity reportedly having neurological syndromes.[235, 236] Cautionary reviews have also been published that suggest such claims remain speculative and that the current science does not support claims one way or another.[237] The entity, termed nonceliac gluten sensitivity, has been claimed to be very common, mostly undiagnosed, but a recent Italian study does not support this claim with prevalence rates similar to celiac disease.[238] However, the science is far from settled on these issues, and many other mechanisms, some completely unrelated to grain-related proteins, may be causing the syndromes in people. One possibility implicates a group of sugars contained in wheat termed FODMAPS (fermentable oligosaccharides, disaccharides, monosaccharides, and polyols) that may be causing abdominal discomfort, bloating, and diarrhea due to bacteria causing excess gas in the colon as a consequence.[239]

Honey: A Special Case

The association of humans with honeybees and gathering honey may date back very far, likely to our earliest ancestors including the australopithecines. Soon thereafter hominoid brain expansion associated with a meat and fish diet also required back up energy dense foods that were provided by underground storage organs and probably also honey, albeit less reliably. The evidence is indirect. Most traditional societies seek out honey, for example, the Ache from Paraguay consumption of honey is second in importance to meat and the pygmy Congo societies at times derive up to 80% of their calories from honey. The Hadza in Tanzania derive about 15% of the dietary energy from honey.[240] Archeological evidence in the form of rock art depicts honeyseekers in Europe dating back to 8000 years (figure 3.18) and in Southern Africa over 40 000 years.[241]

Fig. 3.18. Honey seeker images from the Levantine rock art, Valencia, Spain, dated eight thousand years ago.
A human figure, thought to be a woman, harvesting honey on a ladder made of lianas surrounded by bees (left image). A more complex ladder, serpentine configuration, with five human figures clambering up it, one or two seen falling off with oversized bees surrounding the ladder (right image)
Reprinted with permission from: Dams M Dams L. Spanish rock art depicting honey gathering during the Mesolithic. Nature 1977; 268:228–230.

Furthermore chimpanzees, gorillas, macaques and orangutans ingest honey when capable of extracting it, some using sticks, but which is difficult for all except humans armed with stone tools and fire. The symbiosis of the greater honeyguide bird (*Indicator indicator*) in most of Africa, leads both honey badgers and humans to wild beehives. The honey badger's (*Mellivora capensis*) claws enable the extraction from beehives.[242] Humans, on the other hand, may have first extracted the honey with the use of fire, which dates back to 0.5–1.5 mya.[243] Honey has beneficial properties that include improvement of glycemic control due to the oligosaccharides contained in honey in addition to glucose and fructose by delaying gastric emptying, slowing rate of digestion and delaying intestinal absorption due to increased intestinal caloric extraction by pathogenic gut microbes. The antidiabetic effect may also be due to lower serum insulin and C-peptide concentrations secretions in response to honey use in healthy men.[244] Honey inhibits the growth of *Helicobacter pylori*, a cause of gastric and duodenal ulcers, and has beneficial effects on gut microbiota. For example, the growth of *Lactobacillus acidophilus* and plantarum is markedly increased.[245] Effects on lipid metabolism include reduced total cholesterol, LDL, and C-reactive proteins and increased HDL. Hormonal effects have also been described with leptin levels reported to be lower in rats given honey instead of sucrose. There was a delayed postprandial ghrelin secretion and increased total peptide YY response.[246, 247]

Honey contains flavonoids and antioxidants, which help reduce the risk of cancer, heart disease, and the probiotics that are found in honey support beneficial bacteria including six species of lactobacilli and 4 species of bifidobacteria. Antibacterial, antifungal properties, blood sugar regulation, and improved athletic performance have also been supported in clinical research.[248]

The Combination of Foods Rather Than the Individual Amounts or Specific Nutrients May Be the Most Important Strategy for Successful Diets

This has been particularly revealing in the very recent meta-analysis of fats in the diet and cardiovascular disease. An analysis of eighty-six studies involving over 600,000 participants did not support current cardiovascular dietary recommendations of low fat diets in the prevention of cardiac disease.[249] The meta-analyses for fish consumption and omega-3 FA intake, however, showed significant results for reducing cerebrovascular disease in 794,000 people. An inverse relationship was found with a relative risk of 0.88 (95% CI: 0.81–96) for >5 servings per week compared to only one.[250]

A purview of the most common diets used and studied indicates they generally all recommend similar macronutrient components and promote fruits and vegetables, avoiding transfatty acids refined sugars and promoting fibrous foods and omega-3 and omega-6 fatty acids. Differences are largely in the recommendations regarding proportions of these such as low or high saturated fat, level of protein intake, avoidance by some of grains and dairy products (Paleo diet), and some have a particularly high intake of spices and phytochemicals (Okinawan diet).

Mediterranean Diet: Epidemiological Evidence for Benefits

The Mediterranean diet places emphasis on fruits, vegetables, meats, seafood, and grains and has been studied the most extensively. A major study assessing the efficacy of the Mediterranean diet in the primary prevention of cardiovascular diseases in high-risk patients revealed that supplementation with this diet with extravirgin olive oil or tree nuts reduced cardiovascular death, myocardial infarction, or a stroke by 30%.[251] Many benefits have been described to date including a significant decrease not only in myocardial infarction but also coronary artery disease and stroke.[252] Furthermore, cerebral white matter (leukoraiosis), or white matter hyperintensity volume (WMHV) reduction, that is associated with cognitive decline was decreased by following this diet. In this important study, using a semiquantitative food questionnaire (on a scale of 0–9) was employed to reflect increasing similarity to the Mediterranean diet (MeDi) pattern (participants n = 1091). WMHV was measured by quantitative MRI and a linear regression model used between MeDi score and log transformed WMHV. Each one pointed increase in MeDi score was associated with a lower log WMHV (B = 0.04, p = 0.01).[253]

A decrease in mild cognitive impairment and conversion to Alzheimer's disease in response to adhrerence to a Mediterranean diet has also been reported.[254]

A Mediterranean diet initiated after myocardial infarction is close to three times more effective in reducing mortality compared to a statin therapy.[255] This was corroborated by the PREDIMED study, which achieved a 30% improvement compared to a low fat diet.[256]

The Paleo Diet Type

The specifics of these diets are based on archeological evidence as well as inferences from those of modern hunter-gatherer groups and exclude relatively recently acquired foods such as grains and dairy products. Emphasis is placed on proteins, avoidance of relatively high intake of phytochemicals, fiber, antioxidants, relatively higher PUFA and MUFA levels and more favorable omega-6 to omega-3 ratio intakes.[257, 258] These have been described by more than one group of researchers and also include the New Evolution Diet, for example.[259]

In clinical studies, the Paleo diet was better than metformin for glucose control for example.[260]

DASH Diet

The DASH (dietary approaches to stop hypertension) diet—developed by the National Heart, Lung and Blood Institute (NHLBI) and supported by the National Institutes of Health (NIH)—emphasizes fruits, vegetables, whole grains, low-fat dairy foods (which includes seafood, red and white meat, fish, nuts, beans) and limits refined sugar foods and drinks. It is promoted for blood pressure reduction supported by several clinical trials as well as appropriate eating in general.[261] As with the Mediterranean diet, the DASH diet has been correlated with slower rates of cognitive decline in older people.[262]

Okinawan Diet

Okinawan residents in Japan are renowned in the number of centenarians, generally long life expectancy, and low incidence of neurodegenerative and cardiovascular disease, which have been attributed to their traditional diet. The characteristics of their diet include low calories, low in saturated fats, relatively high carbohydrate intake, nutritionally dense, high numbers of phytonutrient antioxidants, and flavonoids. There are many similarities to the traditional Mediterranean diet and the DASH diet. In addition, there are many herbs and spices that may well further promote the health of these individuals.[263]

Atkins Diet

The Atkins diet, and its revised Atkins nutritional approach, is a low-carbohydrate diet initially popularized by Robert Atkins but derived from Alfred Pennington.[264] This diet limits consumption of carbohydrates to support ketosis. The previously allowed unlimited amounts of fatty meats and cheeses is no longer promoted. Recent dietary research of the Atkins diet with three other popular diets (Zone, Ornish, Weight Watchers) testing for primary outcomes of weight loss and heart disease risk reduction all resulted in weight loss with no significant difference between the diets.[265] The modified

Adkins diet is increasingly used as a ketogenic diet to treat refractory epilepsy.[266]

Rosedale Diet

This diet promotes a low intake of nonfibrous carbohydrates, moderate to low protein, and relatively high fat intake with the latter to include specifically good (omega-3 and omega-6 fatty acids) and not bad fats (transfatty acids). Other recommendations include the avoidance of refined sugars. One feature perhaps unique to this diet is the promotion of no calorie counting but rather eating when hungry and avoiding late-night dinners—at least three hours prior to retiring.[267]

Fruits and Vegetables Alone May Be a Critical Dietary Factor

There are many mechanisms whereby fruit and vegetables have a cardiovascular and cerebrovascular protective effect, which in turn translates into a neuroprotective effect. These include anti-inflammatory and antioxidant mechanisms, blood pressure lowering, improved microvascular function, and lowering of low-density lipoprotein.[268–270]

A meta-analysis of twenty prospective studies involving 760,629 patients with 16,981 stroke events revealed an inverse relationship with stroke for a high fruit and vegetable consumption with a relative risk of 0.79 (CI: 0.75–0.84). Every 200 gram increase in fruit consumption was associated with a 32% decrease in stroke.[271] This confirms an earlier meta-analysis with similar conclusions of a 26% relative risk of stroke reduction in those achieving more than five servings per day of fruit and vegetables.[272]

Not surprisingly a European study of people, sixty-five years and older supported a relationship between regular fruit and vegetable consumption and a 28% decrease in the risk of dementia in general.[273]

Promising Changes in National Guidelines

Diets recommended by the American Heart Association and American Stroke Association published in 2014 were encouraging in that a change of policy occurred with the recommendation of a Mediterranean diet based on strong current clinical evidence rated as grade IIa level of evidence as well as advising this in favor over a low fat diet.[274] Lifestyle changes alone can be successful in mitigating risk without pharmacotherapeutic agents. In ethnically diverse people (n = 2390), this was studied with the intervention being the application of national guidelines that included the NCEP dietary recommendations.[275]

Alcohol

Evolutionary Insights: Alcohol May Have Been One of the First Chemical Weapons Deployed by Organisms Very Far Back in Time

It is frequently surmised that the domestication of grains about ten thousand years ago was more for the purposes of alcohol production than food supplementation although both are probably the case. However, the first organisms likely to have used alcohol were the yeast family that evolved the ability to manufacture alcohol to out-compete bacteria sometime during the angiosperm evolution about 140 mya during the Cretaceous Period. Yeast organisms are able to tolerate alcohol concentrations of between 10 and 14% whereas bacteria tolerate much lower levels.[276] However, our relationship with alcohol may go back as far as ~55 million years ago at a time of the emergence of primates in the then-tropical world of forests that, thanks to the angiosperm evolution, contained an abundance of fruit. At a similar time, the evolution of venomous snakes with the theory of improved trichromatic color vision in primates occurred, or rather the reemergence of trichromatic color vision, the snake detection theory of Isbell.[277] Not only mammals but also birds and insects use alcohol detection for the detection of sugars in ripe fruit, thanks to its low molecular weight that can be sensed. In a study of alcohol content of unripe, ripe, and overripe fruit by Dudley, these were shown to contain alcohol concentrations of 0%, 0.6%, and 4.5% respectively. This is the theory posited by Robert Dudley of the drunken monkey hypothesis. Even fruit flies use alcohol to fend off preying wasps that are less able to tolerate an alcohol vapor of more than 0.6%, which fruit flies are able to.[276]

Primates, humans, birds as well as several invertebrates have in common an ancestral frugivorous diet. Overripe fruit may have a small amount of different alcohols due to the fermentation of fruit sugars by yeasts, the most common of which is ethanol. Drunkenness from alcohol due to eating overripe fruits has been documented in elephants, especially from overconsumption of marula fruits.[278] The levels of alcohol in fruit and overripe fruit have been estimated at 0.6% and up to 6% respectively, the latter similar to a moderate-strength standard can of beer. Drunkenness has also been described in monkeys, birds, chimpanzees, elephants, butterflies, fruit flies as well as humans.279–281

The interaction of alcohol and early primates may date back to at least 10 million years or more. This is several magnitudes longer than a frequently assumed human alcohol interaction with the discovery of fermentation at the time of the agricultural evolution about 10,000 years ago. This is supported by paleogenetic data concerning digestive alcohol dehydrogenase (ADH4) of our primate ancestors, which was relatively more inefficient at oxidizing alcohol, implying that a change occurred at a time of increasing terrestrial adaptation to the forest floor where the fruit was more likely to fermented and contain higher alcohol than hanging fruit.[282]

The Clinically Beneficial Effects of Alcohol in Humans May Have Evolved Through a Process Known as Hormesis

The low-level exposure over time of a number of chemicals, including alcohol, has been shown to have benefits. High-level exposure of these substances is toxic. For example, an important finding in fruit flies revealed a decrease in mortality as a function of alcohol exposure that was maximal at an alcohol concentration of 3%.[283] The mechanisms of how alcohol exerts this effect are uncertain, but one might be an antimicrobial action.

Table 3.16. Deleterious: Medical and neurological effects of alcohol (comprehensive but not all-inclusive)

General Medical
Pellagra
Optic neuropathy
Tobacco alcohol amblyopia
Fetal alcohol syndrome

Gastrointestinal
Hepatitis and cirrhosis
Hepatic stupor and coma
Hepatocerebral syndrome
Esophageal cancer
Pancreatitis

Cardiovascular
Cardiac arrhythmia (atrial fibrillation)
Myocardial infarction
Cardiomyopathy

Neurological and Psychiatric Disease
Pathologic intoxication
Stroke
Blackouts (a memory loss)
Withdrawal Seizures (rum fits)
Delirium tremens
Wernicke-Korsakoff syndrome
Polyneuropahty
Cerebellar degeneration (particularly anterior vermal)
Marchiafava Bignami disease
Central pontine myelinolysis
Alcoholic myopathy
Alcoholic dementia
Cerebral atrophy
Alcohol dependence

Traumatic Brain Lesions During Intoxication
Subdural hematoma
Cerebral contusions

Beneficial Effects of Alcohol

Reduction in stroke
Reduction in myocardial infarction
Decreased rate of conversion to mild cognitive impairment and
    dementia
Neuropsychological effects – decreased anxiety
Hormesis – low exposure effects that are biologically beneficial
    and are opposite to higher dose toxic effects

Alcohol Metabolism and Action

Alcohol acts on neuronal membranes akin to general anesthetics and inhibits subcortical structures, brainstem, and the reticular formation. It has both a depressant action and excitatory effect. For example, there is a negative effect on glutamate receptors but a stimulant effect on GABA, cannabinoid, and mu opiate receptors, the latter two accounting for the euphoria and well-being associated with alcohol use.[285] Alcohol degradation is due to the biochemical action of alcohol dehydrogenase in the liver yielding acetaldehyde, catalase in the mitochondria and the microsomal ethanol oxidizing system (MEOS). Levels associated with neurological impairment are noted in the table.

Table 3.17. Alcohol level and effects on neurological function[286]

Concentration in mg/dl	Neurological impairment
30	Mild euphoria
50	Mild incoordination
100	Ataxia
200	Confusion
300	Stuperous
400	Deep anesthesia and potentially fatal

These needs to be understood in the context of many other addicting substances. The probability of becoming dependent when you have tried a substance at least once (adapted and modified from Stahl SM). [285]

Substance	Probability of addiction
Tobacco	32%
Heroin	23%
Cocaine	17%
Alcohol	15%
Stimulants	11%
Anxiolytics	9%
Cannabis	9%
Analgesics*	8%
Inhalants	4%
Hyperpalatable foods	?

*287

There Are Many Clinical Benefits of Alcohol That Include the Reduction of Stroke, Dementia, Myocardial Infarction, Gallstones, and Diabetes Mellitus II

There is an almost 30% reduction in the risk of dementia compared to those who do not drink as well as those that drink excessively.[288] There is a J-shaped benefit from alcohol in general with approximately two drinks (one unit equivalent to ten grams of alcohol per day) for men and one drink for nonpregnant women yielding maximum benefit compared to no alcohol. The beneficial effects may be due to decreased platelet inhibition, increase in HDL cholesterol, and lowering of fibrinogen. In those having three or more drinks per day, there is an association with increased risk of alcohol-related conditions, which may trigger hypercoagulable states, cardiac arrhythmias, and hypertension.[289]

Alcohol Is Carcinogenic, but There Are Compounds That Also Prevent Cancer: The Case of Xanthohumol and Reseveratrol

A component of darker beers, xanthohumol, has potent anticarcinogenic properties and a scavenger of reactive oxygen species inhibiting superoxide anion radical and nitric oxide production. It also has anti-inflammatory properties by inhibition of cyclooxygenase-1 and cyclooxygenase-2 activity. It is currently being investigated as a novel and easily available chemopreventive compound.[290] Resveratrol found in red wine has long been thought to have neuroprotective effects in relation to dementia, supported by both animal and clinical studies.[291] However, a large community-based study found no health-associated benefits and urinary resveratrol levels.[292]

There Is a Fine Line Between the Beneficial and Deleterious Effects of Alcohol

The J-shaped mortality risk from alcohol is least with one standard drink per day and already rises in both men and women with two drinks per day.[293] This needs to be compared to the clinical epidemiological data that have shown two drinks per day (1.5 for women) is protective in stroke and cardiovascular disease.[294]

Salt

The human requirement for salt in the diet may be traced very far back over hundreds of millions of years to our marine origins (~500 mya). Our terrestrial occupation in the form of amphibians, beginning about 390 mya, did not change that need because of the design of our sodium/potassium cellular pumps. Much later in our history, during the paleo-climactic change to the relatively hot and dry African climate, perspiration probably contributed to a sodium need. Salt was also scarce in our ancestral plant-rich diet. Our ancestral low-salt environment is in direct contrast to our current salt-abundant environment. This physiological requirement is therefore mismatched today with the persistent psychological reward for salt intake entrained in our dopaminergic, frontal subcortical, nucleus accumbens brain circuitry. The evolutionary need for sodium had acquired a hedonic value. Sodium is one of nature's antidepressants and similar to certain vitamin (B_{12}, folate) and mineral (Mg) deficiencies, lethargy, depressed mood, and impaired attention may occur with sodium deficiency.[295] The environment of relative salt deficiency, of the evolving hominids in the hot, arid environment was further compounded by their dependence on herbivorous diets that were low in sodium content, hence the strong impetus for sodium conservation.[296] Sodium—similar to other physiologically important components such as voluntary exercise, fats, carbohydrates—possesses natural addictive qualities. In recorded history, early empires placed considerable importance on salt, and a major thoroughfare in Rome named Via Salaria along which salt caravans travelled is regarded as the origin of the word *salary*, during which times soldiers were also reportedly paid in salt. Salt was used as a meat and seafood preservative in Scandinavian trade cities. Examples include Lubeck in Denmark, Faslsterbo in Sweden, and Scarborough in England among others, which originated as centers that traded in salt-preserved herring. Salt taxes existed in many cultures including the early Chinese over two thousand years ago and were an important factor in the French revolution. The importance of the salt trade persists historically in the British towns ending in "wich," indicating they were associated with the production or availability of salt, and some cities associated with the salt trade such as Salzburg, Austria, or Salt Town near the Hallein salt mines.[297] The ability of salt as a preservative is due to its osmolarity-induced microbial toxicity. Historically, in human populations there was a wide range of consumption intake, with particularly high levels documented in medieval Sweden related to fish preservation and salted fish diet. Historical records have revealed that up to 100 g per day were commonplace in parts of Sweden. A high salt diet persists in that country.[297–299] The Trobiander people in New Guinea intake of salt is 40–50 mmol Na/10 MJ compared with 100–250 in Sweden, or about 0.5 g per day with no clinical evidence of cardiovascular disease.[300] Paleolithic diets estimate include values of 1–1.5 g/day, but there is marked variation seen clinically and in various diets as well as national guideline recommendations.

Table 3.18. Salt-intake variation and some food salt contents

CDC and FDA Recommendations
1,500 mg if >50 y, if hypertensive, diabetes,
kidney disease or African American
2,300 if over 2y of age and do not have above conditions [301]

Average US Use Per Day 3,400 mg (CDC) [302]

Average Western Diet Consumption 9,000–12,000
mg per day (150–200 mmol/day)[303]

Examples of Very High Intake Recorded in People
100 g (Sweden, seventeenth century)[302]

Examples of Low Intake Recorded in People
Yanamamo Amazonian Indians[304]
~58 mg/day (1 mmol/day)

Vegetarian Diet[305] 750 mg/day

Prehistoric Hunter-Gatherer Intake Estimation[303]
<1,755 mg/day (30 mmol/day)

Estimated Physiological Need[306]
~0.6 mmol/kg/day

High-Salt-Containing Foods
Breads, bagels, pasta, cured meats, chips, pizza, soups[307]

Biochemistry Notes

Salt (NaCl or sodium chloride) is not synonymous with sodium (Na). Chemical formula numerics include $NaCl$, 1 mmol = 58.5 grams, for Na, 1 mmol = 23 grams. One tablespoon of salt = 6 g salt or 2.4 g Na. For the conversion of mmol to mg of sodium, chloride, or sodium chloride, multiply mmol by 23, 35.5, or 58.5 (molecular weights) CDC.

Many people with hypertension are salt sensitive (~ 50%).[308, 309] Black people, in particular, are genetically adapted for efficient sodium retention that was presumably selected by the tropical conditions we evolved in as well as lower sweat rates and lower sweat sodium concentrations. This adaptive trait has become maladaptive with the high salt content of most Western diets.[310]

The Cost of Hypertension

Limiting sodium intake to 1,500 mg per day, which represents half of the average American intake, and if this could be achieved for all would save 150 lives per year and $1.5 trillion over a twenty-year period in the USA.[311] A study of hypertensive people using the DASH (dietary approaches to hypertension) diet that emphasized increased fruit, vegetables, and low-fat and -sodium intake shows reduction of systolic blood pressure by 8–14 mm Hg within a month. [312] However, the situation is much more complex. As with other food substances, such as fats and alcohol for example, the benefits of salt intake follow a U-shaped curve. A recent meta-analysis has concluded that both high- and low-salt intake is associated with increased cardiovascular mortality.[313] There is little evidence for an association of low-sodium diets and reduced cardiovascular or cerebrovascular events in the general population. Contrary to the "salt hypothesis" predictions, a multinational European study found low salt diets increased risk for death from MI and stroke and did not prevent hypertension.[314] The NHLBI's MRFIT database found no health benefits with low sodium diets,[315] nor did the Scottish Heart Health Study find any benefits for those on low-salt diets.[316] Furthermore, the US National Health and Nutrition Examination Survey (NHANES I) showed a 20% increased incidence of myocardial infarcts in those with lowsalt diets compared to normal-salt diets,[317] which were confirmed by the NHANES II and NHANES III results.[318] Concluding comments of a meta-analysis of clinical trials that included the Cochrane library, Medline, and Embase were that intensive salt reduction lead to small blood pressure reductions and no clear health benefits on cardiovascular events and mortality.[319] Adequate magnesium intake instead may be important. Magnesium is present in sea salt and has beneficial blood pressure lowering effects, opposing that of sodium, with clinical studies showing a significant reduction in systolic blood pressure.[320]

Nature's Protective Strategies: Antioxidants and Caloric Restriction

Antioxidant Notes

Terrestrial plants were needed to produce nonmarine antioxidants such as polyphenols and tocopherols among others during the angiosperm evolution since the last two hundred million years. The production of many antioxidant pigments countered the reactive oxygen species, which were the by-products of photosynthesis.[321] Since then, most living organisms require oxygen to exist but with the potential of damaging reactive oxygen species such as hydrogen peroxide, superoxide anion, hypochlorous acid, and hydroxyl radicals. The evolution of antioxidants by organisms were necessary to prevent oxidative damage to cellular structures, including proteins, lipids, and DNA.[322]

Susceptibility to oxidative damage is an important feature of our brain attributed to its high metabolic load and relative abundance of oxidizable material (PUFA). Antioxidants include berries, polyphenols, micronutrients, spices, tocopherol, and curcumin that provide protection from membrane lipid peroxidation, which also impacts synaptic plasticity. Berries, for example, contain tanins and polyphenols, which increase hippocampal plasticity in rats (measured by HSP 70 and IGF-1), protect against kainite induced damage, and improve memory and learning.[323, 324] Alpha lipoic acid found in a number of foods, including spinach, broccoli, potatoes is a coenzyme in the mitochondria and shown to improve memory function in the Alzheimer's disease mouse model.[325, 326]

Curcumin ameliorates lipid peroxidation and nitric oxide–based radicals and consequently may be the reason for the low incidence of Alzheimer's disease in India.[327] Curcumin has been studied in relation to the known action of macrophages and microglia. As innate immune cells are responsible for clearance of waste products and pathogens in the brain, this was tested in a human study of macrophages using venous blood. The compound bisdemethoxycurcumin may have potential therapeutic promise in Alzheimer's disease through the repair of the transcriptional deficits of Alzheimer's disease macrophages.[328]

Curcumin and vitamin E both may ameliorate the effects of a high transfat and saturated fat diet supporting the premise that oxidative stress may mediate the effects of diet on plasticity. Flavanols include various fruits, cocoa, beans, ginkgo biloba tree, and in particular the plant-derived flavanol, (-) epicathechin, crosses the BBB and has been reported to elevate indices of synaptic spine density and angiogenesis as well as increased hippocampus-dependent memory in mice. Furthermore, these were facilitated by concomitant exercise.[329]

Lycopenes

Found in tomatoes as well as other vegetables and fruits have been shown to cause coronary vasodilatation—up to 53% in people with cardiovascular disease.[330]

Antioxidants: Berries, Spices, and Herbs

With the premise that a usual diet constitutes over 25,000 bioactive ingredients, a study by Carlsen et al. examined over 3,100 spices, herbs, and other supplements to assist in understanding the complex relationship between these and health and illness. Overall plant-based foods had much higher antioxidant values than animal-based foods and in particular the highest antioxidant values as tested by the FRAP (ferric reducing ability of plasma) method and reported in mmol/100 g.[331] Although many different food groups have antioxidant potential, berries are known to have particularly high quantities of phytochemicals (tannins, lignans, flavonoids, stilbenoids, phenolic acid), among which the following had the highest values. Analysis of 119 berries revealed particularly high values in dried amla (Indian gooseberry, mean values of 261.5 mmol/100 g), dried wild bilberries (48.3 mmol/100 g), zereshk (red sour berries) (27.3 mmol/100 g), and dog rose (24.3 mmol/100 g). Testing of 425 different herbs and spices revealed maximal values for cloves, followed by peppermint, allspice, cinnamon, oregano, thyme, sage, rosemary, saffron, and estragon (mean range: 44 to 277 mmol/100 g).[332]

Table 3.19. An antioxidant classification

Substance	Found in Phytochemicals
Flavanoids	Grapes, red wine (resveratrol), blueberries, cranberries, tea
Favanols	Fruit and vegetables
Flavonones	Citrus fruits
Flavonols	Wine, tea, cocoa, fruits, beans Anthocyanidins
Anthocyanidins	Blue, red, and purple fruits
Lycopene	Tomatoes, watermelon, pink grapefruit
Lutein	Dark-green leafy vegetables
Lignan	Seeds, oatmeal
Phytic acid	Grains, beans

Vitamins

Vitamin E	Seeds, nuts, avocados, olive oil, wheat, green vegetables
Vitamin C	Citrus fruits, green vegetables, tomatoes, potatoes
Vitamin A	Yellow and orange vegetables and fruits, mango, carrots
Vitamin D	Eggs, seafood, beef liver, lichen

Minerals

Selenium	Seafood, red meat, white meat, wheat, eggs, garlic

Oxidants and Stimulants: Coffee, Tea, and Cocoa Coffee

Contrary to prior reports of increased risk for cardiovascular disease, a recent meta-analysis (479,689 subjects, 10,003 stroke cases) reported a decreased risk of stroke with intake of two cups per day (RR of 0.87).[333] This has been attributed to caffeine, diterpenes, and polyphenols as well as possibly some of the several hundred other bioactives contained in coffee. For example, another polyphenol, chlorogenic acid, has both antioxidant and antihypertensive effects attributed to nitric oxide–induced vasodilation. A small rise of BP

(~8.1 mmg Hg systolic) occurs after one to two cups ingestion (200–300 mg of caffeine), but chronic use is not associated with hypertension. Although the diterpenes (cafestol, kahweol) may raise cholesterol, LDL, and triglycerides, this can be countered by the use of the filters.[334–337]

Human epidemiological and animal studies support a protective role for coffee with respect to Alzheimer's disease. For example, a case control study of 124 people was associated with a reduced risk of dementia in the group with mild cognitive impairment.[338,339]

Green and Black Tea

Teas contain flavanoids with theaflavins and thearubigins, present in black tea, and catechins in green tea, which is unfermented. Oolong tea is partially fermented. The beneficial mechanisms of these, particularly flavanoids, include both hypocholesterolemic effects and enhancement of nitric oxide and improved endothelial function in the cardiovascular and cerebrovascular systems. Clinical studies have shown a 20% reduced stroke risk in Japanese population (n = 82369) consuming green tea (four or more cups/day), and in a Swedish study with black tea (four or more cups/day) consumers (n = 74961) a similar 21% reduction in stroke risk for both ischemic and hemorrhagic stroke.[340, 341]

Cacao

Chocolate contains flavonoids (mostly flavan-3-ols) that have anti-inflammatory and antioxidant effects, increasing endothelial nitric oxide with vasodilation and blood pressure reduction effects. Clinical studies summarized by meta-analyses revealed systolic and diastolic blood pressure reduction reduced insulin concentrations, insulin resistance, and decreased platelet aggregation.[342, 343]

Routine Vitamin Supplementation: Do Not Use

Unless a deficiency syndrome is present, such as pellagra, beri-beri, scurvy, or Wernicke's encephalopathy, current recommendations are not to supplement with vitamins or micronutrients. Review of numerous studies found no benefit and some even the potential for harm with routine supplementation. The recent prominent editorial entitled "Enough Is Enough: Stop wasting money on vitamin and mineral supplements" is a good summary of the status to date.[344] Unless there is a demonstrated clinical and/or laboratory abnormality consistent with a vitamin deficiency, there is currently no support for using these. They are not only expensive but also potentially dangerous, including an increased risk of cancer.

Vitamin D deficiency has been linked to a number of illnesses, including multiple sclerosis and dementia. Meta-analyses had already shown that a low serum vitamin D concentration was associated with cognitive impairment and Alzheimer dementia.[345] A prospective study of incidence all cause dementia and Alzheimer's disease revealed a substantial risk associated with low (<25 nmol/L), hazard ratio 2.25 and deficient (>25–<50 nmol/L), hazard ration 1.53 compared to people with normal levels.[346]

A recently launched wrist-worn device, Sunfriend, monitors UV light exposure that is individualized to be just enough to make sufficient Vitamin D, depending on people's skin sensitivity (scale of 1 to 11) to the sun, and also alerts against overexposure to ultraviolet light and sunburn www.sunfriend.com.

Caloric Restriction Is Beneficial

Fasting, for example, with caloric restriction, elevates levels of BDNF, which likely mediates the beneficial effects on synaptic plasticity. From an evolutionary point of view, the thrifty gene hypothesis proposes that our genome has adapted to benefit from intermittently minimal caloric intake by reducing free radical formation. Even alternate-day caloric restriction resulted in improved cardiovascular disease and diabetes risk profiles.[347]

There Is a Cooperative Process Between Diet and Exercise and Lifestyle Factors That Involve Epigenetic and Molecular Mechanisms

Sleep, exercise, diet, and environmental influences affect our brain health and cognition via epigenetic events (methylation, transcriptional activation, post-translational modifications).[348] Molecular mechanisms are also operative, with the BDNF system susceptible to epigenetic modifications. Silent information regulator 2 (SIRT2), a member of the sirtuin protein family, an important modulator of genomic stability, acts by silencing the function of certain genes. A diet high in omega-3 FA increases SIRT expression in the rat hippocampus for example.[349, 350]

Our Bodies and Those of Our Resident Microbes Work Together in Sickness and in Health; We Are Superorganisms with a Hologenome

There is an extensive host microbiome interaction within our bodies at an intracellular, genomic, intercellular, and cerebral network level. The epigenetic component of the gut brain axis is regarded as the mediator of the genetic and environmental interface.[351] We can be viewed as a superorganism (us and our bugs) that is termed the holobiont, and the hologenome refers to the combined genetic material (us and our bugs) working together, hence superorganisms with a hologenome. The hologenome theory of evolution was first conceived by Richard Jefferson, reviewed recently by Zilber Rosenberg. This is of great importance in evolution and our dietary configurations. Large organisms evolve relatively slowly mostly by way of natural selection, but the symbiosis with the rapid pace of evolving microbes suggests they play an important role not only in the rapid adaptation for us, for example, with new foods but also in the formation of new species. An environmental stressor (change in climate for example) may translate into a change in the microbiota, which accommodates much more rapidly than the host. The ability to change a biological response in our bodies within our own lifetime may be explained by this theory.[352]

Table 3.20. Definition of terms

Microbiome
The microorganisms within us (bacteria, viruses)—hence the term *microbiota* and *symbiont* (conferring mutual advantages)

Holobiont
The host (us) and our microorganisms

Hologenome
The host (us) genome and the microbial genome together

Psychobiome
The effect of gut organisms (bacteria, viruses) on our mind, such as mood, depression, and anxiety

A New Theory: Tuberculosis (TB) Provided Nutrients During Time of Meat Deficiency?

Inclusion of more meat in the diet was associated with key micronutrients such as nicotinamide (vitamin B_3) and tryptophan intake, both of which are poorly obtained from plants. Gut resident TB microbes excrete nicotinamide and are thought to have augmented supplies when nicotinamide levels were low. TB mycobacterium are thought to have coevolved with humans. Disease causation, mostly pulmonary, occurred only during times of poor or meat deficient diet.[353, 354]

Most importantly changes in the diet can translate into rapid changes in the diversity of microbiota, which can be beneficial or deleterious and also be transmitted to the next generation.[355] This underscores the importance of cooperation between our bugs and us and is reminiscent of how collaboration among humans themselves allows us to leap ahead much more quickly with respect to innovations and accomplishments.

A Personalized Food Intake Approach

Physiologically, what we eat impacts our health and longevity. Foods influence the genetic instruction of our cells and body. The emerging field of nutrigenomics is the study of foods and their constituents on gene expression and the influence on health and illness with the hope of an eventual personalized dietary advice tool[356] akin to the generalized personal medicine movement.[357, 358]

There are many good diets, each with their own attributes. These diets represent variations on a theme of the type of foods our ancestors were forced to eat at certain times. For example, the Neanderthal high-fat and -meat diet was similar to an Atkins diet whereas the Rosedale and Paleo are similar. The Mediterranean is similar but emphasizes a large proportion of grains, which may need revision given the emerging concerns about gluten-related enteropathy.

The Legacy Diet

The many mainstream diets, some of which have been enunciated, reveal no substantial differences. They have more similarities than differences with most recommendations similar. Each diet has one or more features though that differ. For example, the Okinawan diet has a high intake of phytochemicals, herbs, and spices. The Paleo diet completely excludes grains and dairy products. In general these are all very close to the ancestral type of diet. The term legacy diet was chosen because it contains the added allusion to the evolving component of our metabolism by virtue of epigenetics, genetics, and environmental stressors such as climatology and biosphere. Inherent in the name too is the extreme range of diets that current hunter-gatherer groups, for example, are adapted to from the almost pure meat and fat diet of the Inuit to the almost wholly vegetarian diets of the South American agriculturalists. For example, the Quechua of Peru have discovered ways of negating the alkaloids in potatoes that grow in their region. The lock-and-key model proposed by Katz, for incorporating cultural adaptations concerning food processing and optimization, is therefore important in designing diets. This is exemplified by the cultural variations between South America, Africa, and India, for example, with respect to maize processing with malnutrition due to pellagra in the latter countries and not in South America. Other examples include the human adaptation to lactose, amylose, and grains. This is important, for the much-varied race ethnicity and cultural components are tightly interwoven with dietary preferences and customs evident today.[359]

1. Guiding principles

a. We need to understand that our nutritional inheritance has a wide variation.

b. We are a work in progress with both chimpanzee and carnivore gut anatomy.

c. Both high carbohydrate and high meat diets seem to work for humans.

d. There are substances our bodies can make and others not; hence, essential nutrients.

e. Diet is so important because of epigenetics and the gene expression effect that alters our bodies and minds.

2. Supplying what the body was designed for

There are no strict rules with respect to proportions or calorie counting, but only general guidelines. The closer one can follow an ancestral type of diet as the overall general guiding principle, the better. Some of the guidelines include the following:

a. Meat, whether red or white, should be from free-ranging animals.

b. Fish should be preferably wild in origin, and shellfish should be evaluated for potential heavy metals such as mercury and arsenic.

c. Fruit and vegetable consumption should be fibrous (oranges instead of orange juice).

d. Maintain an antinutrient awareness with respect to grains, which should probably not be consumed in excess.

3. Avoiding what the body does not need

a. Avoidance of insecticides and toxins

b. Avoidance of meats contaminated with unnecessary antibiotic use

c. Avoidance of unnecessary vitamins and supplements

d. Water purification, be aware of potential heavy metals (arsenic, mercury).

4. Nutrition is intimately tied to sleep and exercise

a.   During our diurnal cycle, ghrelin increases with lack of sleep, which initiates hunger and feeding. Hence, the best diet adherence can be derailed if sleep is impaired.

b.   Physical activity and nutrition are synergistic, and both stimulate brain growth factors such as BDNF.

5. Microbiome awareness and monitoring

a.   Avoid unnecessary antibiotic use.

b.   Consider use of probiotics, in yoghurts for example.

c.   There is a "Godzilla" within us of 200 trillion cells. Respect it.

6. Dosage differentiating beneficial therapeutic effect from toxicity

a.   Request a nutrition prescription and consult with a nutritionist or dietician for a nutrition plan in the same way a pharmacist provides further insights into dosage, side effects, and possible alternatives with prescribed medications.

b.   Utilize apps for tracking food content, calories, and amounts such as the MyFitnessPal app, the world's largest food, nutrition, and calorie database.

Table 3.21. The legacy diet: A semiquantitative, dietary monitoring method, macronutrient index, with a maximum theoretical possible score of 100

Macronutrient Index   **/100**

Scale 0–5 0-never

1-once per week

2-twice per week

3-three times per week

4-four times per week

5-five to seven days per week

Beneficial Foods Category Add Points   Score

1. Fruits deciduous – apples, pears, plums, grapes, berries
2. Fruits tropical – mango, papaya, pineapple
3. Fruits citrus – oranges, grape-fruit, mandarin
4. Vegetables – broccoli, cabbage, cauliflower, tomatoes, peas
5. Tubers – potatoes, sweet potatoes, yams, carrots, cassava
6. Leafy vegetables – lettuce, spinach
7. Complex starches – maize, rice
8. Grains (whole, not refined) – oats, barley, rye, wheat, bran, muesli
9. Legumes – beans, lentils, peas, peanuts
10. Meat (red) – preferably range free or bison
11. Meat (white) – chicken, turkey (preferably free ranging)
12. Fish – pelagic (preferably wild)
13. Shellfish – oysters, clams, mussels, scallops
14. Crustacean – shrimp, lobster
15. Nuts, seeds
16. Eggs – preferably from free-ranging hens
17. Milk – preferably whole milk
18. Yoghurt with probiotics, cheese
19. Coffee – preferably ground beans, black or green tea, dark chocolate
20. Alcohol ≤ 30 g/d for men (2 units), ≤ 20 g/d for women (1.5 units)

Deleterious Foods Category: Subtract Points   Score

1. Added refined sugar (sucrose, HFCS)
2. Sodas, soft drinks, diet or regular
3. Transfatty acid containing foods
4. Processed meats
5. Fat-free dairy products (yoghurt, milk)

References

1. Gomez-Pinilla F. Brain Foods: the effects of nutrients on brain function. *Nature Reviews Neurosci* 2008; 9:568–578.

2. Vaynman S, Gomez-Pinilla F. Revenge of the "sit": how lifestyle impacts neuronal and cognitive health through molecular systems that interface energy metabolism with neuronal plascticity. *J Neurosci Res* 2006; 84:699–715.

3. Montiel-Castro AJ, González-Cervantes RM, BravoRuiseco G, Pacheco-López G. The microbiota-gut-brain axis: neurobehavioral correlates, health and sociality. *Front Integr Neurosci.* 2013 Oct 7; 7:70.

4. Petrof EO, Khoruts A. From stool transplants to nextgeneration microbiota therapeutics. *Gastroenterology.* 2014; 146:1573–82.

5. Pessoa L. On the relationship between emotion and cognition. *Nature Review Neurosci* 2008; 9:148–158.

6. Lindbergh S. Food and Western Disease. Health and Nutrition from an Evolutionary Perspective. WileyBlackwell, Oxford 2010.

7. De Lorgeril M, Salen P, Martin JL et al. Mediterranean diet, traditional risk factors and the rate of cardiovascular complications after myocardial infarction: final report of the Lyon Diet Heart Study. *Circulation* 1999; 99:779–85.

8. VITATOPS Trial Study Group. Collaborators (385). B vitamins in patients with recent transient ischaemic attack or stroke in the VITAmins TO Prevent Stroke (VITATOPS) trial: a randomised, double-blind, parallel, placebo-controlled trial. *Lancet Neurol.* 2010; 9:855–865. doi: 10.1016/S1474-4422(10)70187-3.

9. Farina N, Isaac MG, Clark AR, Rusted J, Tabet N. Vitamin E for Alzheimer's dementia and mild cognitive impairment. *Cochrane Database Syst Rev.* 2012 Nov 14; 11:CD002854. doi: 10.1002/14651858.CD002854.

10. Schürks M, Glynn RJ, Rist PM, Tzourio C, Kurth T. Effects of vitamin E on stroke subtypes: meta-analysis of randomised controlled trials. *BMJ.* 2010 Nov 4; 341:c5702. doi: 10.1136/bmj.c5702.

11. Estruch R, Ros E, Salas-Salvadó J et al. Primary prevention of cardiovascular disease with a Mediterranean diet. Collaborators (233). *N Engl J Med.* 2013 Apr 4; 368(14):1279–90.

12. Catalioto RM1, Maggi CA, Giuliani S. Intestinal epithelial barrier dysfunction in disease and possible therapeutical interventions. *Curr Med Chem.* 2011; 18:398–426.

13. Luckey TD. Introduction to intestinal microecology. *Am J Clin Nutr* 1972; 25:1292–1294.

14. Gill SR et al., Metagenomic analysis of the human distal gut microbiome. *Science* 2006; 312:1355–1359.

15. Morris GL, Gloss D, Buchhalter J, Mack KJ, Nickels K Harden C. Evidence based guideline update: vagus nerve stimulation for the treatment of epilepsy: report of the guideline development subcommittee of the American Academy of Neurology. *Epilepsy Curr* 2013; 13:297–303.

16. Clark KB, Naritoku DK, Smith DC, Browning RA, Jensen RA. Enhanced recognition memory following vagus nerve stimulation in human subjects. *Nature Neuroscience* 1999; 2:94–99.

17. Follesa P et al. Vagus nerve stimulation increases norepinephrine concentration and gene expression of BDNF and bFGF in the rat brain. *Brain Res* 2007; 1179:28–34.

18. Helke C et al. Axonal transport of neurotrophins by visceral afferent and efferent neurons of the vagus nerve of the rat. *J Comp Neurol* 1998; 393:102–117.

19. Nibuya M, Morinobu S, Duman RS. Regulation of BDNF and trk mRNA in rat brain by chronic electroconvulsive seizure and antidepressant drug treatments. *J Neurosci* 1995; 15:7539–7547.

20. Vaynman s, Ying Z, Wu A, Gomez-Pinilla F. Coupling energy metabolism with a mechanism to support brain derived neurotrophic factor mediated synaptic plasticity. *Neuroscience* 2006; 139:1221–1234.

21. Nawa H, Carnahan J, Gall C. BDNF protein measured by a novel enzyme immunoassay in normal brain after seizure: partial disagreement with mRNA levels. *Eur J Neurosci* 1995; 7:1527–1535.

22. Torres-Aleman I. Insulin like growth factors as mediators of functional plasticity in the adult brain. *Horm Metab Res* 1999; 31:114–119.

23. Johnson-Farley NN, Patel K, Kim D, Cowen DS. Interaction of FGF-2 with IGF-1 and BDNF in stimulating Akt, EFK and

neuronal survival in hippocampal cultures. *Brain Res* 2007; 1154:40–49.

24. Akbar M, Calderon F, Wen Z, Kim HY. Docosahexanoic acid : a positive modulator of Akt signaling in neuronal survival. *Proc Natl Acad Sci. USA* 2005; 102:10858–10863.

25. Sacks FM. Metabolic syndrome: epidemiology and consequences. *J Clin Psychiatry* 2004; 65:3–12.

26. Thomas RH Meeking MM, Mepham JR et al. The enteric bacterial metabolite propionic acid alters brain and plasma phospholipid molecular species: further development of a rodent-modelofautismspectrumdisorders. *JNeuroinflamm* 2012; 9:153 doi: 10.1186/1742-2094-9-153.

27. Cryan JF, Dinan TG. Mind-altering microorganisms: the impact of the gut microbiota on brain and behaviour. *Nature Reviews Neuroscience* 2012; 13:701–712.

28. Krabbe KS et al. Brain derived neurotrophic factor (BDNF) and type 2 diabetes. *Diabetologica* 2007; 50:431–438.

29. Toyooka K et al. Decreased levels of brain derived neurotrophic factor in serum of chronic schizophrenic patients. *Psychiatry Res* 2002; 110:249–257.

30. Duman RS. Synaptic plasticity and mood disorders. *Mol Psychiatry* 2002;&:S29–S34.

31. Pepino MY1, Love-Gregory L, Klein S, Abumrad NA. The fatty acid translocase gene CD36 and lingual lipase influence oral sensitivity to fat in obese subjects. J *Lipid Res.* 2012; 53:561–6.

32. Kessler DA. The End of Overeating. Taking Control of the Insatiable American Appetite. Emmaus, Philadelphia, Rodale, 2009.

33. Ziauddeen H, Farooq S, Fletcher P. Obesity and the brain. How convincing is the addiction model? *Nature Reviews Neuroscience* 2012; 13:279–286.

34. Eaton SB, Eaton III SB, Konner MJ. Paleolithic nutrition revisited: A twelve year retrospective on its nature and implications. *European Journal of Clinical Nutrition* 1997; 51:207–216.

35. Otten JJ, Hellwig JP Meyers LD (eds). Dietary reference intakes: the essential guide to nutrient requirements. Washington DC: National Academies Press 2006.

36. Institute of Medicine of the National Academies (IOM, 2005). Dietary Reference Intakes: Energy, Carbohydrate, Fiber, Fat, Fatty Acids, Cholesterol, Protein, and Amino Acids. Washington DC: National Academic Press.

37. World Health Organization (WHO, 2007). Protein and Amino Acid Requirements in Human Nutrition Report of the Joint WHO/FAO/UNU Expert Consultation. WHO Technical Report Series, no 935. Geneva: WHO.

38. Committee on Diet and Health, National Research Council: Diet and Health. Washington, DC: National Academy Press 1989:263–265.

39. Butrum DP, Eaton SB. NCI dietary guidelines. *Am J Clin Nutr* 1988; 48:888–895.

40. Eaton SB, Konner MJ. Paleolithic nutrition: a consideration of its nature and current implications. *N Engl Jnl Med1985*; 312:283–289.

41. Eaton SB, Eaton SB III, Konner MJ. Paleolithic nutrition revisited: twelve year retrospective on its nature and implications. *European Journal of clinical nutrition* 1997; 51:207–216.

42. Samaras D, Samaras N, Lang PO, Genton L, Frangos E, Pichard C. Effects of widely used drugs on micronutrients: a story rarely told. *Nutrition.* 2013; 29:605–10.

43. Myers SS, Zanobetti A, Kloog I et al. Increasing CO_2 threatens human nutrition. *Nature* 2014; 510:139–142.

44. Kleiber M. Body size and metabolism. The Fire of Life: An Introduction to Animal Energetics Wiley, 1961, New York.

45. Leonard WR, Robertson ML, Snodgrass JJ, Kuzawa CW. Metabolic correlates of hominid brain evolution. *Comp Biochem Physiol A* 2003; 135:5–15.

46. Wrangham RW, Jones JH, Laden G, Pilbeam D, Conklin-Brittain N. The Raw and the Stolen. Cooking and the Ecology of Human Origins. *Curr Anthropol.* 1999; 40:567–594

47. Sailer LD, Gaulin SJC, Boster JS, Kurland JS. Measuring the relationship between dietary quality and body side in primates. *Primates* 1985; 26:14–27.

48. Gaulin SJC. A Jarman/Bell model of primate feeding niches. *Hum Ecol* 1979; 7:1–20.

49. Leonard WR, Snodgrass JJ, Robertson ML. Effects of brain evolution on human nutrition and metabolism. *Ann Rev Nutr* 2007; 27:311–327.

50. Anton SC, Potts R, Aiello LC. Evolution of early Homo: An integrated biological perspective. *Science* 2014; 345:45

51. Milton K. The critical role played by animal source foods in human (Homo) evolution. *Journal of Nutrition* 2003; 133:388S–389S.

52. Leonard WR, Robertson ML. Evolutionary perspectives on human nutrition: the influence of brain and body size on diet and metabolism. *Am J Hum Biol* 1994; 6:77–88.

53. Perry GH, Dominy NJ, Claw KG et al. Diet and the evolution of human amylase gene copy number variation. *Nat Genet* 2997; 39:1256–1260.

54. Laden G, Wrangham R. The rise of hominids as an adaptive shift in fallback foods: plant underground storage organs (USOs) and australopith origins. *J Hum Evol.* 2005; 49:482–498.

55. Katz SH, Hediger ML, Valleroy LA. The anthropological and nutritional significance of traditional maize processing techniques in the New World. In: Watts ES, Johnston FE, Lasker GW (eds). Biosocial interrelations in population adaptation. Chicago IL, Aldine 1975.

56. Katz SH, Hediger ML, Valleroy LA. Trandtional maize processing techniques in the New World. *Science* 1974; 184:765–773

57. Katz SH. Food and bio-cultural evolution: a model for the investigation of modern nutritional problems. In Johnstone FE (ed): Nutritional Anthropology. Alan R Liss Publications, New York, 1987.

58. Watt EW, Pico-Reatequi E, Gahagan HE, Buskirk ER. Dietary intake and coronary risk factors in Peruvian Quenchua Indians. *J Am Diet Assoc* 1976; 68:535–537.

59. Leonard WR, Thomas RB. Changing dietary patterns in the Peruvian Andes. *Ecol Food Nutr* 1998; 21:245–263.

60. Johns T. The origins of human diet and medicine. Tucson, Arizona: University of Arizona Press, 1990.

61. Schrimshaw NS, Murray EB (eds). The acceptability of milk and milk products in populations with a high prevalence of lactose intolerance. *Am J Clin Nutr* 1988; 48 (suppl1):1083–1159.

62. Katz SH, Schall JI. Fava bean consumption and biocultural evolution. *Med Anthropol* 1979; 4:459–477.

63. Cryan JF, Dinan TG. Mind-altering microorganisms: the impact of the gut microbiota on brain and behaviour. *Nature Reviews Neuroscience* 2012; 13:701–712.

64. Denes AS, Jekely G, Arendt D et al. Molecular architecture of the annelid nerve cord supports common origin of nervous system centralization in the bilateria. *Cell* 2007; 129:277–288

65. Azpirof F. Intestinal perception: mechanisms and assessment. *Br J Nutr* 2005; 93:S7–12.

66. Marlow FW. The Hadza Hunter Gatherers of Tanzania. University of California Press, Los Angeles 2010.

67. Mann GV, Spoerry A, Jarashow D, Gray M. Atherosclerosis in the Masai. *Am J Epidemiol* 1972; 95:26.

68. Mann GV, Shaffer RD, Anderson RS, Sandstead HH. Cardiovascular disease in the Masai. *J Atheroscler* 1964; 4:289.

69. Gaulin SJC, Konner M. On the natural diets of primates, including humans. In Wurtman R, Wurtman J (eds): Nutrition and the Brain (volume 1). New York, Raven Press, 1979 pp 1–86.

70. Dufour DL. Nutritional ecology in the tropical rain forest of Amazonia. Am J *Hum Biol* 1992; 4:197–207

71. Eaton SB, Konner M. Paleolithic nutrition. A consideration of its nature ad current implications. *New Engl J Med* 1985; 312:283–289.

72. Larsen HB. Kenyan dominance in distance running. *Comparative Biochemistry and Physiology* 2003; 136 (part A):161–170

73. Scott RA et al. Demographic characteristics of elite Ethiopian distance runners. *Medicine and Science in Sports and Exercise* 2003; 35:1727–1732.

74. Christensen DL, Van Hall G, Hambraeus L. Food and macronutrient intake of male adolescent Kalenjin runners in Kenya. *Br J Nutr.* 2002; 88:711–7.

75. Onywera VO, Scott RA, Boit MK, Pitsiladis YP. Demographic characteristics of elite Kenyan endurance runners. *Journal of Sport Sciences* 2006; 24:415–422.

76. Anderson O. Running Science. The ultimate nexus of knowledge and performance. Human Kinetics. Champaign IL, 2013.

77. Kay R. Diets of early Miocene African hominoids. *Nature* 1977; 268:628–630.

78. Angel JL. Paleocolog, paleodemography and health. In: Polgar S, ed. Population, ecology and social evolution. The Hague: Mouton, 1975:167–190.

79. Nickens PR. Stature reduction as an adaptive response to food production in Mesoamerica. *J Archaeol Sci* 1976; 3:31–41

80. Cordain L, Eaton SB, Brand Miller J, Mann N, Hill K. The paradoxical nature of hunter gatherer diets: meat based, yet non atherogenic. *Eur J Clin Nutr* 2002; 56:S42-S52.

81. Cordain L. Implications of the Plio-Pleistocene hominin diets for modern humans. In Ungar P (ed) Evolution of the human diet: The known, unknown and the unknowable. Oxford, Oxford University Press 2007.

82. Barr SB, Wright JC. Postprandial energy expenditure in whole food and processed food meals. *Food and Nutrition Research* 2010; 54. doi: 10.3402/fnr.v54i0.5144.

83. Cordain, L., Miller, J.B., Eaton, S.B., et al. Plant-animal subsistence ratios and macronutrient energy estimations in worldwide hunter-gatherer diets. *Am J Clin Nutr* 2000; 71:682–92.

84. Darwin C. The Voyage of the Beagle: A Naturalist's Voyage Round the World. White Star Publications. Via Candido Sassone 22/24, 13100, Vercelli, Italy. Original publication 1839.

85. World Health Organization Protein and Amino Acid Requirements in Human Nutrition. Report of the Joint WHO/FAO/UNU Expert Consultation. WHO Technical Report Series no 935, Geneva, 2007.

86. Simopoulos, A.P. Evolutionary aspects of diet and essential fatty acids. *World Rev Nutr Diet* 2001; 88:18–27.

87. Brady ST, Siegel GJ, Albers RW, Price DL (Eds). Basic Neurochemistry, Eighth edition, Elsevier Academic Press, New York 2012.

88. Smyth EM, Fitzgerald GA. The eicosanoids: prostaglandins, thromboxanes, leukotrienes and related compounds. In Katzung BG, Masters SB, Trevor AJ (eds): Basic and Clinical Pharmacology, Eleventh edition. McGraw Hill Lange, New York, 2009.

89. Chowdhury R, Warnakula S, Kunutsor S, Crow F, Ward HA, Johnson L, Franco OH, Butterworth AS, Forouhi Ng, Thompson SG, Khaw KT, Mozaffarian D, Danesh J, Di Angelantonio E. Association of Dietary, Circulating, and Supplement Fatty Acids With Coronary Risk: A Systematic Review and Meta-analysis. *Ann Intern Med.* 2014; 160(6):398-406-406. doi:10.7326/M13-178.

90. Siri-Tarino PW, Sun Q, Hu FB, Krauss RM. Meta-analysis of prospective cohort studies evaluation the association of saturated fat with cardiovascular disease. *Am J Clin Nutr* 2010; 91:535–546.

91. Mann GV. Current Concepts. Diet-Heart: End of an Era. *New Engl J Med* 1977; 297:644–650.

92. Mann GV. Coronary heart disease. The dietary sense and nonsense. An evaluation by scientists. Janus Publishing Company London, 1993.

93. Nago N, Ishikawa S, Goto T, Kayaba K. Low cholesterol is associated with mortality from stroke, heart disease, and cancer: the Jichi Medical School Cohort Study. *J Epidemiol* 2011; 21:67–74.

94. Blackburn H, Taylor HL, Keys A. Coronary heart disease in seven countries. XVI. The electrocardiogram in prediction of five-year coronary heart disease incidence among men aged forty through fifty-nine. *Circulation.* 1970 Apr; 41(4 Suppl):I154–61.

95. Musunuru K. Atherogenic dyslipidaemia: cardiovascular risk and dietary intervention. *Lipids* 2010; 45:907–14

96. Malhotra A. Saturated fat is not the major issue. Let's bust the myth of its role in heart disease. *BMJ* 2013; 347:f6340 doi: 10.1136/bmj.f6340.

97. Rong Y, Chen I., Zhu T et al. Egg consumption and risk of coronary heart disease and stroke: dose-response meta-analysis of prospective cohort studies. *BMJ* 2013; 346:e8539 doi: 10.1136/bmj.e8539.

98. Bazzano LA, Hu T, Reynolds K, Yao L, Bunol C, Liu Y, Chen CS, Klag MJ, Whelton PK, He J. Effects of low-carbohydrate and low-fat diets: a randomized trial. *Ann Intern Med.* 2014; 161:309–18. doi: 10.7326/M14-0180.

99. Texon M. A hemodynamic concept of atherosclerosis with particular reference to coronary occlusion. *Arch Intern Med* 1957; 99:418.

100. Texon M, Imparato AM, Lord JW, Helpern M. The experimental production of arterial lesions: furthering the hemodynamic concept of atherosclerosis. *Arch Intern Med* 1962; 110:50–52.

101. Clarke EM, Thompson RC, Allam AH et al. Is atherosclerosis fundamental to human aging? Lessons from ancient mummies. J Cardiol. 2014 May; 63(5):329–34. doi: 10.1016/j.jjcc.2013.12.012.

102. Leonard WR, Robertson ML Snodgrass JJ, Kuzawa CW. Metabolic correlates of hominid brain evolution. *Comparative Biochemistry and Physiology* 2003; 136:5–15.

103. Navarrete A, van Schaik CP, Isler K. Energetics and the evolution of human brain size. *Nature* 2011; 480:91–93 and Potts R. Big brains explained. *Nature* 2011; 480:43–44.

104. Sol D. Revisiting the cognitive buffer hypothesis for the evolution of large brains. *Biology Letters* 2009; 5:130–133

105. Wilder RM. The effects of ketonemia on the course of epilepsy. *Mayo Clin Proc* 1921; 2:307–308.

106. Kossoff EH, McGrogan JR, Bluml RM, Pillas DJ, Rubenstein JE, Vining EP. A modified Adkins diet is effect for the treatment of intractable pediatric epilepsy. *Epilepsia* 2006; 47:421–424

107. Thakur KT, Probasco JC, Hocker SE, Roehl K, Henry B, Kossoff EH, Kaplan PW, Geocadin RG, Hartman AL, Venkatesan A, Cervenka MC. Ketogenic diet for adults in super-refractory status epilepticus. *Neurology* 2014; 82:665–670.

108. Moriguchi T, Greiner R,S, Salem N. Behavioral deficits associated with dietary induction of decreased brain docosahexanoic acid concentration. *J Neurochem* 2000; 75:2563–2573.

109. Hibbeln JR. Fish consumption and major depression. Lancet 1998; 351:1213 and Horrobin DF. Schizophrenia: the illness that made us human. *Med Hypotheses* 1998; 50:269–288.

110. Freeman MP, Rapaport MH. Omega-3 fatty acids and depression: from cellular mechanisms to clinical care. *J Clin Psychiatry* 2011; 72:258–259.

111. Flachs P, Horakova O, Brauner P et al. Polyunsaturated fatty acids of marine origin upregulate mitochondrial biogene-

sis and induce ß-oxidation in white fat. *Diabetologica* 2005; 48:2365–2375.

112. Wu A, Ying Z, Gomez-Pinilla F. Dietary Omega-3 fatty acids normalize BDNF levels, reduce oxidative damage and counteract learning disability after traumatic brain injury in rates. *J Neurotrauma* 2004; 21:1457–1467.

113. Osendarp SJ et al. Effect of a 12 month micronutrient intervention on learning and memory in well nourished and marginally nourished school aged children: 2 parallel, randomized placebo controlled studies in Australia and Indonesia. *Am J Clin Nutr* 2007; 86:1082–1093.

114. Wu A, Molteni R, Ying Z, Gomez-Pinilla F. A saturated fat diet aggravates outcome of traumatic brain injury on hippocampal plasticity and cognitive function by reducing brain derived neurotrophic factor. *Neuroscience* 2003; 119:365–373.

115. Fitzgerald KC, O'Reilly EJ, Falcone GJ. Dietary omega 3 polyunsaturated fatty acid intake and risk of amyotrophic lateral sclerosis. *JAMA Neurology* 2014; 71:1102–1110.

116. Lyons TW, Reinhard CT, Planavasky NJ. The rise of oxygen in Earth's early ocean and atmosphere. *Nature* 2014; 506:307–315.

117. Crawford MA, Bloom M, Broadhurst CL, Schmidt WF, Cunnane SC, Galli C, Gehbremeskel K, Linseisen F, Lloyd-Smith. J, Parkington J. Evidence for the unique function of docosahexanoic acid during the evolution of the modern hominid brain. *Lipids* 1999; 34:S39–S47

118. Williams G, Crawford MA. Comparison of the fatty acid component in structural lipids from dolphins, zebra and giraffe: Possible evolutionary implications. *J Zool Lond* 1987; 213:673–684.

119. Rightmire GP, Deacon HJ. Comparative studies of late Pleistocene human remains from Klasies River mouth, South Africa. *J Human Evolution* 1991; 20:131–156.

120. Pfeiffer S, Zehr MK. A morphological and histological study of the human humerus from the Border Cave. *J Human Evolution* 1996; 31:49–59.

121. Brauer G, Singer R. The Klasies Zygomatic Bone: Archaic or modern? *J Human Evolution* 1996; 30:161–165.

122. Parkington JE. The impact of systematic exploitation of marine foods on human evolution. Colloquia of the Dual Congress of the International Association of the Study of Human Paleontology and the International Study of Human Biologists, Sun City, South Africa, June 28–July 4, 1998.

123. Broadhurst CL, Cunnane SC, Crawford MA. Rift Valley lake fish and shellfish provided brain specific nutrition for early Homo. *Br J Nutr* 1998; 79:3–21.

124. Crawford MA, Ghebremeskel K, Phylactos AC. Are deficits of arachnidonic acid and docosahexanoic acis responsible for the neural and vascular complications of preterm babies? *Am J Clin Nutr* 1997; 66:1032S-1041S.

125. Suzuki H, Manabe S, Wada O, Crawford MA. Rapid incorporation of docosahexanoic acid from dietary sources into brain microsomal, synaptosomal, and mitochondrial membranes in adult mice. *Internat J Vit Res* 1997; 67:272–278.

126. Crawford MA, Bloom M, Broadhurst CL, Schmidt WF, Cunnane SC, Galli C, Gehbremeskel K, Linseisen F, Lloyd-Smith J, Parkington J. Evidence for the unique function of docosahexanoic acid during the evolution of the modern hominid brain. *Lipids* 1999; 34:S39-S47.

127. Albert CM, Hennekens CH., O'Donnell CJ, Ajani UA, Carey VA, Willett WC, Ruskin JN, Manson JE. Fish consumption and risk of sudden cardiac death. *JAMA* 1998; 279:23–28.

128. Harris WS. Fish oils, and plasma lipid and lipoprotein metabolism in humans. A Critical review. *J Lipids Res1989*; 30:785–807.

129. Siegel G, Ermilov E. Omega-3 fatty acids: benefits for cardio-cerebro-vascular diseases. *Atherosclerosis* 2012; 225(2):291–5.

130. Mazereeuw G1, Lanctôt KL, Chau SA, Swardfager W, Herrmann N. Effects of ω-3 fatty acids on cognitive performance: a meta-analysis. *Neurobiol Aging.* 2012; 33:1482. e17–29.

131. Simopoulos, A.P. Evolutionary aspects of diet and essential fatty acids. *World Rev Nutr Diet* 2001; 88:8–27.

132. Gow RV, Sumich A, Vallee-Tourangeau F, Crawford MA, Ghebremeskel K, Bueno AA, Hibbeln JR, Taylor E, Wilson DA, Rubia K. Omega-3 fatty acids are related to abnormal emotion processing in adolescent boys with attention deficit

hyperactivity disorder. *Prostaglandins Leukot Essent Fatty Acids.* 2013; 88:419–29.

133. Crawford MA. Diet and cancer and heart disease. *Nutr Health* 2014; 22:67–78.

134. Crawford MA, Broadhurst CL. The role of docosahexaenoic and the marine food web as determinants of evolution and hominid brain development: the challenge for human sustainability. *Nutr Health* 2012; 21(1):17–39.

135. Muskiet FAJ et al. Is DHA Essential? Lessons from DHA status regulation our ancient diet, epidemiology and randomized controlled trials. American Society of Nutritional Sciences *J Nutri* 2003; 134:183–186.

136. Leonard WR, Snodgrass JJ, Robertson ML. Evolutionary perspectives on fat ingestion and metabolism in humans. In Montmayeur JP, le Coutre J (eds). Fat detection: Taste, texture and post ingestive effects. CRC Press, Boca Raton 2010 and Toepel et al. 2009.

137. Milton K. Distribution patterns of tropical plant foods as an evolutionary stimulus to primate mental development. *American Anthropologist* 1981; 83:534–548.

138. Milton K. Foraging behavior and the evolution of primate intelligence. In: Marchiavellian intelligence: Social expertise and the evolution of intellect in monkeys, apes and humans. Byrne R, Whiten A (eds) Oxford University Press, Oxford, 1988.

139. Davignon J, Gregg RE Sing CF. Apolipoprotein E polymorphisms and atherosclerosis. *Atherosclerosis* 1988; 8:1–21.

140. Davignon J. Apolipoprotein E and atherosclerosis: beyond lipid effect *Atheroscler Thromb Vas Biol* 2005; 25:267–269.

141. Kay R. Diets of early Miocene African hominoids. *Nature* 1977; 268:628–630.

142. Eaton SB, Konner M. Paleolithic nutrition. A consideration of its nature ad current implications. *New Engl J Med* 1985; 312:283–289.

143. Leonard WR, Robertson ML. Comparative primate energetics and hominid evolution. *Am J Phys Anthropol* 1997; 102:265–181.

144. Crawford MA, Bloom M, Broadhurst CL et al. Evidence for the unique function of docosahexanoic acid during the evolution of the modern human brain *Lipids* 1999; 34:S39-S47.

145. Crawford MA, Bloom M, Cunnane SC et al. Docosahexanoic acid and cerebral evolution. *World Rev Nutr Diet* 2001; 88: 6–17.

146. Simopoulos AP. Evolutionary aspects of diet: the omega-6/omega-3 ratio and the brain. *Mol Neurobiol* 2011; 44(2):203–15.

147. Crawford MA. Docosahexaenoic acid in neural signaling systems. *Nutr Health* 2006; 18(3):263–76.

148. Crawford MA, Broadhurst CL, Guest M, Nagar M, Wang Y, Ghebremeskel K, Schmidt WF. A quantum theory for the irreplaceable role of docosahexanoic acid in neural signaling throughout evolution. *Prostaglandins, Leukotrienes and Essential Fatty Acids* 2013; 88:5–13.

149. Sinclair AJ. Long chain polyunsaturated FA in the mammalian brain, in: *Proceedings of the Nutrition Society* 1975; 34:287–291.

150. Brenna JT, Salem Jr N, Sinclair AJ, Cunnane SC. Alpha linolenic acid supplementation and conversion to n-3 long chain polyunsaturated fatty acids in humans. *Prostaglandins, Leukotrienes and Essential Fatty Acids* 2009; 80:85–91.

151. Crawford MA, Blood M, Broadhurst CL, Schmidt WF, Cunnane SC, Galli C, Ghebremeskel K, Linseisen F, Lloyd Smith J, Parkington J. Evidence for the unique function of DHA during the evolution of the modern hominid brain. *Lipids* 2009; 34:S39-S47.

152. Crawford MA, Broadhurst CL, Guest M, Nagar M, Wang Y, Ghebremeskel K, Schmidt WF. A quantum theory for the irreplaceable role of docosahexanoic acid in neural signaling throughout evolution. *Prostaglandins, Leukotrienes and Essential Fatty Acids* 2013; 88:5–13.

153. Brown KS, Marean CW, Jacobs Z, Schoville BJ, Oestmo S, Fisher EC, Bernatchez J, Karkanas P, Matthews T. An early and enduring advanced technology originating 71,000 years ago in South Africa. *Nature* 2012; 491:590–3.

154. Marean CW, Bar-Matthews M, Bernatchez J et al. Early human use of marine resources and pigment in South Africa during the Middle Pleistocene. *Nature* 2007 Oct 18; 449(7164):905–8.

155. Bradbury J. Docosahexaenoic acid (DHA): an ancient nutrient for the modern human brain. *Nutrients* 2011; 3(5):529–54.

156. German JB. Dietary lipids from an evolutionary perspective: sources, structures and functions. *Matern Child Nutr.* 2011; 2:2–16.

157. Polyunsaturated fatty acids and their metabolites in brain function and disease. *Nature Reviews Neuroscience* 2014; 15:771–785.

158. Pinot M, Vanni S, Pagnotta S et al. Polyunsaturated phospholipids facilitate membrane deformation and fission by endocytic proteins. *Science* 2014; 345:693–697.

159. Crawford MA, Broadhurst CL, Guest M, Nagar M, Wang Y, Ghebremeskel K, Schmidt WF. A quantum theory for the irreplaceable role of docosahexanoic acid in neural signaling throughout evolution. *Prostaglandins, Leukotrienes and Essential Fatty Acids* 2013; 88:5–13.

160. Darwin C. On the origin of species by means of natural or the preservation of favoured races in the struggle for life. Sixth edition. John Murray, London 1872 and Stade G. (Consulting Editorial Editor) Barnes and Noble Classics, New York, 2004, p171–172.

161. Testa-Silva G, Verhoog MB, Linaro D et al. High bandwith synaptic communication and frequency tracking in human neocortex PLOS Biology 2014; 12:1–13 e1002007.

162. Gawrisch NV, Eldho NV, Holte LL. The structure of DHA in phospholipid membranes. *Lipids* 2003; 38:445–452.

163. Owen OE, Morgan AP, Kemp HG, Sullivan JM, Herrera MG, Cahill GF, Jr: Brain metabolism during fasting. *J Clin Invest* 1967, 46:1589–1595.

164. Cahill GF Jr, Veech RL. Ketoacids? Good medicine? *Trans Am Clin Climatol Assoc.* 2003; 114:149–61.

165. Cahill GF Jr. Starvation in man. *New Eng J Med* 1970; 282:668–75.

166. Guzman M, Blazquez C: Is there an astrocyte–neuron ketone body shuttle? *Trends Endocrinol Metab* 2001, 12:169–173.

167. Gasior M, Rogawski MA, Hartman AL: Neuroprotective and disease modifying effects of the ketogenic diet. *Behav Pharmacol* 2006, 17:431–439.

168. Hasselbalch SG, Madsen PL, Hageman LP, Olsen KS, Justesen N, Holm S, Paulson OB: Changes in cerebral blood flow and carbohydrate metabolism during acute hyperketonemia. *Am J Physiol* 1996, 270:E746-E751.

169. Pellerin L, Pellegri G, Martin JL, Magistretti PJ: Expression of monocarboxylate transporter mRNAs in mouse brain: support for a distinct role of lactate as an energy substrate for the neonatal vs. adult brain. *Proc Natl Acad Sci U S A* 1998, 95:3990–3995.

170. Veech RL, Chance B, Kashiwaya Y, Lardy HA, Cahill GF Jr. Ketone bodies, potential therapeutic uses. *IUBMB Life* 2001; 51:241–7.

171. White H, Venkatesh B. Clinical Review: Ketones and brain injury. *Critical Care* 2011; 15:219 http://ccforum. com/content/15/2/219.

172. Ziegler DR, Ribeiro LC, Hagenn M, Siqueira IR, Araujo E, Torres IL, Gottfried C, Netto CA, Goncalves CA: Ketogenic diet increases glutathione peroxidase activity in rat hippocampus. *Neurochem Res* 2003, 28:1793–1797.

173. Klein RG, Edgar B. The Dawn of Culture. New York, John Wiley & Sons, 2002.

174. Freeman JM, Vining EP, Kossoff EH, Pyzik PL, Ye X, Goodman SN. A blinded, crossover study of the efficacy of the ketogenic diet. *Epilepsia.* 2009; 50:322–5.

175. Kobow K, Kaspi A, Harikrishnan KN, Kiese K, Ziemann M, Khurana I, Fritzsche I, Hauke J, Hahnen E, Coras R, Mühlebner A, El-Osta A, Blümcke I. Deep sequencing reveals increased DNA methylation in chronic rat epilepsy. *Acta Neuropath* 2013; 126:741–756.

176. Cahill GF, Veech RL. Ketoacids? Good Medicine? *Transactions of the American Clinical and Climatological Association* 2003; 114: 149–163.

177. Milton, Katharine (2000). "Diet and Primate Evolution." In Alan Goodman, Darna Dufour, & Gretel Pelto. Nutritional Anthropology: Biocultural Perspectives on Food and Nutrition. Mountain View, California: Mayfield Publishing Company. pp. 46–54.

178. Laden G, Wrangham R. The rise of the hominids as an adaptive shift in fallback foods: plant underground storage organs (USOs) and australopith origins. *J Hum Evol* 2005; 49:482–498.

179. Teaford MF, Ungar PS. Diet and the evolution of the earliest human ancestors. *Proc Natl Acad Sci USA* 2000; 97:13506–13511.

180. McHenryHM.Relativecheek-toothsizein*Australopithecus*. *Am J Phys Anthropol* 1984; 64:297–306.

181. McHenry HM. Introduction to the fossil record of human ancestry. In: The Primate fossil record. Hertwig C (Ed). Cambridge University Press, Cambridge 2002:401–405.

182. McHenry HM. How big were early hominids? Evol Anthropology 1992; 1:15–20 and McHenry HM. Behavioral ecological implications of early hominid body size. *J Hum Evol* 1994; 27:77–87.

183. Grine FE, Kay RF. Early hominid diets from quantitative image analysis of dental microwear. *Nature* 1988; 333:765–768

184. Teaford MF, Ungar PS. Diet and the evolution of the earliest human ancestors. *Proc Natl Acad Sci* 2000; 97: 13506–13511.

185. Wood B, Strait DS. Patterns of resource use in early Homo and Paranthropus. *J Hum Evol* 2004; 46:19–162.

186. Grine FE Martin LB. Enamel thickness and development in *Australopithecus* and Paranthropus. In: Grine FE (Ed) Evolutionary History of the "Robust" Australopithecines. Aldine de Gruyter, New York 1988; 3–42.

187. Macho, GA, Thackeray JF. Computed tomographic and enamel thickness of maxillary molarsof Plio Pleistoncen honins from Sterkfontein, Swartkrans and Kromdraai (South Africa): an exploratory study. *Am J Phys Anthropol* 1992; 89:133–143.

188. Wrangham RW, Jones JH, Laden G, Pilbeam D, Conklin-Brittain N. The Raw and the Stolen. Cooking and the Ecology of Human Origins. *Curr Anthropol.* 1999; 40:567–594.

189. Kay RF. In: Adaptations for foraging in nonhuman primates: contributions to an organismal biology of prosimians, monkeys and apes. Eds Rodman PS Can JGH. Columbia University Press, New York 1984:21–53.

190. Neel JV. Diabetes Mellitus: a "thrifty" genotype rendered detrimental by "progress"? *Am J Hum Genet* 1962; 14:353–362.

191. Wells JC. Environmental quality, developmental plasticity and the thrifty genotype: a review of evolutionary models. *Evol Bioinform Online* 2007; 19:109–120.

192. Shetty PS, James WPT. Body mass index: a measure of chronic energy deficiency. FAO Food and Nutrition Paper, no. 50. Rome. FAO, 1994.

193. Flegal KM, Carroll MD, Ogden CL, Johnson CL. Prevalence and trends in obesity among US adults, 1999– 2000. *JAMA.* 2002; 288(14):1723–1727.

194. WHO Web site: http://www.who.int/mediacentre/ factsheets/ fs311/en./

195. Hubert HB. The importance of obesity in the development of coronary risk factors and disease: the epidemiologic evidence. *Annu Rev Public Health.* 1986; 7:493–502

196. Adams KF, Schatzkin A, Harris TB, et al. Overweight, obesity, and mortality in a large prospective cohort of persons 50 to 71 years old. *N Engl J Med.* 2006; 355(8):763–778.

197. Karam JG, McFarlane SI. Tackling obesity: new therapeutic agents for assisted weight loss. Diabetes, Metabolic Syndrome and Obesity: *Targets and Therapy* 2010:3 95–112.

198. Hanover LM, White JS. Manufacturing, composition, and applications of fructose. *Am J Clin Nutr.* 1993; 58(5 Suppl):724S-732S.

199. BeMiller JN. One hundred years of commercial food carbohydrates in the United States. *J Agric Food Chem.* 2009; 57:8125–9.

200. Ng SW, Slining MM, Popkin BM. Use of caloric and non-caloric sweeteners in US consumer packaged foods, 2005–2009. *J Acad Nutr Diet.* 2012; 112(11):1828–34.

201. Bray GA, Popkin BM. Dietary sugar and body weight: have we reached a crisis in the epidemic of obesity and diabetes?: health be damned! Pour on the sugar. *Diabetes Care.* 2014; 37:950–6.

202. Stanhope KL. Role of fructose-containing sugars in the epidemics of obesity and metabolic syndrome. *Annu Rev Med.* 2012; 63:329–43.

203. Basciano H, Federico L, Adeli K. Fructose, insulin resistance, and metabolic dyslipidemia. *Nutr Metab (Lond).* 2005; 21;(1):5.

204. van Buul VJ, Tappy L, Brouns FJ. Misconceptions about fructose-containing sugars and their role in the obesity epidemic. *Nutr Res Rev.* 2014; 27(1):119–30.

205. Ganguly R, Piernce GN. Trans fat involvement in cardiovascular disease. *Mol Nutr Food Res* 2012; 56:1090–1096

206. Martin-Calvo N, Martínez-González MA, Bes-Rastrollo M, Gea A, Ochoa MC, Marti A. Sugar-sweetened carbonated beverage consumption and childhood/adolescent obesity: a case-control study. *Public Health Nutr.* 2014; 31:1–9.

207. Bernstein AM1, de Koning L, Flint AJ, Rexrode KM, Willett WC. Soda consumption and the risk of stroke in men and women. *Am J Clin Nutr.* 2012; 95(5):1190–9.

208. Gardener H, Rundek T, Markert M, Wright CB, Elkind MS, Sacco RL. Diet soft drink consumption is associated with an increased risk of vascular events in the Northern Manhattan Study. *J Gen Intern Med.* 2012; 27(9):1120–6.

209. de Koning L, Malik VS, Rimm EB, Willett WC, Hu FB. Sugar-sweetened and artificially sweetened beverage consumption and risk of type 2 diabetes in men. *Am J Clin Nutr.* 2011; 93:1321–1327.

210. Fowler SP, Williams K, Resendez RG, Hunt KJ, Hazuda HP, Stern MP. Fueling the obesity epidemic? Artificially sweetened beverage use and long-term weight gain. *Obesity* (Silver Spring). 2008; 16:1894 –1900.

211. Johnson RJ, Sanchez-Lozada LG, Nakagawa T. The effect of fructose on renal biology and disease. *J Am Soc Nephrol.* 2010; 21:2036–9.

212. Li H, Zou Y, Ding G. Dietary factors associated with dental erosion: a meta-analysis. *PLoS One.* 2012; 7(8):e42626. doi: 10.1371/journal.pone.0042626.

213. Barclay AW1, Brand-Miller J. The Australian paradox: a substantial decline in sugars intake over the same timeframe that overweight and obesity have increased. *Nutrients.* 2011; 3(4):491–504.

214. Veith WB, Silverberg NB. The association of acne vulgaris with diet. *Cutis.* 2011; 88:84–91.

215. Vos MB. Nutrition, nonalcoholic fatty liver disease and the microbiome: recent progress in the field. *Curr Opin Lipidol.* 2014 Feb; 25(1):61–6.

216. Cao XL, Corriveau J, Popovic S. Levels of bisphenol A in canned soft drink products in Canadian markets. *J Agric Food Chem.* 2009 Feb 25; 57(4):1307–11.

217. Suez J, Korem T, Zeevi D et al. Artificial sweeteners induce glucose intolerance by altering the gut microbiota. *Nature* 2014; doi.org/10/1038/nature3793; 2014.

218. Abbott A. Sugar substitutes linked to obesity. Artificial sweetener seems to change gut microbiome. *Nature* 2014; 513:290.

219. Parker, M. The Sugar Barons: Family, Corruption, Empire and War. London: Hutchinson, London 2011

220. Ponting, Cl. World History: A New Perspective. Chatto & Windus, 2000, London.

221. BeMiller JN. One hundred years of commercial food carbohydrates in the United States. *J Agric Food Chem.* 2009; 57:8125–9.

222. Flegal KM, Campbell SM, Johnson CL. Increasing Prevalence of Overweight among US Adults. The National Health and Nutrition Examination Surveys 1960 to 1991. *JAMA* 1994; 272:205–211.

223. Bray GA, Nielsen SJ, Popkin BM. Consumption of high fructose corn syrup in beverages may play a role in the epidemic of obesity. *Am J Clin Nutr* 2004; 80:1090.

224. Melanson KJ, Zukley L, Lowndes J et al. Effects of high fructose corn syrup and sucrose consumption on circulating glucose, insulin, leptin and ghrelin and on appetite in normal-weight women. *Nutrition* 2007; 23:103–112.

225. Johnson RK, Appel LJ, Brands M et al. Dietary Sugar Intake and Cardiovascular Health. A Scientific Statement from the American Heart Association. *Circulation* 2009; 120:1011–1020.

226. Petry N, Egli I, Zeder C et al. Polyphenols and phytic acid contribute to low iron availability from common beans in young women. *J Nutr* 2010; 140:1977–1982.

227. Gaitan E, Lindsay RH, Reichart RD et al. Antithyroid and goitrogenic effects of millet: role of C-glycosylflavones. *J Clin Endocrinol Metab* 1989; 68:707–714.

228. Kitts DD, Weiler K. Bioactive proteins and peptides from food sources. Applications of bioprocesses used in isolation and recovery.

229. *Curr Pharm Des* 2003; 9:1309–1323. Larsen CS. Animal Source Foods and Human Health during Evolution. *J Nutr* 2003; 133:38935–38975.

230. Ludvigsson JF, Bai JC, Biagi F et al. Diagnosis and management of adult celiac disease: guidelines from the British Society of Gastroenterology. *Gut* 2014; 63:1210–1228.

231. Kleslich M, Errazuriz G, Posselt HG et al. Brain White Matter Lesions in Celiac Disease: A Prospective Study of 75 Diet Treated Patients. *Pediatrics* 2001; 108:e21.

232. Sapone A, de Magistris L, Pietzak M et al. Zonulin upregulation is associated with increased gut permeability in subjects with type I diabetes and their relatives. *Diabetes* 2006; 55:1443–1449.

233. Farrell RJ, Kelly CP. Current concepts: Celiac sprue. *N Engl J Med* 2002; 346:180–188 and Hadjivassiliou M. Gluten sensitivity from gut to brain. Lancet Neurology 2010; 9:318–330

234. Hadjivassiliou M, Sanders DS, Grünewald RA, Woodroofe N, Boscolo S, Aeschlimann D. Gluten sensitivity: from gut to brain. *Lancet Neurol* 2010 Mar; 9(3):318–30. doi: 10.1016/S1474-4422(09)70290-X.

235. Holmes GKT. Neurological and psychiatric complications in coelica disease. In: Gobbi G, Anderman F, Naccarato S, Bachini G (eds). Epilepsy and other neurological disorders in coelic disease. London, John Libbey 1997.

236. Briani C, Zara G, Aleedeini A et al. Neurological complications of celiac disease and autoimmune mechanisms: a prospective study. *J Neuroimmunol* 2008; 195:171–175.

237. Geddes L. *New Scientist* 2014, July 12:28–31.

238. Volta U, Bardella MT, Calabrò A, Troncone R, Corazza GR; Study Group for Non-Celiac Gluten Sensitivity. An Italian prospective multicenter survey on patients suspected of having non-celiac gluten sensitivity *BMC Med* 2014; 12:85. doi: 10.1186/1741-7015-12-85.

239. Gibson PR, Shepherd SJ. Evidence-based dietary management of functional gastrointestinal symptoms: The FODMAP approach. *J Gastroenterol Hepatol.* 2010; 25:252–8.

240. Marlowe FW, Berbesque JC, Wood B, Crittenden A, Porter C, Mabulla A. Honey, Hadza, hunter-gatherers and human evolution. *Journal of Human Evolution* 2014; 71:119–128.

241. Dams M, Dams L. Spanish rock art depicting honey gathering during the Mesolithic. *Nature* 1977; 268:228–230.

242. Isack HA, Reyer HU. Honeyguides and Honey Gatherers: Interspecific Communication in a Symbiotic Relationship. *Science* 1989; 243:1343–1346.

243. Wrangham RW, Machanda Z. Honey exploitation by chimpanzees and hunter-gatherers indicates an ancient use of fire by humans. The 82nd Annual Meeting of the American Association of Physical Anthropologists, 2013.

244. Munstedt K, Sheybani B, Hauenschild A et al. Effects of basswood honey comparable glucose fructose solution, and oral glucose tolerance test solution on serum insulin, glucose and C peptide concentrations in healthy subjects. *J Med Food* 2008; 11:424–428.

245. Chick H, Shin HS, Ustunol Z. Growth and acid production by lactic acid bacteria and bifidobacteria grown in skim milk containing honey. *J Food Sci* 2001; 66:478–481.

246. Nemoseck TM, Carmody EG, Furchner–Evanson A et al. Honey promotes lower weight gain, adiposity and triglycerides than sucrose in rats. *Nutr Res* 2011; 31:55–60.

247. Erejuwa OO, Sulaiman SA, Ab Wahab MS. Honey – a novel antidiabetic agent. *International Journal of Biological Sciences* 2012; 8:913–934.

248. Ajibola, Chamunorwa JP, Erlwanger KH. Nutraceutical values of natural honey and its contribution to human health and wealth. *Nutrition and Metabolism* 2012; 9:1–12.

249. Chowdhury R, Warnakula S, Kunutsor S, Crow F, Ward HA, Johnson L, Franco OH, Butterworth AS, Forouhi Ng, Thompson SG, Khaw KT, Mozaffarian d, Danesh J, Di Angelantonio E. Association of Dietary, Circulating, and Supplement Fatty Acids With Coronary Risk: A Systematic

Review and Meta-analysis *Ann Intern Med.* 2014; 160(6):398-406-406. doi:10.7326/M13-1788.

250. Chowdhury R, Stevens S, Gorman D et al. Association between fish consumption, long chain omega 3 fatty acids and risk of cerebrovascular disease: systematic review and meta analysis. *BMJ* 2012; 345:e6698. doi: 10.1136/bmj. e6698.

251. Estruch R, Ros E, Salas-Salvadó J et al. Primary prevention of cardiovascular disease with a Mediterranean diet. Collaborators (233). *N Engl J Med.* 2013 Apr 4; 368(14):1279–90

252. O'Donnell MJ et al. Risk Factors for ischemic and intracerebral hemorrhagic stroke in 22 countries (Interstroke study): a case control study. *Lancet* 2010; 376:112–123.

253. Gardener H, Scarmeas N, Gu Y, Boden Albala B, Elkind MSV, Sacco RL, De Carti C, Wright CB. Mediterranean diet and white matter hyperintensity volume in the Northern Manhattan Stroke Study. *Arch Neurol* 2012; 69:251–256.

254. Scarmeas N, Stern Y, Mayeaux R, Manly JJ, Schupf N, Luchsinger JA. Mediterranean diet and mild cognitive impairment. *Archives Neurol* 2009; 66:216–225.

255. Iqbal R et al. A higher intake of prudent diet associated with 30% reduction in AMI globally (Interheart Study). *Circulation* 2008; 118; 1929–1937.

256. Estruch R, Ros E, Salas-Salvadó J et al. Primary prevention of cardiovascular disease with a Mediterranean diet. Collaborators (233). *N Engl J Med.* 2013 Apr 4; 368(14):1279–90.

257. Cordain L, Eaton SB, Sebastian A, Mann N, Lindeberg S, Watkins BA, O'Keefe JH, Brand-Miller J. Origins and evolution of the Western diet: health implications for the 21st century. *Am J Clin Nutr.* 2005; 81:341–54.

258. Cordain L, Eaton SB, Miller JB, Mann N, Hill K. The paradoxical nature of hunter-gatherer diets: meat-based, yet non-atherogenic. *Eur J Clin Nutr.* 2002; 56 Suppl 1:S42–52.

259. De Vany A. The New Evolution diet. Rodale, New York, 2011.

260. Lindberg S, Jonsson T, Granfeldt Y et al. A Paleolithic diet improves glucose tolerance more than a Mediterranean-like diet in individuals with ischemic heart disease *Diabetologia* 2007; 50:1795–1807.

261. Karanja N, Erlinger TP, Pao-Hwa L, Miller ER, Bray G. "DASH Diet for High Blood Pressure: From Clinical Trial to Dinner Table." *Cleveland Clinic Journal of Medicine* 2004; 71: 745–53.

262. Tangney CC, Li H, Wang Y, Barnes L, Schneider JA, Bennett DA, Morris MC. Relation of DASH and Mediterranean like dietary patterns to cognitive decline in older persons. *Neurology* 2014; 83:1410–1416.

263. Willcox BJ, Willcox DC, Todoriki H, Fujiyoshi A, Yan K, He Q, Curb JD, Suzuki M. Caloric Restriction, the Traditional Okinawan Diet, and Healthy Aging. The Diet of the World's Longest-Lived People and Its Potential Impact on Morbidity and Life Span. *Annals of the New York Academy of Sciences.* 2007; 1114:434–455.

264. Pennington AW. Weight Reduction. *Journal of the American Medical Association* 1958; 166: 2214–2215.

265. Dansinger ML, Gleason JA, Griffith JL, Selker HP, Schaefer EJ. Comparison of the Atkins, Ornish, Weight Watchers, and Zone diets for weight loss and heart disease risk reduction: a randomized trial. *JAMA* 2005; 293:43–53.

266. Kossoff EH, Cervenka MC, Henry BJ, Haney CA, Turner

267. Z. A decade of the modified Atkins diet (2003–2013): Results, insights, and future directions. *Epilepsy Behav.* 2013; 29:437–42.

268. Rosedale R, Westman EC, Konhilas JP. Clinical experience of a diet designed to reduce aging. *J Appl Res* 2009; 9:159–165.

269. Woodside JV, Young IS, McKinley MC. Fruit and vegetable intake and risk of cardiovascular disease. *Proc Nutr Soc* 2013; 72:399–406.

270. Zhao D, Qi Y, Zheng Z et al. Dietary factors associated with hypertension. Nat Rev Cardiol 2011; 8:456–465 and Holt EM. Steffen LM, Moran A et al. Fruit and vegetables consumption and its relation to markers of inflammation and oxidative stress in adolescents. *J Am Diet Assoc* 2009; 109:414–421.

271. Radhika G, Sudha V, Mohan SR et al. Association of fruit and vegetable intake and cardiovascular risk factors in urban south Indians. *Br J Nutr* 2008; 99:398–405.

272. Hu D, Huang J, Wang Y, Zhang D, Qu Y. Fruits and vegetables consumption and risk of stroke. A meta-analysis of prospective cohort studies. *Stroke* 2014; 45:1613–1619.

273. He FJ, Nowson CA, MacGregor GA. Fruit and vegetable consumption and stroke: meta-analysis of cohort studies. *Lancet* 2006; 367:320–326.

274. Barberger-Gateau P, Raffaitin C, Letenneur L, Berr C, Tzourio C, Dartigues JF, Alpérovitch A. Dietary patterns and risk of dementia: the Three-City cohort study. *Neurology* 2007; 69:1921–30.

275. Kernan WN, Ovbiagele B, Black HR et al. Guidelines for the prevention of stroke in patients with stroke and transient ischemic attack. *Stroke* 2014; 45:2160–2236.

276. Gordon NF, Salmon R, Franklin BA, Sperling LS, Hall L, Leighton RF, Haskell WL. *Am J Cardiol* 2004; 94:1558–1561.

277. Dudley R. The Drunken Monkey. Why we drink and abuse alcohol. University of California Press, Los Angeles 2014.

278. Isbell LA. The fruit the tree and the serpent. Harvard University Press, Cambridge, Massachusetts 2009.

279. Morris S. Myth, marula and elephant: an assessment of voluntary ethanol intoxication of the African elephant (Loxodonta Africana) following feeding on the fruit of the marula tree (Sclerocarya birrea). *Physiological and Biochemical Zoology* 2006; 79:363–369.

280. Milton K. Ferment in the family tree: does a frugivorous dietary heritage influence contemporary patterns of human ethanol use? *Integr Comp Biol.* 2004; 44(4):304–14.

281. Kinde H, Foate E, Beeler E et al. Strong circumstantial evidence for ethanol intoxication in Cedar Waxwings (Bombycilla cedrorum). *Journal of Ornithology* 2012; 153:995–998.

282. Miller WE. Intoxicated lepidopterans: how is their fitness affected and why do they tipple? *Journal of Lepidoterists Society* 1997; 51:277–287.

283. Carrigan MA, Uryasev O, Frye CB, Eckman BL, Myers CR, Hurley TD, Benner SA. Hominids adapted to metabolize ethanol long before human-directed fermentation. *Proc Natl Acad Sci U S A* 2015; 112:458–463.

284. Parsons P. Ecobehavioral genetics: habitats and colonists. *Annual Review of Ecology and Systematics* 1983; 14:35–55.

285. Parsons P. The hormetic zone: an ecological and evolutionary perspective based upon habitat characteristics and fitness selection. *Quarterly Review of Biology* 2001; 76:459–467.

286. Stahl SM. Stahl's Essential Psychopharmacology, Third edition. Cambridge University Press, Cambridge, 2008.

287. Ropper AH, Samuels MA, Klein JP. Adams and Victor's Principles of Neurology, 10th ed. McGraw Hill, New York, 2014.

288. Kuehn BM. Patients warned about risks of drugs used for analgesics, fevers, addiction. *JAMA* 2009; 301(22):2315–6.

289. Anstey KJ, Mack HA, Cherbuin N. Am J Geriatr Psychiatry 2009; 17:542–555.

290. Furie K, Kasner SE, Adams RJ et al. Guidelines for the prevention of stroke in patients with stroke or transient ischemic attack. A guideline for healthcare professionals from the American Heart Association/American Stroke Association *Stroke* 2011; 42:227–276.

291. Gerhauser C, Alt A, Heiss E, Gamal-Eldeen A, Klimo K, Knauft J, Neumann I, Scherf HR, Frank N, Bartsch H, Becker H. Cancer chemopreventive activity of Xanthohumol, a natural product derived from hop. *Mol Cancer Ther.* 2002 Sep; 11:959–69.

292. Lif F, Gong Q, Dong H, Shi J. Resveratrol, a neuroprotective supplement for Alzheimer's disease. *Curr Pharm Des* 2012; 18:27–33.

293. Sembra RD et al. Resveratrol levels and all cause mortality in older community dwelling adults. *JAMA Intern Med* 2014; 174:1077–84.

294. Di Castelnuovo A et al. Alcohol dosing and total mortality in men and women: an updated meta analysis of 34 prospective studies. *Archives of Internal Medicine* 2006; 166:2437–2445.

295. Gill JS, Zezulka AV, Shipley MJ et al. Stroke and alcohol consumption. *N Engl J Med* 1986; 315:1041–1046.

296. Morris MJ, Na ES, Johnson AK. Salt Craving: the psychobiology of pathogenic sodium intake. *Physiology and Behavior* 2008; 94:709–721.

297. Cirillo M, Capasso G, Di Levo VA, De Santo NG. A history of salt. *Am J Nephrol* 1994; 14:426–431.

298. Kurlanksy M. Salt: A World History. Penguin Books, New York 2002 and Conte F, Conte C, Conte P. The biological secrets of salt. Glazier Graphics and Illustrations, Bend, Oregon 2012.

299. MacGregor GA, Wardener HE. Salt, diet and health. Cambridge. Cambridge University Press 1998.

300. Stamler J. The INTERSALT study: background, methods, findings and implications. Am J Clin Nutr 1997; 65:626S-642S and Hulthén L1, Aurell M, Klingberg S, Hallenberg E, Lorentzon M, Ohlsson C. Salt intake in young Swedish men. *Public Health Nutr* 2010; 13:601–5.

301. Lindeberg, S, Nilsson-Ehle, P, Terént, A, Vessby, B, and Scherstén, B. Cardiovascular risk factors in a Melanesian population apparently free from stroke and ischaemic heart disease. The Kitava study. *J Intern Med* 1994; 236: 331–340.

302. Mitchell AR. The clinical biology of sodium. New York: Elsevier, 1995.

303. MacGregor GA, Wardener HE. Salt, diet and health. Cambridge. Cambridge University Press 1998.

304. Eaton, S, Konner, M. Paleolithic nutrition. A consideration of its nature and current implications. *N Engl J Med* 1985; 312:283–9. Mancilha-Carvalho, JJ, de Oliveira R, Esposito RJ. (1989). Blood pressure and electrolyte excretion in the Yanomamo Indians, an isolated population. *J Hum Hypertens* 1989; 3:309–14.

305. Lev-Ran A, Porta M. Salt and hypertension: a phylogenetic perspective. *Diabetes Metabolic Res Rev* 2005; 21:118–131.

306. Michell AR. Physiological aspects of the requirement for sodium in mammals. *Nutr Res Rev* 1989; 2:149–60.

307. Stamler J, Rose G, Stamler R, Eiliott P, Dyer A, Marmot M. INTERSALT study findings. Public health and medical care implications. *Hypertension* 1989; 14:570–577.

308. Strazzullo P, Galletti P. Genetics of salt sensitive hypertension. *Curr Hypertens Rep* 2007; 9:25–32.

309. de Wardener HE, MacGregor GA. Harmful effects of dietary salt in addition to hypertension. *J Hum Hypertens* 2002; 16:213–223.

310. Denton D. The hunger for salt: An anthropological, physiological and medical analysis. New York, SpringerVerlag 1982.

311. Jacobson MF. Salt: The forgotten killer. Washington DC. Center for Science in the Public Interest 2005.

312. Williams B, Poulter NR, Brown MJ, et al. Guidelines for management of hypertension: report of the fourth working party of the British Hypertension Society, 2004-BHS IV. *J Hum Hypertens* 2004; 18:139–85.

313. Graudal N1, Jürgens G, Baslund B, Alderman MH. Compared with usual sodium intake, lowand excessive-sodium diets are associated with increased mortality: A meta-analysis. *Am J Hypertens.* 2014; 27(9):1129–37.

314. Stolarz-Skrzypek K, Kuznetsova T, Thijs L, et al. Fatal and non-fatal outcomes, incidence of hypertension and blood pressure changes in relation to urinary sodium excretion. *JAMA* 2011; 305:1777–1785.

315. Stamler J, Neaton JD, Cohen JD, Cutler J. Multiple risk factor intervention trial revisited: a new perspective based on nonfatal and fatal composite endpoints, coronary and cardiovascular, during the trial. *J Am Heart Assoc.* 2012; 1(5):e003640. doi: 10.1161/JAHA.112.003640.

316. Tunstall-Pedoe H, Woodward M, Tavendale R, A'Brook R, McCluskey MK. Comparison of the prediction by 27 different factors of coronary heart disease and death in men and women of the Scottish Heart Health Study: cohort study. *BMJ* 1997; 315:722–729.

317. Alderman MH, Cohen H, Madhavan S. Dietary sodium intake and mortality: the National Health and Nutrition Examination Survey NHANES 1. *Lancet* 1998; 351:781–785.

318. Cohen HW, Hallpern SM, Fang J, Alderman MH. Sodium intake and mortality in the NHANES II follow up study. Am J Med2006; 119 and Cohen HW, Hallpern SM, Alderman MH. Sodium intake and mortality in the third National Health and Nutrition Examination Survey NHANES III. *J Gen Inern Med* 2008; 23:1297–1302.

319. Hooper L, Bartlett C, Davey Smith G, Ebrahim S. Systematic review of long term effects of advice to reduce dietary salt in adults. *BMJ* 2002; 325(7365): 628 Review.

320. Sarkkinen ES, Kastarinen MJ Niskanen TH, Karjalainen PH et al. Feasibility and antihypertensive effect of replacing regular

salt with mineral salt rich in magnesium and potassium in subjects with mildly elevated blood pressure. *Nutr J.* 2011; 10:88 doi: 10.1186/1475-2891-10-88.

321. Benzie, I. Evolution of dietary antioxidants. *Comparative Biochemistry and Physiology* 2003; 136: 113–26. doi:10.1016/S1095-6433(02)00368-9.

322. Murray RF, Harper HW, Granner DK, Mayes PA, Rodwell VW (2006). Harper's Illustrated Biochemistry. New York: Lange Medical Books/McGraw-Hill. ISBN 0-07-146197-3.

323. Galli R, Bielinksi DF, Szprengiel A, Shukitt-Hale B, Jospeh JA. Blueberry supplemented diet reverses age related decline in hippocampal HSP 70 neuroprotection *Neurobiol Aging* 2006; 27:344–350.

324. Duffy KB, Spangler EL, Devan BD et al. A blueberry enriched diet provides cellular protection against oxidative stress and reduces kainite induced learning impairment in rats. *Neurobiol Aging* 2008; 29(11):1680-9.

325. Quin JF, Bussiere JR, Hammond RS et al. Chronic dietary alpha lipoic acid reduces deficits in hippocampal memory of aged Tg 2576 mice. *Neurobiol Aging* 2007; 8: 213–225.

326. Holmquist L, Stuchbury G, Berbaum K et al. Lipoic Acid as a novel treatment for Alzheimer's disease and related dementias. *Pharmacology Ther* 2007; 113:154–164.

327. Ganguli M, Chandra V, Kamboh MI et al. Apolipoprotein E polymorphism and Alzheimer disease: the Indo-US Cross National Dementia Study. *Arch Neurol* 2000; 57:824–830.

328. Fiala M, Liu PT, Espinosa-Jeffrey A et al. Innate immunity and transcription of MGAT-III and Toll-like receptors in Alzheimer's disease patients are improved by bisdemethoxycurcumin. *PNAS* 2007; 104:12849–12854.

329. van Praag H, Lucero MJ, Yeo GW et al. Plant derived flavanol (-) epicatechin enhances neurogenesis and retention of spatial memory in mice. *J Neurosci* 2007; 27:5869–5878.

330. Mordente A, Guantario B, Meucci E et al. Lycopene and cardiovascular diseases: an update. *Curr Med Chem.* 2011; 18:1146–6.

331. Benzie IF, Strain JJ: The ferric reducing ability of plasma (FRAP) as a measure of "antioxidant power": the FRAP assay. *Anal Biochem* 1996; 239:70–76.

332. Carlsen MH, Halvorsen BL, Holte K et al. The total antioxidant content of more than 3,100 foods, beverages, spices, herbs and supplements used worldwide. *Nutrition Journal* 2010; 9:3, doi:10.1186/1475-2891-9-3.

333. Larsson SC, Orsini N. Coffee consumption and risk of stroke: a dose response meta analysis of prospective studies. *Am J Epidemiol* 2011; 174:993–1001.

334. Larsson SC. Coffee, tea and cocoa and the risk of stroke. *Stroke* 2014; 45:309–314.

335. Steffen M, Kuhle C, Hensrud D, Erwin PJ, Murad MH. The effect of coffee consumption on blood pressure and the development of hypertension: a systematic review and meta-analysis. *J Hypertens* 2012; 30:2245–2254.

336. Cai L, Ma D, Zhang Y, Liu Z, Wang P. The effect of coffee consumption on serum lipids: a meta analysis of randomized controlled trials. *Eur J Clin Nutr* 2012; 66:872–877.

337. Bonita JS, Mandarano M, shuta D, Vinson J. Coffee and cardiovascular disease: in vitro, cellular, animal and human studies. *Pharmacol Res* 2007; 55:187–198.

338. Gross G, Jaccaud E, Huggett AC. Analysis of the content of the diterpenes, cafestol and kahweol in coffee brews. *Food Chem Toxicol* 1997; 55:547–554.

339. Cao C, Lowenstein DA, Lin X et al. High blood caffeine levels in MCI linked to lack of progression to dementia. *J Alzheimers Dis* 2012; 30:559–572.

340. Kokubo Y, Iso H, Sait I et al. The impact of green tea and coffee consumption the reduced risk of stroke incidence in Japanese population: The Japan public health center based stud cohort. *Stroke* 2013; 44:1369–1374.

341. Larsson SC, Virtamo J, Wolk A. Black tea consumption and risk of stroke in women and men. *Ann Epidemiol* 2013; 23:157–160.

342. Larsson SC. Coffee, Tea and Cocoa and the risk of stroke. *Stroke* 2014; 45:309–314.

343. Ostertag LM, O'Kennedy N, Kroon PA, Duthie GG, de Roos B. Impact of dietary polyphenols on human platelet function – a critical review of controlled dietary intervention studies. *Mol Nutri Food Res* 2010; 54:60–81.

344. Guallar E, Stranges S, Mulrow C, Appel LJ. Enough is Enough: Stop wasting money on vitamin and mineral supplements. *Ann Intern Med.* 2013; 159:850–851.

345. Balion C, Griffith LE, Stifler L et al. Vitamin D, cognition and dementia: a systematic review and meta-analysis. *Neurology* 2012; 79:1397–1405.

346. Littlejohns TJ, Henley WE, Annweiler C et al. Vitamin D and the risk of dementia and Alzheimer disease. *Neurology* 2014; 83:920–928.

347. Halagappa VK, Guo Z, Pearson M et al. Intermittent fasting and caloric restriction ameliorate age related behavioral deficits in the triple transgenic mouse model of Alzheimer's disease. *Neurobiol Dis* 2007; 26:212–220.

348. Pereira AC, Huddleston DE, Brickman AM et al. An in vivo correlate of exercise induced neurogenesis in the adult dentate gyrus. *Proc Natl Acad Sci USA* 2007; 104:5638–5643.

349. Xue B, Yang Z, Wang X, Shi H. Omega-3 polyunsaturated fatty acids antagonize macrophage inflammation via activation of AMPK/SIRT1 pathway. *PLoS One.* 2012; 7:e45990. doi: 10.1371/journal.pone.0045990.

350. Jung SB, Kwon SK, Kwon M, Nagar H, Jeon BH, Irani K, Yoon SH, Kim CS Docosahexaenoic acid improves vascular function via up-regulation of SIRT1 expression in endothelial cells. *Biochem Biophys Res Commun.* 2013 Jul; 437:114–9. doi: 10.1016/j.bbrc.2013.06.049.

351. Stilling RM, Dinan TG, Cryan JF. Microbial genes, brain & behaviour-epigenetic regulation of the gut-brain axis. *Genes Brain Behav.* 2014; 13:69–86. doi: 10.1111/ gbb.12109.

352. Zilber-Rosenberg I, Rosenberg E. Role of microorganisms in the evolution of animals and plants: the hologenome theory of evolution. *FEMS Microbiol Rev.* 2008; 32:723– 35. doi: 10.1111/j.1574-6976.2008.00123.x.

353. Williams AC, Dunbar RI. Big brains, meat, tuberculosis, and the nicotinamide switches: co-evolutionary relationships with modern repercussions? *Int J Tryptophan Res.* 2013; 15:73–88.

354. Williams AC, Dunbar RI. Big brains, meat, tuberculosis and the nicotinamide switches: Co-evolutionary relationships with

modern repercussions on longevity and disease? *Med Hypotheses.* 2014; 83(1):79–87.

355. RosenbergE,SharonG,Zilber-RosenbergI.Thehologenome theory of evolution contains Lamarckian aspects within a Darwinian framework. *Environ Microbiol* 2009; 11:2959– 62. doi: 10.1111/j.1462-2920.2009.01995.x

356. Müller M, Kersten S. Nutrigenomics: Goals and Perspectives. *Nature Reviews Genetics* 2003; 4:315–322.

357. Stilling RM, Dinan TG, Cryan JF. Microbial genes, brain & behavior – epigenetic regulation of the gut-.brain axis. *Genes Brain Behav* 2014; 13:69–86

358. Arnold C. The Other You. *New Scientist,* 12 January 2012:31–34.

359. Katz SH. Food and bio-cultural evolution: a model for the investigation of modern nutritional problems. In Johnstone FE (ed): Nutritional Anthropology. Alan R Liss Publications, New York, 1987.

4

Sleep Health

Humans are controlled by circadian (twenty-four-hour) rhythms consequent to the Earth's rotation, and we observe a diurnal rhythm, having abandoned our primordial mammalian nocturnal rhythm about 60 mya. Natural light is the most significant influence on our various circadian rhythms. We are a collection of body clocks, a master clock, the superior chiasmatic nucleus (SCN), and many peripheral tissue body clocks that have been entrained by the Earth's rotation. Laboratory sleep analysis with electroencephalography, functional brain imaging, and neurochemical analyses reveal a complicated interplay of many neurotransmitter systems in the brain involved in normal sleep.

The myriad sleep-related syndromes are not always a consequence to the malfunctioning of these systems, but many may be best explained from an evolutionary trade-off perspective.[1] The sleeping brain, with its seeming complexity of five different sleep stages over a ninety-minute period, repeated six times during a typical night, is regarded as a sleep quality, predator-risk trade-off—the frequent cycling into a stage 2 very light sleep having evolved to facilitate easier awakening in case of predator threat.[2]

Epidemiology and Scope of the Problem

Currently in the United States, 30% of daytime workers and 44% of night-shift workers sleep less than the recommended eight hours per night (or daytime sleep), averaging less than six hours. In comparison to data from the 1960s, only 3% of people had such curtailed sleep.[3] Apart from the personal toll of tiredness, impaired concentration, and memory loss, there are serious medical consequences including cardiovascular disease, stroke, obesity, diabetes, and depression that in 2013 affected between fifty to seventy million people in the United States. Other medical problems include a marked increase in sleep breathing disorder driven by the obesity epidemic, death from traffic accidents due to sleep-deprived individuals ranking second behind drunk driving.[4] Furthermore, lack of sleep affects the immune system adversely and may also be carcinogenic.[5]

Poor Sleep in Adults Causes Daytime Sleepiness, but Children May Be Overactive and Inattentive

Overall, children too, are getting less sleep on days they attend school compared to one hundred years ago (by about 1.2 hours). Rather than presenting with daytime sleepiness like adults, many present with hyperactivity and inattentiveness, perhaps contributing to the surge in attention-deficit hyperactivity disorder (ADHD) diagnoses as well as the obesity epidemic.[6, 7]

Emerging Causes

A Web-accessed database, the Munich chronotype questionnaire, designed by Till Roenneberg has highlighted what is termed social jet lag. Due to shift work or day work schedules, many people have disconnected with their central clock and internal rhythms. This circadian dysynchrony results in impaired attention, working memory, and general medical disorders such as cardiovascular disease and metabolic disorders. One of the factors identified is the use of artificial lighting at nighttime, which continues to stimulate the SCN and interferes with melatonin release, which normally initiates sleep onset. The retinal cells, intrinsic photosensitive retinal ganglion cells (ipRGCs), are particularly sensitive to blue wavelengths (wavelengths 460–480 nm) generated by light-emitting diodes (LED) of smart phones, computers, and television screens (figure 4.1).

Fig. 4.1. Natural light varies throughout the day
Light emitting diode (LED) lights 450–475 (nm).
Modified from: Hecht J. New Scientist June 30, 2012:43-45

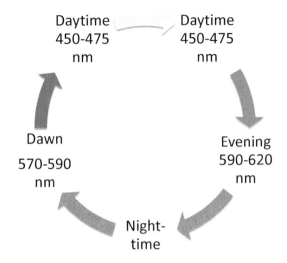

One of the options is controlling color composition of solid state lighting, for example, with a higher component of red light, which is less disruptive to ipRGCs and melatonin release. Another recommendation is considering designing work schedules according to an individual's chronotype .[8]

Neurobiological Overview of Sleep

Primates had evolved from tactile and olfactory sensation as their prime sensory organs to using vision as the dominant sense. However, the eye processes not only visual percepts from the environment through its retinal rod and cone cells but also light intensity, frequency, and duration by a third type of retinal cell, the ipRGCs, and comprise of 1–3% of retinal ganglion ganglion cells. The ipRGCs utilize a photopigment (melanopsin), which activates the SCN, which in turn quells the production of melatonin (which is sleep inducing) that is secreted by the pineal gland (figure 4.2).

Fig. 4.2. Light impinges on the retinal ipRGCs (blue) is relayed to the SCN (red) in the hypothalamus, which in turn stimulates the pineal gland (yellow) to release melatonin.

Abbreviations: ipRGC's – intrinsic photosensitive retinal ganglion cells, SCN – suprachiasmatic nucleus

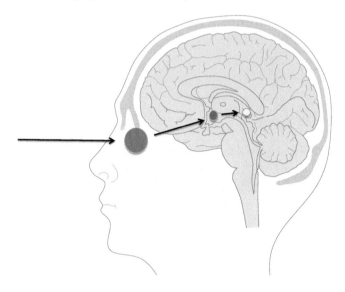

The ipRGCs are also excitatory in that they activate the hypothalamic orexin neurons that mediate arousal, which is deficient in narcolepsy for example.[9] In addition to melatonin, the pineal gland also secretes pinoline, a neuroprotective antioxidant .[10]

The central SCN pacemaker keeps both twenty-four-hour time as well as seasonal time and tied to the SCN are peripheral body clocks that express a network of clock genes, which in turn influence metabolism and the immune system. Alterations to light exposure are regarded as a risk factor for a number conditions such as depression, cardiovascular disease, and metabolic diseases. The central SCN transmits information to peripheral tissue body clocks. Approximately 10% of the genome in cells is concerned with circadian oscillation, and the ~20,000 cells in the SCN influence peripheral tissue body clocks via a molecular network of transcriptional factors. These can also act as epigenetic modifiers, which, in turn, influence metabolism as well as cognition and memory.[11] For example, the connection of the SCN to the peripheral body clocks in the amygdala and habenula may explain the role of depression in response to irregular light exposure or nonalignment with the solar day.[12]

Brain lesions in the hypothalamus and brain areas adjacent to the caudal (posterior) third ventricle are associated with excessive sleep, and lesions in the rostral (front) third ventricle regions are associated with excessive wakefulness. Lesions in the posterior hypothalamus are associated with narcolepsy (intermittently falling asleep).[13] Functional imaging studies with PET brain scanning has confirmed the importance of these critical areas showing increased activation of the hypothalamus as well as the amygdala, medial prefrontal cortex, and upper brainstem in people with insomnia.[14]

Theories of Sleep Promotion and Wakefulness Can Be Considered in Terms of a Neurotransmitter Interplay of WakePromoting and Sleep-Inducing Systems [15] (figures 4.3 and 4.4)

Fig. 4.3. The chemistry of the wake-sleep cycle

Abbreviations: Ach Acetylcholine, NA – noradrenaline, 5HT – 5 hydroxytryptamine (serotonin), HA – histamine, DA – dopamine, ATP – adenosine triphosphate, POA – preoptic area, MnPn – median preoptic nucleus, SCN – suprachiasmatic nucleus, GABA – gamma amino butyric acid

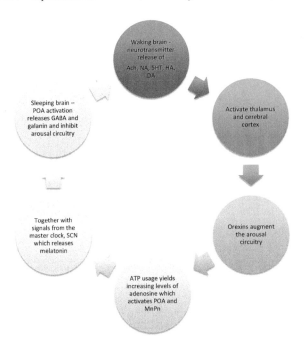

Fig. 4.4. Wake-producing systems: Acetylcholine (purple), noradrenaline (yellow), serotonin (green), dopamine (blue), histamine (pink), orexin (orange).

Sleep producing neurons from VLPO and MnPn (red) producing neuromodulators, GABA and galanin that inhibit the wake producing neurons. Modified from Saper CG, Lu J, Chou TC, Gooley J. The hypothalamic integrator for circadian rhythms. Trends in Neurosciences 2005; 28:152–157

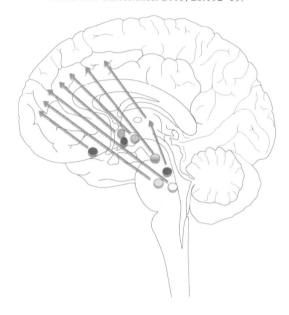

1. Wake-promoting systems that do not affect rapid eye movements (REM)

   a.   Serotonin (5-HT): Nuclei from the dorsal and median raphe nucleus in the midbrain project widely to the cortex, limbic system, and diencephalon

   b.   Noradrenaline (NA): Neurons project from the locus coeruleus from the posterior pons to the cortex and diencephalon

   c.   Histamine: Neurons project from the tuberomammillary nucleus of the hypothalamus, not only to the neocortex, but also brainstem and spinal cord

   d.   Orexin: Neurons project from the hypothalamus to the cortex and brainstem

2. Wake-promoting systems with REM affected

    a.   Acetycholine (Ach): A cluster of acetycholine neurons in the pons and midbrain (PPT, LDT, RF) project widely to the cortex, thalamus, and hypothalamus. In addition, a fourth group, the basal forebrain group, specifically projects to the limbic system.

    b.   Dopamine (DA): Neurons project from the substantia nigra and ventral tegmental area to the cortex.

    c.   Glutamate: Neurons are widely distributed in all cortical areas and reticular formation. Glutamate is the principal excitatory neurotransmitter of the brain

3. The sleep-inducing system originates in the lower pons and upper medulla

The preoptic area (POA) and median preoptic nucleus (MnPN) cells are involved in promoting sleep, a finding first noted by Von Economo in 1915. Both MnPN and VLPO (ventrolateral preoptic) neurons are active during sleep and express glutamic acid decarboxylase (GAD), which produces the inhibitory neurotransmitter GABA and galanin. These are also activated by elevated adenosine levels by exercise, for example (which rise with decreased ATP production, an inhibitory neuromodulator that indicate a need for sleep).[16] Increased adenosine levels are, therefore, regarded as neuroprotective in the setting of reduced brain energy reserves (ATP). Adenosine promotes sleep effects through activating the inhibitory adenosine (A1) receptors on cholinergic cells (promotion of wakefulness) that originate from the basal forebrain. Other sleep-promoting agents include pro-inflammatory cytokines (IL-1Beta, LI), prostaglandin D2, and growth hormone—all of which act on the POA and basal forebrain.[17] Nitric oxide (NO) is produced in response to reactive oxygen species (ROS), cytokines, inflammation and glutaminergic stimulation, and sleep may therefore serve as a protective role in response to oxidative stress, and sleep deprivation may lead to neuronal damage.[18]

Sleep and wakefulness theories include the concept of a so-called flip-flop switch, and any one the components can lead to impaired sleep (figure 4.5).

Fig. 4.5. Sleep-wake flip-flop switch

Modified from: Siegel JM. Sleep mechanisms and phylogeny. In; Kryger MH, Roth T, Dement WC (eds). Principles and Practice of Sleep Medicine, 5th ed. Elsevier Saunders, St Louis, Missouri, 2011 andSaper CB, Chou TC, Scammell TE. The Sleep Switch. Trends in Neurosciences 2001;2 4:726–731.

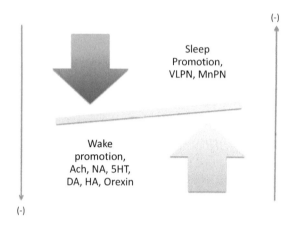

The Neurotransmitter Interplay Results in an Intricate Sequence of Sleep Stages That Was Forged in Our Evolutionary Past (See Below)

The thalamocortical circuit activity can be discerned by EEG analysis, which has resulted in sleep staging (N1/N2/N3/REM) according the rhythms and frequency analysis.

Awake EEG rhythms include alpha (8–13Hz) and beta (14–25 Hz), whereas during sleep and in pathological states, theta (5–7 Hz) and delta (0.5–4 Hz) occur. Other rhythms such as sigma (12–16 Hz) and gamma (30–80) may be identified. Sleep stages are largely based on frequency but also on the patterns and combinations of the rhythms seen on EEG as well as recordings of eye movements (EOG) and limb movements (EMG). They are classified as the following:

N1 – Mainly theta rhythm 4–7 Hz, slow eye movements seen with EOG, EMG.

N2 – Further slowing in theta range, sleep spindles appear (sigma 12–16 Hz) that may include both slow spindles (12–14Hz) in frontal leads and fast spindles (14–16Hz) in central and parietal leads. K complexes (large negative upward waves and subsequent positive downward deflection) may be seen.

N3 – Delta waves (0.5–4 Hz), high amplitude, occasional sleep spindles.

REM – Rapid eye movements seen by electro oculogram (EOG) and electromyogram (EMG). Ocular muscles maintain tone during sleep whereas skeletal muscles do not. However, skeletal muscle twitches, middle ear muscle activity (MEMAs), as well as periorbital potentials (PIPs) may be discerned. During the average night sleep of about eight hours, usually six cycles of approximately ninety minutes occur with progressive lengthening of REM in the latter part of sleep. EEG staging combined with other measurements (EMG, EOG, airflow, abdominal and chest movements, oxygen saturation), together called polysomnography (sleep study), enable delineation of a number of sleep-related conditions and pathologies.[19]

The combination of the electrical activity in the brain during sleep and monitoring of limb movements, oxygen, and breathing has resulted in the diagnosis of over a dozen relatively common sleep disorders. Almost all are treatable, but each has specific management: pharmacological, behavioral, or lifestyle correction.

Table 4.1. Neurological sleep disorders Sleep Breathing Disorder

Sleep apnea – central, obstructive, mixed

Sleep-Related Movement Disorders
Periodic limb movement disorder
Rhythmic movement disorder

Sleep-Related Epilepsy
Nocturnal frontal lobe epilepsy

REM Sleep Behavior Disorder (Vocalizations, Motor Behaviors)
Disorders of arousal from non-REM sleep
Confusional arousals, sleepwalking, sleep terrors

Parasomnimas
Sleep-related dissociative disorder
Sleep-related groaning (catathrenia)

Nocturnal Panic Attacks Nocturnal Wandering
Dementia and other cognitive impairments

Overview of Some of These More Common Sleep-Related Conditions

Sleep Disorder Breathing (SDB) Syndromes

One of the most common sleep disorders diagnosed by polysomnography or one of the portable monitoring devices includes obstructive sleep apnea, or less-severe breathing disturbance termed hypopnea. A much rarer condition termed respiratory effort arousals (RERAs) may also be diagnosed by sleep studies. Apnea (no airflow recorded via the nose or mouth) is diagnosed when there is ten or more seconds airflow cessation or there is 90% or greater airflow reduction for at least ten seconds. Hypopnea is diagnosed if there is 30–90% airflow decrease for ~10 seconds as well as a >4% oxygen desaturation. There is a complex relationship between SDB, cardiovascular, and cerebrovascular disease. [20]

Table 4.2. Prevalence of moderate to severe SDB in cardiovascular and cerebrovascular diseases

Drug-resistant hypertension	80%
Congestive heart failure	50%
Atrial fibrillation	50%
All hypertension	35%
Coronary artery disease	30%
Angina	30%

Obstructive sleep apnea (OSA) grading system

Definition of OSA: Apnea hypopnea index
(AHI) of five per hour or more

> Mild: 5–14
> Moderate: 15–29
> Severe: >30

The condition of central sleep apnea is diagnosed by polysomnography when no respiratory or abdominal effort as well as cessation of airflow is noted. Treatment is tailored to the individual, which often includes weight loss, alcohol curtailment, and frequently continuous positive airways pressure (CPAP) therapy, auto CPAP (adjusts pressures to level of obstruction), BIPAP or bilevel PAP (higher inspiration, lower during expiration pressures), oral devices such as tongue-retaining device, mandibular positioning device (with CPAP intolerance), soft palate lifting device, and various surgical options such as septoplasty, uvulopalatopharyngoplasty, glossectomy, maxillomandibular advancement depending on the particular anatomy and pathophysiology.

Hypersomnias (Excessive Sleep or Sleepiness)

Narcolepsy is the most common form of hypersomnia and is now understood to be an autoimmune disease. The syndrome may include sleep paralysis, daytime somnolence, cataplexy, hypnopompic hallucinations (sleep onset hallucinations), automatic behavior, periodic leg movement disorder, and REM sleep behavior disorder. Loss of orexin neurons in the posterior lateral hypothalamus has been established with autoantibodies produced (occurring mostly in those with HLADQB1*0602 genotype). There is preliminary evidence with a relationship to influenza epidemics. Diagnosis is by the multiple sleep latency test (MSLT) (EEG based). An MSLT with <8 minutes sleep onset is abnormal. Sleep onset REM periods (SOREMP) or REM sleep occurring within fifteen minutes of sleep onset and low CSF hypocretin levels in CSF, <110 pg/ml or 0 is diagnostic. Treatment options include Amphetamines, Methylphenidate, Modafanil, Armodafanil, Sodium Oxybate, Tricyclic antidepressants, selective serotonin reuptake inhibitors (SSRI), selective serotonin and noradrenaline reuptake inhibitors (SNRI), and histamine agents that stimulate H1 receptors. Future treatment may include Hypocretin-1 replacement.

REM Sleep Behavior Disorder

Upper pontine neurons generate REM sleep and lesions in this area may impair the integrity of REM sleep. Loss of muscle tone (atonia) during REM sleep normally prevents acting out one's dreams. With lesions in this region, there is intermittent lack of atonia (no muscle tone) during REM phase, with the development of REM sleep behavior. There is about a 30% association with Parkinson's disease and Lewy body disease.

Unraveling the Cause of Chronic Insomnia Often Requires Some Detective Work, but If Applied, Can Be Rewarding

Chronic insomnia affects about 10% of the population. Once the initial list of possible implicating agents or conditions have been excluded (secondary insomnias), primary insomnia may be diagnosed. Some of the more common causes of secondary insomnia include the following:

1. Poor sleep hygiene—prebedtime electronic use (TV, computers), bright lights, excessive noise, and extending the workday by answering e-mails. All of these may increase cortisol release. Not abiding to sleep hygiene rules is very common but the easiest to rectify.

2. Anxiety, stress, depression, posttraumatic stress disorder—release adrenaline and cortisol (normally suppressed during sleep)

3. Medications—steroids, antidepressants, antihypertensives, decongestants, weight loss medications (stimulants)

4. Chronic medical illness—acid reflux (GERD), chronic pulmonary disease, heart failure (nocturnal dyspnea), cancer, arthritis, cancer, hyperthyroidism

5. Any conditions that cause pain, polyuria (frequent urination)
6. Snoring and sleep disorder breathing (sleep apnea)
7. Stimulants—tea, coffee, soft drinks, energy drinks, chocolate, substance abuse
8. Alcohol—increases initial slow wave sleep but disrupts subsequent REM sleep with waking at 2:00–3:00 a.m. and disrupts dreaming and memory
9. Micronutrient deficiency—vitamin B, C, calcium, magnesium deficiency
10. Hormonal imbalance, estrogen level fluctuation may affect melatonin release

The Entity Termed Primary Insomnia Is Considered to Be the Most Common Sleep Deficiency Syndrome

In this syndrome, insomnia is caused by hyperarousal. Polysomnographic studies show near normal amount of sleep, but more detailed inspection of EEG analysis reveals abnormalities of certain frequencies such as excess gamma frequency activity (> 30 Hz), which is associated with waking cortical activity. There is a discrepancy, therefore, on what the sleep laboratory indicators reveal and the quality of sleep people experience. In primary insomnia, researchers have also documented more average activity of both beta-1 (14–20 Hz) and beta-2 (20–35 Hz) during the NREM sleep phase. In people with major depression, there may, for example, be an excess of overall omega activity (45.0–125 Hz).[21] This has led to the concept of the hyperarousal model of primary insomnia, with an inability to lessen arousal when asleep. In another study using EEG spectral power analysis, comparing people with good sleep and those with primary insomnia, elevation of beta and sigma frequencies during stage 2 (NREM phase) sleep was recorded. Spiegelhalder et al. maintain that the beta activity is indicative of cortical arousal while the sigma activity is regarded as "a sleep-protecting neural activity" with both activities at the same time being the reason for the subjective experience of non-rejuvenating poor sleep in primary insomnia.[22]

Sleep Deprivation Causes Problems with Cognition, Memory, Metabolism, Coronary Artery Disease, Stroke, Obesity, Hypertension, and Immune System Impairment

Cognition and Dementia

Reduced sleep to four to six hours per night for two weeks resulted in cognitive impairment and inattention in a study performed by Van Dongen et al.[23] and people with sleep disturbance are more likely to develop neurodegenerative disease such as Alzheimer's and Parkinson's disease within two to four years according to the SHARE trial.[24] Sleep-deprived mice led to a marked rise in their brain amyloid beta concentration. Sleep disturbance may be one of the earliest Alzheimer's disease manifestations, and sleep apnea may almost double the risk overall of developing dementia.[25]

Amyloid-ß production is increased by neural activity in the awake state and is reduced or cleared during sleep. This has been attributed to the dilated interstitial space increases of about 60%, noted in rodents and presumably the same applies to humans. This process doubles the clearance of radio-labeled amyloid-ß in the sleep state. Natural sleep induced a 60% increase in the interstitial space and is associated with a profound increase in exchange of CSF within the interstitial fluid. In turn, the interstitial flow increases the rate of clearance of beta-amyloid in the sleep state (figure 4.6).[26]

Fig. 4.6. Restorative function of sleep: Removal of neurotoxic waste that accumulates in the waking state.

Sleep and anesthesia is associated with a 60% increase in the interstitial fluid space that promotes flushing of metabolites including ß-amyloid Reproduced with permission from: Xie L et al. Sleep Drives Metabolite Clearance from the Adult Brain. Science 2013; 342:373–377.

Diagrams showing how wakefulness is associated with suppression of the influx of cerebrospinal fluid tracers (CSF) tracers (% volume diagram) in mice:

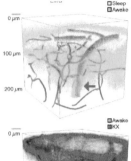

Top figure - CSF tracer injected and shown in awake state (yellow) and sleep state (green). Arteries shown in blue (red arrow)

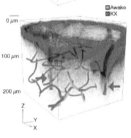

Lower figure) CSF tracer injected. The awake state (yellow) and anesthetized (red) states are contrasted. Arteries appear in blue (red arrows)

Sleep deprivation, therefore, interferes at a molecular level with amyloid-ß deposition. In a sleep study of healthy middle-aged men, monitored by polysomnography and cerebrospinal fluid determinations of amyloid ß-42, the 6% decrease that was found after one night of unrestricted sleep was not seen in those with sleep deprivation. The brain area most active in the awake state, the default mode network, is also the site of amyloid-ß accumulation.[27] The implications are that chronic sleep disturbance increases brain levels of amyloid-ß42 and the risk of Alzheimer's disease.[28]

Furthermore, in a community study (147 adults) using the Pittsburgh Sleep Quality Index and MRI scan based atrophy evaluation showed that poor sleep quality was correlated with reduced brain volume. In particular, this affected the right superior frontal cortex in the cross-sectional analyses. In the longitudinal analyses, it correlated with atrophy in frontal, temporal, and parietal region. The study was controlled for engagement in physical exercise as well as blood pressure and body mass index.[29]

Cardiovascular (Hypertension)

In a small controlled trial of people with early hypertension that slept for less than seven hours per night, extending their sleep by only one hour (six-week study period) altered the blood pressure from stage 1 hypertension 142/82 to the normal 128/74. Those who did not extend their sleep time (control group) registered no beneficial blood pressure decrease.[30]

Metabolic Derangement and Obesity

Many epidemiological studies have suggested that sleep duration is tied to energy intake and shorter sleep is tied to an elevated body mass index. The possible mechanisms include an increase in food intake perhaps due to appetite regulation changes relayed by leptin and ghrelin or an overall decreased energy expenditure, such as less exercise. Lower leptin levels and higher ghrelin levels have been documented with shorter sleep times. For example, data from the Cleveland Family Study showed that each hour of sleep reduction led to an approximately 6% increase in leptin levels. Overall reduced sleep as well as reduction in REM sleep were correlated with inflammatory adipokine elevations, including leptin and visfatin and insulin resistance.[31–35]

Immune System and Genes

Curtailing sleep time elevates inflammatory factors interleukin-6 and C-reactive protein (CRP), which cause low-grade inflammation associated with vascular disease, diabetes.[36]

Sleep affects gene activity (the transcriptome), and in one study, one week of insufficient sleep altered the activity of 711 genes, including those with stress responses, immune system, and cellular metabolism. However, the restricted sleep also affected several genes involved in overall gene regulation.[37] Genetic variation in clock genes also influences susceptibility to dementia, and activity of the clock gene PER1 has been linked with those who are early risers or night owls [38]. In addition, genetic influences have been documented on the variation found in people in response to sleep deprivation.[39]

Evolutionary Insights into the Complex Nature of Sleep Regulation, Sleep Cycles, and Implications for Sleep Hygiene

Animals use states of dormancy to cope with specific environmental challenges. A most obvious case is hibernation during time of extreme cold. Aside from a seasonal time of dormancy, more frequent states include torpor (temperature may drop 4–5 degrees C) and daily sleep (a 30% energy reduction occurs in nonrapid eye movement (NREM) sleep compared to quiet waking state). Among mammals there may be a marked variation in activity from hibernation to prolonged sleeplessness, and marine animals appear less influenced by the circadian rhythms and more by marine tidal effects. Walrus have been noted to be active for days without sleep as are orcas in the postpartum period. Cetaceans are able to engage one hemisphere in sleep as noted by unilateral slow wave activity while they continue swimming with appropriate motor activity. One species of seal adjust their sleep to the terrestrial environment and when in the water also display the asymmetric hemispheric sleep pattern associated with activity of one flipper and one being inactive.[40]

The Two Sleep Stages, NREM and REM, Developed in Early Mammals in Conjunction with Warmbloodedness and Was Used to Improve Their Memory

Sleep evolution is thought to have been driven by the need of animals to adapt and learn, especially with the development of vision as the main sense organ and the consequent need for sensorimotor responses, either predation or evasion. A memory store to guide such activity is an obvious advantage. REM and NREM sleep appear to have been adaptations that evolved in the immediate ancestors to mammals during the Triassic period (240–200 mya) in conjunction with the development of euthermia or warm-bloodedness. NREM sleep is likely to have arisen about 180 mya in monotremes (egg-laying mammals) with the early evolution of warm-bloodedness. REM sleep is thought to have evolved about 130 mya and is likely to have developed from the twilight sleep during which there was presumably no or little need for motor activity for thermoregulation. The evolution of REM sleep in birds and mammals diverged relatively early, associated with homeothermia in both groups. The REM capability allowed enhanced cognitive skills, problem solving and communication. Furthermore, if they incur REM sleep deprivation, this leads to impaired temperature regulation.[41] The lack of muscle contraction at this time may eventually have translated into the atonia that is part of REM sleep and enabled the fast brain wave activity typical of the waking brain, important in forming memory of motor and sensory inputs without motor activity disrupting sleep. The stimulation of their neuronal circuitry by these sleep stages, fast wave activity during REM (coordinated activity by fast waves) and slow wave activity during NREM (uncoordinated activity by slow waves), was exapted presumably to bind information in a temporal sense in their circuits and so maintain long-term memories. Marine mammals have excellent memories, which is achieved by their NREM sleep as they have little REM sleep and birds have even less. Birds may, in some instances, similar to marine mammals, be able to engage in NREM unihemispherically.[42]

Our Primate Ancestors Evolved in a Temperature Maximum Epoch and Became the Best Adapted Mammals in a Tropical World

The oldest fossil primate skeleton recovered to date is that of the ancestral primate *Archicebus achilles*, which evolved in Eastern Asia near the present-day Yangzte River in China, about 55 mya. The elevated temperatures of the Paleocene-Eocene thermal maximum about 55.8 mya (PETM) provided mammals and early primates high-density foods such as fruits and insects.[43, 44]

Although occurring much later in our evolutionary history, a review of extant primate sleeping arrangements that can be observed today can be insightful. Monkeys, for example, sleep high up in trees to avoid predators and do not in any way modify their sleeping sites. Gelada baboons that inhabit the savanna sleep on the side of a cliff face to avoid carnivore predation. The sleep architecture of monkeys is characteristic of predominant early stage and light sleep. The primates (orangutans, chimpanzees bonobos), on the other hand, typically build nests in trees, which decreases likelihood of falls that range from five to twenty meters above the ground and which allows a horizontal sleep position. However, chimpanzees show a preference for ground sleep when this is feasible such as under conditions devoid of predators.[45] Gorillas, presumably because of their large size, are less at risk to predators and are ground sleepers[46] (figure 4.7).

What kind of sleep arrangements the australopithecines had in the period of 4.5–2.0 mya is debatable as they peregrinated from the arboreal to the terrestrial lifestyle. However, with the advent of *Homo erectus* about 1.8 mya, a formal tree-to-ground transition for sleeping arrangements is regarded as a major achievement in human evolution. This occurred at the same time with the use of fire and tool production, all of which were mutually protective. The evidence from Swartkrans in South Africa supports the use of fire at about 1.4 mya, which also led to a nutritional improvement with a higher-quality diet possible in addition to the protection afforded by fire.[47]

Fig. 4.7. The tree-to-ground transition improved sleep in early hominins, aided by the discovery of fire.
Baboons slept on the side of cliffs, monkeys on tree branches and chimpanzees were at risk of falling out of their elevated nests.
Art work by Todd Soper, concept and design by author

The tree-to-ground transition had pivotal cognitive sequelae, most notably enhancement of episodic memory. One of the most important functions of sleep is the processing of memory, in particular the consolidation of memory. The other processes involved in memory, namely encoding and retrieval, occur during wakefulness. Consolidation involves transformation of newly formed memories that are still in the labile phase into the existing memory network.[48] Importantly too, REM and dreaming are regarded as a neural platform for creativity and innovation.[49]

Table 4.3. Slow wave and REM sleep electrical activity and neurotransmitters (adapted from Diekelmann)[48]

Slow-Wave Sleep	REM Sleep
Early sleep	Late sleep
Spindle, sharp wave riplet	PGO waves, theta activity
Acetycholine decreased	Acetylcholine increased
NA and 5HT unchanged	NA and 5HT decreased
Cortisol decreased	Cortisol increased

Legend

Pontogeniculate occipital waves
NA – noradrenaline
5HT – 5 hydroxytryptamine (serotonin)

Procedural Memory Enhancement

Studies in rats revealed that REM sleep strengthened as well as consolidated visuospatial memories, which are regarded as equivalent to procedural memory.[50] Both REM sleep and stage N1 (previously stage 2) sleep are associated with procedural memory improvement, but the degree of complexity (visual discrimination) may be relegated to different sleep stages, with REM and motor skill procedural memory probably a function of stage N1 sleep. From an evolutionary point of view, the different sleep stages may have become associated with strengthening different memory subtypes.[51]

The Origin of the Sleep Cycles May Be a Compromise Between Obtaining Good-Quality Sleep and Predator Risk

The ninety-minute cycling of stages, N1-N3 and REM sleep—usually six cycles—occur in a typical night and is regarded as a trade-off between obtaining good-quality sleep and diminishing predator risk. Stage N1 sleep is the lightest sleep and comprises about 50% of sleep time and represents a periodic lightening of sleep to facilitate possible predator perception.[52] This is buttressed by studies of dream analysis in two groups, children and hunter-gatherer groups. Revonsuo formulated his threat simulation theory on information gleaned from dream reports of modern children in which animal characters (lions, tigers, bears, snakes, gorillas) that they have not typically encountered comprise of a large part of their dreams (20–45%). Present-day hunter-gatherers (Mehinaku Indians of Brazil) dream analysis indicated that frequent confrontations with animals increase components of anxiety and aggression in their dreams (60%). These findings are interpreted as one of the functions of dreaming being to serve as a simulation of threatening experiences dating to the ancestral environment or as virtual rehearsal mechanism. This translates into REM and dreaming, enabling novel connections to be made between concepts and ideas and ultimately to creativity and innovation.[53-55]

Functions of Sleep: Neuro-Protection, Memory, Metabolic Regulation, Emotion Cognition, Creativity

Table 4.4. The biological and neurological merits of sleep

Whole Organism
Predator avoidance, recuperate energy, facilitates healing processes

Brain Neuroprotection
Nitric oxide is released in response reactive oxygen species during sleep.[56]

Cognition
Consolidation of episodic, semantic, and procedural memory
Dreaming, mood elevation, and creativity.[57-59]

Metabolic
Glucose metabolism regulation, restoration of glycogen stores[60]
Sleep loss leads to increased risk of obesity and metabolic syndrome[61]

Immune Function
Interleukin 1 (IL-1) and tumor necrosis factor (TNF), both released by neuronal activity, enhance NREM sleep[62]

Endocrine
Growth hormone release[63]

Molecular
Slow wave sleep prunes synaptic connections formed during waking with the elimination of those synapses that are "weakly potentiated"[64]
Sleep facilitates protein folding in the endoplasmic reticulum[65]

Molecular Mechanisms of Sleep Functions:
The Synaptic Homeostasis Hypothesis

About two-thirds of daily energy consumptions is attributed to synaptic activity. While experiences by the organism or person are stored in synaptic activity and weighting of synapses, the information somehow needs to be incorporated and integrated with the existing circuitry. This is the function of sleep whereby the individual is uncoupled from the environment and the synaptic plasticity is assimilated. The slow wave activity during NREM sleep is a manifestation of large groups of neurons firing together, which is involved in synaptic pruning. Weak synapses determined by AMPA receptor activity are eliminated.[66–68]

The microglia are the cells in the brain responsible for the pruning, termed microglial topiary (figure 4.8).[69, 70]

Fig. 4.8. Microglia and topiary. Pruning of synapses (green and red arrows) during sleep by microglia (yellow)

Figure credit: Tremblay ME, Lowery RL, Majewska AK. Microglial interactions with synapses are modulated by visual experience. PLoS Biology 2010; 8:e1000527 and Tremblay ME, Stevens B, Sierra A, Wake H, Bessis A, Nimmerjahn A. The role of microglia in the healthy brain. Journal of Neuroscience 2011; 45:16064–16069.

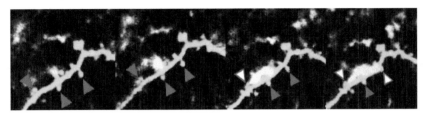

Sleep has restorative functions that involve the removal of neurotoxic compounds that accumulate with cerebral activity during the waking state. Experiments in mice (real-time tetra-methylammonium diffusion and two-photon imaging) revealed a 60% increase in the interstitial space during natural sleep that facilitated exchange of interstitial fluid and cerebrospinal fluid. This has the effect of flushing out metabolic waste, termed glymphatics.[71, 72]

The Dreaming Brain: Insights from Recent Neurobiological Advances

Electrical activity studies have revealed that during NREM sleep, the slow wave (theta, delta waves) begin in the frontal lobes and propagate posteriorly, whereas in REM sleep, gamma waves (30–80 and 80–150 Hz) are present, which are also associated with waking functions, concerned with attention and working memory. The gamma waves across different brain regions are thought to be the mechanism whereby the brain links different sensory domains during REM sleep.[73, 74] Dreaming during NREM occurs, but with less likelihood of recall. During REM sleep, activation of areas different to the wake state occurs, such as activation of the amygdala and medial prefrontal areas (fear circuitry, hence anxious dreams).[75] The atonia during REM prevents skeletal muscle activity—that is, preventing the acting out of dreams. Hobson's activation synthesis hypothesis (ASH) helps explain the visual hallucinations during dreams arising from pontine signals to the occpital cortex (PGO waves).[76]

We spend approximately one-third of our lives sleeping, and of the sleep time, almost one-third is spent dreaming. The dream functions known so far include consolidation of new learning with the more REM possible the better the recall. Many accounts by artists, engineers, scientists have noted their creative solutions to become apparent to them after a specific dream. An oft-cited example is that of Kekule's snake biting its tail and the chemical ring structure of the benzene.[77] In a kind of hybrid sleep state, called lucid dreaming, sleep has properties of both the waking state as well as being involved in a dreaming state. This has been studied by quantitative EEG, which demonstrated a 40 Hz activity in the frontal regions of the brain. The frontal areas are normally active during waking and deactivated in REM sleep. Athletes, for example, target lucid dreaming to achieve complex motor acts more quickly (figure 4.9).[76, 78, 79]

Fig. 4.9. Quantitative EEG and lucid dreaming
Frontal areas are very active during waking but deactivated during REM. In lucid dreaming a 40 Hz power increase may be observed in frontal areas (power scale blue to red, 0.5%–1.5%). Additionally, coactivation is necessary to activate the frontal regions enabling recognition of the real state without waking and aborting the dream. Reproduced with permission from Voss U, Holzmann R, Tuin I, Hobson JA. Lucid dreaming: a state of conscious with features of both waking and non-lucid dreaming. Sleep 2009; 32:1191–1200.

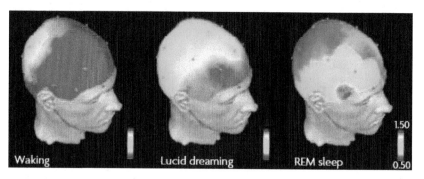

Hobson's AIM Model

Allan Hobson, a leading researcher in dream neuroscience, has advanced his four-dimensional AIM model, which helps elucidate the different brain states during sleep, waking, dreaming, and lucid dreaming. This occurs as a result of the cholinergic (mediates REM) and aminergic (no REM) neurons and the ponto-geniculate (PGO) spikes. The fourth dimension is time. In summary the components of the AIM are as follows:

(A) Activation—extensive brain regions that are active during waking are also active during REM sleep but not slow wave (NREM) sleep.

(I) Internal activation and inhibition of motor activity and sensory input is mediated by the brainstem.

(M) Modulation of neural circuitry and neurons by neurotransmitters. Specifically during REM there is cholinergic activity and suppression of aminergic activity (except for dopamine).

The absence of three wake-state neuromodulators with dopamine remaining active may explain the visual hallucinations, lack of self-awareness, and dream bizarreness that is reported by individuals. This is akin to its role in psychotic illness and may explain some of the cognitive characteristics of dreaming such as the visual hallucinations, the bizarreness, the lack of self-reflective awareness, and the amnesia. Hobson's 3-D State Space AIM showing normal transitions with the AIM state space from waking to NREM and REM is depicted in figure 4.10.[76]

Fig. 4.10. 3-D state space AIM model.
Normal transitions depicted by the AIM state space from
waking to NREM and REM where activation is on the x-axis,
modulation on the y-axis and input, output gating represented
by the z-axis (a). Disease states such as minimally conscious state
and the hybrid condition referred to as lucid dreaming (b).
With permission from: Hobson JA. REM sleep and
dreaming: toward a theory of protoconsciousness.
Nature Neuroscience Reviews 2009; 10:803–813

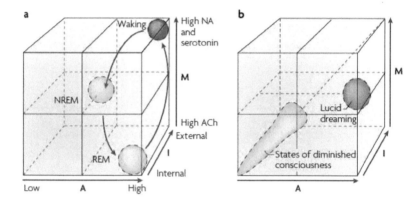

Table 4.5 The benefits of dreaming: Effects on memory, mood, and creativity[80–83]

1. Dreaming facilitates the different memory networks.
2. Emotional health—Dreaming modulates waking emotional states including mood and depression.
3. Creativity and solutions due to activation of disparate brain regions. This widespread kind of activation does not occur during the waking state. Brain areas restricted to logical and familiar processes are less active in REM sleep.

Excesses and Abnormal Dreaming

Brain lesions such as strokes, infections, or tumors may specifically impact the neural circuitry or neurotransmitter systems that mediate dreaming. The described syndromes to date include the following:[84–86]

Charcot's Variant
Isolated loss of specific aspects of dreams such as color, faces, movement

> Etiology–dementia, carbon monoxide poisoning, stroke, cerebral trauma
> Brain regions affected – bilateral occipitotemporal lesions

Willbrand's Variant (Global Anoneria) Global loss or suppression of dreaming

> Etiology—hydrocephalus, stroke, and cerebral trauma Brain regions affected—bilateral occipitotemporal lesions

Anoneirognosis (Dream/Reality Confusion)

> Etiology—Parkinson's disease, dopamine reduction, dopamine blocking drugs
> Brain regions affected—lesions in the anterior diencephalon or basal forebrain

Posttraumatic Stress Disorder (PTSD) Recurring flashbacks, hyperarousal, nightmares

> Cause—traumatic experiences
> Atrophy of the prefrontal cortex, amygdala, hippocampus
> Responsive to Prazosin—antinoradrenergic agent

Physics Insights into the Neuroscience of Sleep: Criticality and Sleep

Criticality refers to a physics principle observed in the natural world that include very large numbers of interacting components. Some examples include flocks of migrating birds, grains and collapsing sand piles, heating water (suddenly transforming from liquid to vapor for example), and clinical seizures. These can suddenly reach what is termed a critical point resulting in a so-called avalanche of activity. The brain and its networks are thought to operate near a critical point in order to enhance information processing. This may confer a kind of flexibility to cope and manage unpredictably that is so often encountered in the environment and allow biological systems to readjust and refashion themselves more rapidly. This may underlie evolutionary processes itself.[87]

Functional MRI and EEG are modalities that are able to interrogate the brain circuits that are organized in spatio-temporal domains that underlie anatomical and functional connectivity among various brain regions.[88] These large interconnected neuronal systems are considered to operate near a critical transition and are termed resting state networks or systems of collective activity. These underlie cognition in the brain. For optimal expression of inherent ability, complex systems are hypothesized to be operating near a critical point, poised at a knife edge between stability and volatility, or order and disorder.[89] Pearlmutter and Houghton have advanced their "tuning for criticality" role of sleep and dreaming function whereby they contend that, among other functions of sleep, one is a protective capacity against "super-critical behavior," which may be potentially disruptive to brain functioning. The synaptic plasticity and pruning that takes place during sleep and dreaming are thought to optimize the brain's future responses to similar waking stimuli.[90, 91]

Recommendations for Improved Sleep and Sleep Hygiene[92, 93]

1. Adhere to night-time sleep hygiene methods such as maintaining low ambient temperatures and noise.
2. LED light use should be curtailed prior to retirement.
3. Avoid substances/stimulants such as caffeine, sodas, prior to retiring (exogenous).
4. Avoid activities that impair sleep such as high-level cognitive activity (endogenous).
5. Limit substances that interfere with sleep architecture (alcohol).
6. Become physically fit to avoid sleep apnea.
7. Become cognitively fit to enhance cognitive reserve.
8. Respect the twenty-four-hour solar light cycle with set, regular hours for retiring and waking.
9. Abide by your chronotype and juxtapose as far as possible with work schedules.

10. Augmenting the twenty-four-hour sleep-wake cycle with brief daytime sleep (power naps) improves cognitive performance and reduce mortality.
11. Monitor sleep with simple, unobtrusive, actigraphic devices to gain insights into personal sleep characteristics such as duration and changes in response to activities.

References

1. Nesse R, Dawkins. Evolution: Medicine's most basic science. In: Warrell DA, Cox TM, Firth JD, Benz EJJ (Eds). Oxford Textbook of Medicine, Fifth edition, Oxford University Press, Oxford 2010.

2. Lima S, Rattenborg N, Lesku J, Amlaner C. Sleeping under the risk of predation. *Animal Behavior* 2005; 70:723–736.

3. Luckhaupt SE, Tak S, Calvert GM. The prevalence of short sleep duration by industry and occupation in the National Health Interview Survey. *Sleep* 2010; 33:149–159.

4. Colten, HR, Altevogt, BM (eds). Sleep Disorders and Sleep Deprivation: An Unmet Public Health Problem, National Academies Press, Washington DC, 2006.

5. Costa G. Shift work and breast cancer. *G Ital Med Lav Ergon* 2010; 32:454–7.

6. Matricciani L, Olds T, Petkov J et al. *Sleep Med Rev* 2012; 16:203–211.

7. Hjorth MF, Quist JS, Andersen R et al. Change in sleep duration and proposed dietary risk factors for obesity in Danish school children. *Pediatr Obes.* 2014 Sep 24. doi: 10.1111/ijpo.264.

8. Roenneberg T. Chronobiology: the human sleep project. *Nature* 2013; 498(7455):427–8.

9. Hattar S, Liao HW, Takao M, Berson DM, Yau KW. Melanopsin-Containing Retinal Ganglion Cells: Architecture, Projections, and Intrinsic Photosensitivity. *Science* 2002:295:1065–1070. DOI: 10.1126/science. 1069609.

10. Tang GY, Ip AK, Siu AW. Pinoline and N-acetylserotonin reduce glutamate-induced lipid peroxidation in retinal homogenates. *Neurosci Lett.* 2007; 412:191–4.

11. Masri S, Sassone-Corsi P. The circadian clock: a framework linking metabolism, epigenetics and neuronal function. *Nature Neuroscience Reviews* 2013; 14:69–75.

12. LeGates TA, Fernandez DC, Hattar S. Light as a central modulator of circadian rhythms, sleep and affect. *Nature Neuroscience Reviews* 2014; 14:443–545.

13. Von Economo, C. Sleep as a problem of localization. *J Nerv Ment Dis* 1930; 71:249–259.

14. Desseilles M, Dang-Vu T, Schabus M et al. Neuroimaging insights into the pathophysiology of sleep disorders. *Sleep* 2008; 31:777–794.

15. Siegel JM. Sleep mechanisms and phylogeny. In; Kryger MH, Roth T, Dement WC (eds). Principles and Practice of Sleep Medicine, Fifth edition. Elsevier Saunders, St Louis, Missouri, 2011.

16. McCarley RW. Neurobiology of REM and NREM sleep. *Sleep Med* 2007; 8:302–330.

17. Krueger JM, Rector DM, Churchill L. Sleep and cytokines. *Sleep Med Clin* 2007; 2:161–169.

18. Eiland MM, Ramanathan LGS, Gilliland M et al. Increases in amino cupric silver staining in the supraoptic nucleus after sleep deprivation. *Sleep Res* 2002; 945:1–8.

19. Pace-Schott EF, Hobson AJ. The Neurobiology of Sleep and Dreaming. In: Squire LR, Berg D, Bloom FE, duLac S, Ghosh A, Spitzer NC (eds). Fundamental Neuroscience. Fourth edition. Academic Press, New York 2013.

20. Ayas NT, Hirsch AA Laher I et al. New frontiers in obstructive sleep apnea. *Clin Sci (London)* 2014; 127; 209–216.

21. Perlis ML, Smith MT, Andrews PJ, Orff H, Giles DE. Beta/Gamma EEG activity in patients with primary and secondary insomnia and good sleeper controls. *Sleep* 2001; 24:110–117.

22. Spiegelhalder K, Regen W, Feige B, Holz J, Piosczyk H, Baglioni C, Riemann D, Nissen C. Increased EEG sigma and beta power during NREM sleep in primary insomnia. *Biol Psychol* 2012; 91:329–33. doi: 10.1016/j. biopsycho.2012.08.009.

23. Van Dongen HPA, Maislin G, Mullington JM, Dinges DF. The cumulative cost of additional wakefulness: dose-response effects on neurobehavioral functions and sleep physiology from chronic sleep restriction and total sleep deprivation. *Sleep* 2003; 26:117–126.

24. Sterniczuk R, Theou O, Rusak B, Rockwood K. Sleep disturbance is associated with incident dementia and mortality. *Curr Alzheimer Res.* 2013; 10(7):767–75.

25. Yaffe K, Laffan AM, Harrison SL, et al. Sleep-disordered breathing, hypoxia, and risk of mild cognitive impairment and dementia in older women. *JAMA* 2011; 306:613–619.

26. Xie L, Kang H, Xu Q et al. Sleep drives metabolic clearance from the adult brain. *Science* 2013; 342:373–377

27. Jagust WJ, Mormıno EC. Lifespan brain activity, ßamyloid and Alzheimer's disease. *Trends Cogn Sci* 2011; 15:520–526

28. Ooms S, Overeem S, Besse K, Olde Rikkert M, Verbeek M, Classen JAHR. Effect of 1 night of total sleep deprivation on cerebrospinal fluid ß-amyloid 42 in healthy middle aged men. A randomized clinical trial. *JAMA Neurology* 2014; 71:971–977.

29. Sexton CE, Storsve AB, Walhovd, KB et al. Poor sleep quality is associated with increased cortical atrophy in community-dwelling adults. *Neurology* 2014; 83:967–973.

30. Haack ME, Serrador J, Cohen D, Simpson N, MeierEwert H, Mullington JM. J *Sleep Res.* 2012; 22:295–304. doi: 10.1111/jsr.12011.

31. Bayon V, Leger D, Gomez-Merino D, Vecchierini MF, Chennaoui M. Sleep debt and obesity. *Ann Med.* 2014; 46(5): 264–72.

32. Broussard JL, Ehrmann DA, Van Cauter E, Tasali E, Brady MJ. Impaired insulin signaling in human adipocytes after experimental sleep restriction: a randomized, crossover study. *Ann Intern Med.* 2012; 157(8):549–57.

33. Gildner TE, Liebert MA, Kowal P, Chatterji S, Josh Snodgrass J. Sleep duration, sleep quality, and obesity risk among older adults from six middle-income countries: Findings from the study on global ageing and adult health (SAGE). *Am J Hum Biol.* 2014. doi: 10.1002/ajhb.22603.

34. Hayes AL, Xu F, Babineau D, Patel SR. Sleep duration and circulating adipokine levels. *Sleep* 2011; 34:147–52.

35. St-Onge MP. The Role of Sleep Duration in the Regulation of Energy balance: Effects on Energy intakes and Expenditure. *Journal of Clinical Sleep Medicine* 2013; 9(1):73–80. doi. org/10.5664/jcsm.2348.

36. Haack M, Sanchez E, Mullington JM. Elevated inflammatory markers in response to prolonged sleep restriction are associated with increased pain experience in healthy volunteers *Sleep* 2007; 30:1145–1152.

37. Archer SN, Laing EE, Möller-Levet CS. Mistimed sleep disrupts circadian regulation of the human transcriptome.*Proc.*

Natl Acad. Sci. USA 2014; 111:E 682–91. doi: 10.1073/pnas.1316335111.

38. Lim AS, Chang AM, Shulman JMA common polymorphism near PER1 and the timing of human behavioral rhythms. *Ann Neurol.* 2012; 72:324–334.

39. Goel N, Banks S, Mignot E, Dinges DF. DQB1*0602 predicts inter-individual differences in physiologic sleep, sleepiness, and fatigue. *Neurology* 2010; 75:1509–1519

40. Siegel JM. Sleep viewed as a state of adaptive inactivity. *Nature Reviews Neuroscience* 2009; 10:747–753.

41. Allison T, Twyver H. The evolution of sleep. *Natural History 1970*; 79:56–65.

42. Kavanu JL. REM and NREM sleep as natural accompaniments of the evolution of warm bloodedness. *Neuroscience and Biobehavioral Reviews* 2002; 26:889–906

43. Marshall M. Archicebus Achilles and into Africa New Scientist June 2013.

44. Ni X, Gebo DL, Dagosto M et al. The oldest known primate skeleton and early haplorhine evolution. *Nature* 2013; 498(7452):60-4DOI:10.1038/nature12200.

45. Stewart FA, Pruetz JD. Do chimpanzee nests serve an anti predatory function? *A J Primatol* 2013; 75:593–604

46. Anderson, J 1998. Sleep, sleeping sites, and sleep related activities: Awakening to their significance. *American Journal of Primatology* 46:63–75.

47. Wrangham, RW, Jones, JH, Laden, G, Pilbeam, D, Conklin-Brittain, NL 1999. The raw and the stolen: Cooking and the ecology of human origins. *Current Anthropology* 40:567–594.

48. Diekelmann S, Born J. The memory function of sleep. *Nature Neuroscience Reviews* 2010; 11:114–126.

49. Wynn T, Coolidge FL. The Implications of the Working Memory Model for the Evolution of Modern Cognition Int J Evol Biol. 2011:741357. 10.4061/2011/741357.

50. Winson, J. The meaning of dreams. *Scientific American* 1990; 263:89–96.

51. Walker MP, Strickgold R. Sleep dependent learning and memory consolidation. *Neuron* 2004; 44:121–133.

52. Lima S, Rattenborg N, Lesku J, Amlaner C. Sleeping under the risk of predation. *Animal Behavior* 2005; 70:723–736.

53. Revonsuo A. The reinterpretation of dreams: An evolutionary hypothesis of the function of dreaming. *Behavioral and Brain Sciences* 2000; 23:877–901.

54. Franklin MS, Zyphur MJ. The role of dreams in the evolution of the human mind. *Evolutionary Psychology* 2005; 3:59–78.

55. Coolidge FL, Wynn T. The effects of tree to ground sleep transition in the evolution of cognition in early Homo. *Before Farming* 2006(4).DOI: 10.3828/bfarm.2006.4.11.

56. Calabrese V, Mancuso C, Calvani M et al. Nitric oxide in the central nervous system: neuroprotection versus neurotoxicity. *Nat Rev Neurosci* 2007; 19:766–775.

57. Drago V, Foster PS, Heilman KM, Arico D, Montagna P, Ferri R. Cyclic alternating pattern in sleep and its relationship to creativity. *Sleep Med* 2011; 12:361–366.

58. Walker MP. The role of sleep in cognition and emotion. *Ann NY Acad Sci* 2009; 1156:168–197.

59. King D, DeCicco T. The relationship between dream content and physical health, mood and self control. *Dreaming* 2007; 17:127–239.

60. Benington JH, Heller HC. Implications of sleep deprivation experiments for our understanding of sleep homeostasis. *Sleep* 1999; 22:1033–1043.

61. Benington JH, Heller HC. Restoration of brain energy metabolism as the function of sleep. *Prog Neurobiol* 1995; 45:347–360.

62. Krueger JM, Rector DM, Churchill L. Sleep and Cytokines. *Sleep Medicine Clinics* 2007; 2:161–169.

63. Kim E, Grover LM, Bertolotti D, Green TL. Growth hormone rescues hippocampal synaptic function after sleep deprivation. *Am J Physiol Regul Integr Comp Physiol.* 2010; 298:R1588-96. doi: 10.1152/ajpregu.00580.2009.

64. Tononi G, Cirelli C. Sleep function and synaptic homeostasis. *Sleep Medicine Reviews* 2006; 10:49–62.

65. Naidoo N. Cellular stress/the unfolded protein response: Relevance to sleep and sleep disorders. *Sleep Medicine Reviews* 2009; 13:195–204.

66. Bushey D, Tonoi G, Cirelli G. Sleep and Synaptic Homeostasis: Structural evidence in Drosophila. *Science* 2011; 332:1576–1581.

67. Nere A, Hashimi A, Cirelli C, Tononi G. Sleep dependent synaptic down selection: Modeling the benefits of sleep on memory consolidation and integration. *Front Neurol* 2013; 4:143.

68. Tononi G, Cirelli C. Perchance to Prune. *Scientific American* August 2013; 34–39.

69. Tremblay ME, Stevens B, Sierra A, Wake H, Bessis A, Nimmerjahn A. The role of microglia in the health brain. *Journal of Neuroscience* 2011; 45:16064–16069.

70. Costandi M. *New Scientist* Oct 12, 2013:44–47.

71. Xie L et al. Sleep Drives Metabolite Clearance from the Adult Brain. *Science* 2013; 342:373–377.

72. Underwood E. Sleep: The Brain's Housekeeper? *Science* 2013; 342:301.

73. Kahn D, Pace Schott EF, Hobson JA. Consciousness in waking and dreaming: the roles of neuronal oscillation and neuromodulation in determining similarities and differences. *Neuroscience* 1997; 78(1):13–38

74. Corsi-Cabrera M, Guevara MA, del Río-Portilla Y. Brain activity and temporal coupling related to eye movements during REM sleep: EEG and MEG results. *Brain Res* 2008; 1235:82–91.

75. Nielsen T, Levin R. Nightmares: a new neurocognitive model. *Sleep Med Rev* 2007; 11:295–310.

76. Hobson JA. REM sleep and dreaming: toward a theory of protoconsciousness. *Nature Neuroscience Reviews* 2009; 10:803–813

77. Benfey OT. August Kekulé and the birth of the structural theory of organic chemistry in 1858. *Journal of Chemical Education* 1958; 35:21–23.

78. Voss U, Holzmann R, Tuin I, Hobson JA. Lucid dreaming: a state of consciousness with features of both waking and non-lucid dreaming. *Sleep* 2009; 32:1191–1200.

79. Cai DJ, Mednick EM, Harrison EM, Kanady JC, Mednick SC. REM, not incubation, improves creativity by priming associative networks. *Proceedings of the National Academy of Science USA (PNAS)* 2009; 106:10130–10134.

80. Cartwright R. Dreaming as a mood regulation system. In: Kryger MH, Roth T, Dement WC (Eds). Principles and Practice of Sleep Medicine, Fifth Edition. Elsevier Saunders 2011, New York.

81. King D, DeCicco T. The relationship between dream content and physical health, mood and self-control. *Dreaming* 2007; 17:127–239.

82. Kramer M. Nightmares in Vietnam Veterans. *J Am Acad Pyschoanalysis* 1987; 15:67–81.

83. Pace-Schott EF, Hobson AJ. The Neurobiology of Sleep and Dreaming. In: Squire LR, Berg D, Bloom FE, duLac S, Ghosh A, Spitzer NC (eds). Fundamental Neuroscience Fourth edition. Academic Press, New York 2013.

84. Bischof M, Bassetti CL. Total dream loss: a distinct neuropsychological dysfunction after bilateral PCA stroke. *Ann Neurol.* 2004; 56:583–6.

85. Kramer M. Nightmares in Vietnam Veterans. *J Am Acad Pyschoanalysis* 1987; 15:67–81.

86. Raskind MA, Peskind ER, Kanter ED et al. Reduction of nightmares and other PTSD symptoms in combat veterans by prazosin: a placebo-controlled study. *Am J Psychiatry* 2003; 160:371–373.

87. Beggs JM, Timme N. Being Critical of criticality in the brain. *Frontiers in Physiology* 2012; 3:(article 163)1-12. doi 10.3389/fphys.2012.00163.

88. Tagliazucchi E, Balenzuela P, Fraiman D, Chialvo DR. Criticality in large scale brain fMRI dynamics unveiled by a novel point process analysis. *Frontiers in Physiology* 2012; 3(article 15)1–11.

89. Bak P, Tang C, Wiesenfeld K. Self-organized criticality: an explanation of the 1/f noise. *Phys Rev Lett.* 1987; 59:381–384.

90. Pearlmutter BA, Houghton CJ. A new hypothesis for sleep: tuning for criticality. *Neural Comput.* 2009 Jun; 21(6):1622–41. doi: 10.1162/neco.2009.05-08-787.

91. Pearlmutter BA, Houghton CJ. Dreams, mnemonics and tuning for criticality. *Behavioral and Brain Sciences* 2013; 36:625–626.

92. Lhal O, Wispel C, Willigens B, Pietrowsky R. An ultra short episode of sleep is sufficient to promote declarative memory performance. *Sleep Res* 2008; 17:3–10.

93. Naska A et al. Siesta in healthy adults and coronary mortality in the general population. *Arch Intern Med* 2007; 167296–301.

Social Intelligence, Sociality, and Brain Health

Evolutionary Insights

Although sociality among primates is regarded as an important driving force in the evolution of a large and complex brain, it is not limited to apes. Elephants, dolphins, and parrots all pass the so-called mirror test. This test is used as a surrogate for the recognition of the self, implying that the animal then has a concept of self, which is a prerequisite for theory of mind (TOM) or being able to conceive what others in a group may be up to. Humans have particularly visible sclera (whites of the eyes), which are not pigmented, in comparison to primates. Compared to orangutans, the visible area of sclera of humans is two to three times larger and particularly elongated in the horizontal dimension, which accentuates and enhances gaze signals.[1] The human investment in social interaction and cooperation that often demand joint interactions, gaze direction, and following probably played an important role. The ability to communicate, using gaze signals, likely causing evolutionary selection for a gradual loss of scleral pigmentation for the promotion and fostering of social communication has been proposed, termed the cooperative eye hypothesis.[2]

Gaze detection is a particularly important component of social interaction among primates. It is used to determine where another can or cannot see and can enable forming inferences about another's mind (TOM). For example, direct gazing into some primate's eyes is interpreted as a threat, hence the concept of gaze prohibition. Gaze following is a feature among some animals such as apes, goats, and dogs that allows a wider field of vision, a kind group vision. Primate coalitionary conduct is considered to have been a crucial factor during their evolution development, allowing weaker individuals to overcome a dominant male, for example, and allow reconciliation among the group after skirmishes.[3-5]

Social Intelligence, Acting in Concert with Technical and Innovation Correlated with Increasing Brain Size

Several so-called social intelligence hypotheses were suggested to explain the larger brain size of primates. It was postulated that the inherent complexity of the interaction of individuals in a group of fifty to one hundred individuals, which included instances of deception, outwitting another, and forging alliances, was at least one factor in the enlarging primate brain.[6, 7] The frequently referred to Marchiavellian intelligence hypothesis was yet another theory on how deviousness, mind reading, deception, manipulation, and strategizing was an important facet of primate and subsequently human society.[8] In a challenge to these hypotheses, a comparative analysis of instances of innovation, social learning, and of tool episodes reviewed from over one thousand manuscripts from four major primate journals established a positive correlation with these and executive brain volumes. Learning from others, fashioning new tools, and developing new behaviors in the social setting promoted primate brain-size enlargement.[9]

Neurobiological and Neurochemical Insights into Social Behavior

Social behavior is important in many animal species and varies widely, promoting group survival behavior in both invertebrate and vertebrate species, ranging from bees to humans. Differences in behavior depending on social behavior have been described in the round worm *C. elegans* and the marine snail *Aplysia*, for example, and the same applies to mammalian species. The two peptide hormones oxytocin and vasopressin (also known as antidiuretic hormone or arginine vasopressin – AVP) released from the posterior pituitary are key chemical mediators of this process. The responsible cells are located in the hypothalamus in the supraoptic and paraventricular nuclei, and their axons terminate in the posterior pituitary. The direct neural link as opposed to the portal capillary vascular mediated process of the anterior pituitary allows for a quicker mechanism of action and regulation. Of the three known vasopressin receptors (V1, V2, V3), V2 is found in the kidneys, mediating antidiuretic effects and V1a in the smooth muscles, brain, and liver. The V1b are found in the anterior pituitary, which facilitates ACTH secretion. Many and diverse functions are attributed to these hormones.

Table 5.1. Functions of the hormones AVP and Oxytocin[10]

Predominantly AVP Organism
Regulation of salt and water intake
Water intake regulation and appetite for salt
Vasocontriction in response hemorrhage,
especially postpartum hemorrhage
Regulation of the stress response

Vasopressin—affiliative/nonaffiliative
Male behavior—paternal care, scent marking, aggression

Predominantly Oxytocin
Parturition—uterine contraction during delivery
Lactation—mediates gland contraction in
response to suckling stimulus

Oxytocin—Affiliative Facilitates social motivation
Facilitates approach behavior Maternal nurturing
Both
Key role in social behavior Reproduction
Pair bonding

The Seminal Study of the Prairie Voles

Two closely related vole species, the nonmonogamous voles (montane and meadow voles) and the monogamous prairie vole demonstrate different social, pair bonding, and nurturing behaviors. The former tend to be solitary, abandon their young approximately two weeks after birth, and show no social bonding. This is in contradistinction to the prairie pine vole, which demonstrates long-lasting monogamous behavior, with males assisting the females in raising their offspring and demonstrating social attachment. In prairie voles, there are relatively elevated numbers of oxytocin receptors (OTR) in the nucleus accumbens (NA) and a higher density of vasopressin receptors in the ventral pallidal (VP) area. The NA and VP are part of the dopaminergic mesolimbic and opioid reward circuitry of the brain.

Low levels of these receptors are found in the montane and meadow voles. These findings implicate the involvement of the reward pathways of the brain in promoting pair bonding and social bonding.[11, 12] Researchers Lim et al. were able to manipulate these receptors by injection of antagonists into the nucleus accumbens of the voles. Injection of an OTR antagonist into the nucleus accumbens of the female prairie vole blocked pair bonding, and injection of an antagonist in the meadow vole against V1aR (into the ventral pallidum) resulted in partner preference and pair bond formation. The social preference and bond formation are attributed the interaction, therefore, of the V1a receptors and the reward center of the brain, the dopamine receptors in the nucleus accumbens and ventral pallidum. Regarding the male prairie voles, it is arginine vasopressin (AVP) that mediates the behavioral changes. With intraventricular infusion of AVP, the behavioral features of affiliative behavior and partner preference emerged.[13] The implications for humans are clearly that, as mammals, similar mechanisms may be operative.

Distribution of Vasopressin in the LS and VP Prairie and Montane Vole

Fig. 5.1. Vasopressin and the prairie vole

In the nonmonogamous montane vole, vasopressin receptor (V1a) binding is elevated in the lateral septum (LS) and decreased in the ventral pallidum of the basal ganglia (VP) (left figure). In the monogamous prairie vole, the vasopression expression is elevated in the ventral pallidum forming a link between social recognition and reward pathways (right figure)

Figure with permission: Young LJ, Lim MM, Gingrich B. Cellular mechanisms of social attachment. Hormones and Behavior 2001; 40:133–138 and Kandel and Schwartz. Neuroscience 5th Edition. McGraw Hill, New York 2012.

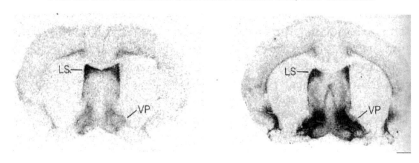

Sociality, Oxytocin, and Nucleus Accumbens (NA)

Social interaction can act as a natural reward mechanism similar to that associated with other basic human drives. In mice, the NA oxytocin receptor inputs impinge from various brain regions, including the serotonergic dorsal raphe nucleus and activation of nucleus accumbens 5HT1 B receptors, which also promotes social interaction. The need for the combined activity of oxytocin and 5HT in the NA for the mediation of the rewarding aspects of social interaction has implications for the social impairment presenting with a wide range of neuropsychiatric conditions, most prominently obsessive-compulsive disorder, autism, and schizophrenia. In this study in mice, the NA associated social reward system involving oxytocin and serotonin are viewed as the precursors for pair bonding, documented in prairie voles.[14]

Primates have an unusual degree of bonding due to the social life, which is uncommon among mammals. Grooming among primates is common and is associated with the triggering of opioid reward mechanisms in their brains. This has major advantages such as in the formation of coalitions. With increasing group size, the logistics of grooming large numbers (> 50) has been calculated to exceed about 20% of total daytime activities. This amount of time allocated to grooming alone (as measured in extant primates) necessitated a new way of communicating, which is one of the theories of language evolution. Dunbar has proposed that laughter may have served as a mechanism of social bonding with increasing group size (estimated to about 100), dating from the time of our Australopithecine past to the subsequent hominins. Supportive arguments include laughter being a shared feature with chimpanzees and humans. Laughter is a social rather solitary occurrence, facilitates social interactions, and as with tactile grooming also initiates, increases endorphin release.[15] Coping with the demands of yet larger group size (>150) was most likely facilitated by the development of first musical protolanguage and then modern language.[16]

Primate social life was also associated with the evolution of mating systems. Sociality occurred only once primates became diurnal. With diurnality and sociality, primates evolved from polygynandry to the two current conditions of harem polygyny and monogamy. Nocturnal primates, however, remained solitary despite evolving to these two mating systems.[17] Pair bonding, among vertebrates and primates, has also been correlated with increasing brain size compared to other forms of mating systems due to increased cognitive demand in maintaining the relationship. From an evolutionary point of view, it appears likely that social living was followed by pair living by about thirty-five million years.[18]

Frontotemporal degeneration is a common type of dementia that is associated with a profound deterioration in empathy and social interaction, often one of the first symptoms. A recent trial of oxytocin administration to such patients in a randomized controlled trial revealed improvements on some measures on a relevant test for such people, the frontal behavioral inventory and neuropsychiatric inventory.[19]

Oxytocin is released from the paraventricular and supraoptic hypothalamic nuclei during physical contact.

Figure 5.2: Baboons grooming with tactile stimulation releasing oxytocin and promoting group cohesion. Baboons have unique and extensive social knowledge, perhaps more so than other primates as they live in groups of up to 100 individuals, much larger than other primate groupsCheney DL, Seyfarth RM. Baboon Metaphysics. University of Chicago Press, 2007, Chicago. Image credit and permission: Artist: Steffen Foerster/Shutterstock.com

Neurobiology of the Social Brain

The social circuitry hubs include a widespread network that involves all the cerebral lobes and subcortical regions:[20–23]

1. The mirror neuron hubs in the inferior frontal gyrus and inferior parietal lobe
2. The medial frontal region and temporo-occipito-parietal theory of mind hubs
3. The temporal lobe superior temporal sulcus
4. The temporal lobe inferior cortex
5. The hippocampal CA2 region
6. The amydala

Fig. 5.3. Schematic social brain circuitry hubs

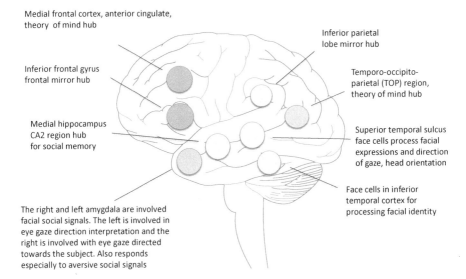

Medial frontal cortex, anterior cingulate, theory of mind hub

Inferior parietal lobe mirror hub

Inferior frontal gyrus frontal mirror hub

Temporo-occipito-parietal (TOP) region, theory of mind hub

Medial hippocampus CA2 region hub for social memory

Superior temporal sulcus face cells process facial expressions and direction of gaze, head orientation

Face cells in inferior temporal cortex for processing facial identity

The right and left amygdala are involved facial social signals. The left is involved in eye gaze direction interpretation and the right is involved with eye gaze directed towards the subject. Also responds especially to aversive social signals

For example, brain areas concerned with gaze monitoring revealed that the direction of gaze activated the left amygdala by functional neuroimaging. When gaze by another was directed towards a person making eye contact, activation was recorded in the right amygdala underscoring the role that the human amygdala has in interpreting facial social signals.[24]

The frugivorous primates were dependent on memory and learning because of the nature of their habitat and food source, which by nature is ephemeral. The temporal challenges associated with the timing of fruit ripening and localizing these in the vast three dimensional arboreal environment, presumably led to the enlargement of brain areas for processing color vision, visual acuity and stereopsis.

These cognitive demands and consequent areas of brain enlargement are thought to have led to the foundations of the circuitry required to process complex social relationships such as changing social interactions, individual behavior, gaze direction and alliances.[25]

Social Memory: A Critical Hub Is the CA2 Region of the Hippocampus

Episodic memory is processed in the entorhinal cortex, dentate gyrus, CA3 and CA1. CA2 appears to be a node for social memory as supported by the findings of a transgenic mouse model. In this model, elective inactivation (genetically) of the pyramidal cell CA2 synaptic connections resulted in impairment of this region and was followed by the inability of the mice to remember their conspecifics (fellow mice) with no change in episodic memory noted. Clinically, decreased numbers of inhibitory neurons in the CA2 in people with bipolar disease and schizophrenia are findings that support the mouse data with possible future treatment implications in neuropsychiatric disease.[26]

Epidemiology: Sociality and Clinical Medicine

Membership in groups makes us healthier and more resilient. A study of one of the largest population based prospective stroke studies (NOMASS), first-ever stroke patients (n = 655), if socially isolated, prior to their stroke, were two times more likely to have a subsequent stroke within five years in comparison to those that had significant personal relationships.[27]

Other Conditions

In addition to the syndrome of stroke, negative health effects of social isolation and lack of social support, have been reported for other medical conditions, including cardiovascular disease, cancer, rheumatoid arthritis and renal disease as well as overall mortality.[28–32] In animal studies involving mice, investigation of oxytocin as a mediator of social neuroprotection after cerebrovascular ischemia demonstrated both anti-inflammatory and antioxidant properties. At the molecular level, decreased levels of proinflammatory cytokines (interleukin 6), decreased neutrophil infiltration, reduced lipopolysaccharide (LPS) and superoxide production by microglial cells, endothelial cells and macrophages were recorded.[33]

From a primary prevention point of view, social interaction was studied in a Swedish longitudinal population based database, albeit together with intellectual stimulation. The relative risk reduction in dementia incidence was an impressive 0.54 (95% CI: 0.34-0.87) for both activities combined.[34]

Supercooperators: Sociality and Present-Day Human Societies

Humans have been described as supercooperators. Nowak has proposed that in addition to the main drivers of evolution, random mutation, and natural selection we have, as a species, the preponderance of what we have achieved is through cooperation with each other. The mechanisms responsible for the high level of cooperativity in our species include five key concepts. Direct and indirect reciprocity refers to helping one another because the favor is likely to be returned. The former is dependent on personal knowledge or acquaintance of the individual whereas indirect reciprocity is dependent on someone's reputation. The third, network reciprocity, stems from the interaction because of residing in close proximity (spatial selection) such as may occur with neighbors. Group selection, the fourth mechanism, is dependent on intergroup competition, and natural selection acts at the group level, due to a particular social organization. The fifth component, kin selection, refers to the preferred or favored cooperation between blood relatives over that with strangers.[35] Looking to the future, he subsequently developed the intergenerational goods game, which studies overexploitation of present-day resources. His findings indicated that if decisions were made by individuals, as opposed to a group voting democratically, overexploitation of the resources occurred.[36]

The importance of operating and cooperating within teams was supported by scientific research, engineering, arts, humanities manuscript publishing, and patents by Wuchty et al. In a review spanning fifty years of 19.9 million manuscripts as well as 2.1 million patents, teams dominated over solo authorship in terms of production as well as high impact research.[37]

From Supercooperators to Superconnections
and the West Side Story

Uzzi and Dunlap have suggested that personal networks have restricted friendship circles or clusters with potential limitation in acquiring new ideas. The ideas should benefit by being exposed to a new cluster of relationships (by an information broker) that may result in improved opportunities. Diversification of contacts is the key concept promoted by them.[38] A similar concept was proposed to explain the success of the West Side Story and the Goldilocks network. Social structures with too many strangers may impede the exchange of new ideas whereas groups characterized by too many personal friends or restricted relationships may also stunt innovation. The right kind of mix or ratio, however, with optimal numbers of clusters interacting with each other may lead to creativity and new concepts. This was the proposed explanation of the success of the West Side Story, one of the most successful musicals.[39]

The overall trend of human evolution has been one of escalating networking. This began with the networking of our own mind first before increasing sensorimotor networks and then, through the working memory faculty, intracortical connectivity. Subsequent extension to the interaction with other minds, or intercortical connectivity, was likely facilitated by the mirror neuron faculty. The brain machine interface extends this connectivity further by enabling direct brain-to-brain communication and foregoing the impediments of our own sensory and motor systems. Brain-to-brain communication refers to the transmission of information between two humans not involving traditional sensory or motor networks. This has been achieved experimentally by the combination of brain-to-computer interfaces with EEG encoding binary 0, 1 information bits, and in a remote subject, computer to brain (transcranial magnetic stimulation) eliciting phosphenes with perception again encoded with 0 and 1 binary bits.[40]

Evolutionary Insights

Our social brain circuitry was designed over several million years for living in relatively small groups of 35 to 50. According to the social brain hypothesis, the neocortical brain volume translates into a natural human group size of 150 (Dunbar's number) (figure 5.4).[41]

Fig. 5.4. Social group size for different monkey and ape species plotted against relative cortex size

Index of relative cortex size (neocortex ratio) is neocortex volume divided by the volume of the rest of the brain

Gamble C, Gowlett J, Dunbar R. *Thinking Big.* "How the evolution of social life shaped the human mind." Thames and Hudson, London 2014

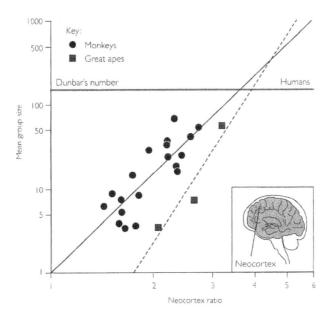

Nowadays our technology has enabled interaction with much larger societal numbers. Gamble, Gowlett, and Dunbar expounded their theory of "the rule of 3 in human communities" with the core group numbering 5 (intimate friends), support group (best friends) of 15, band size (good friends) of 50, communities (friends) of 150, megabands (near acquaintances) of 500, and tribes (far acquaintances) of 1,500. In their view warfare, leadership, and religion were the responses by humans to coping with the increasing group size.[42]

Our understanding, until recently, of the sequence of human events put the agricultural revolution (~10,000 years ago) first, which in turn allowed for increasing group sizes after which warfare, societal structure with leadership, and religion developed as a way of managing the group sizes of thousands and tens of thousands of people. However, the discovery of Göbekli Tepe suggests that agriculture may well have been last.[43] Signs of spirituality and religion were evident much earlier in the archeological record with the discovery of the Franco-Cantabrian cave art in present-day France and Spain dated to about forty thousand years ago.[44]

Social information is critically important to survival and optimum functioning within groups. A noteworthy theoretical perspective, termed the inferential brain hypothesis, has been proposed by Koscik and Tranel to help explain our brain processing within the social domain. They describe the evolutionary trajectory of the human brain from being primarily concerned with perceptual processing to one that performs inferential processing. This emphasizes cognition itself one of the driving forces in brain evolution and enlargement.[45]

The Electronic Age: What It Lacks

Facebook is a manifestation of human sociality, but as with Twitter, texts, e-mails, and Instagrams, there are limits to electronic communication. Despite millions of users, emerging data indicate that Facebook users have not developed group sizes any larger than our hunter-gatherer ancestors remaining between 100 and 250 names.[46] The archeological record informs us that we were gesturing and singling before we developed formal language. Even earlier than this we were grooming (and presumably grunting) and using other body language such as gaze as a form of communication, appeasement, and forming bonds. Our social brain circuitry was fashioned to include several other aspects of communication such as the following:

1. The over 10,000 facial expressions we are capable of that impart vital, subtle, covert, and other nuances to our communication [47].

2. Body language—postures and stances similarly impart nonverbal communication.

3. Speech intonation, prosody, can have the opposite meaning at times to the literal content of the language.

4. Visual and sound information is important in primate and human communication. Dobson's facial mobility index (visual signaling complexity) and vocal signaling are a function of group size in primates [48].

5. Personal touch – the grooming effect put in place over the last fifty million years was associated with oxytocin (bonding) and opiate release that is still very much part of our neural circuitry.

Proposals for Brain Healthy Societal Interaction

1. Form interpersonal face-to-face opportunities because the majority of the communication may be nonverbal and not captured by electronic communication devices.

2. Electronic communication devices are ancillary, not a substitute for face-to-face interactions. They facilitate and complement, not replace.

3. Socialize for brain development. The major fiber network in the brain for emotional and social competency, the uncinate fasciculus, continues to mature well into the fourth decade.[49, 50]

4. Socialize for brain health. Socialization mediates release of oxytocin, vasopressin and endorphins, which have neuroprotective and anti-inflammatory properties.[14]

References

1. Kobayashi H, Kohshima S. Unique morphology of the human eye and its adaptive meaning: Comparative studies on external morphology of the primate eye. *Journal of Human Evolution* 2001; 40:419–435.

2. Tomasello M, Hare B, Lehmann H, Call J. Reliance on head versus eyes in the gaze following of great apes and human infants: the cooperative eye hypothesis. *J Hum Evol* 2007; 52(3):314–20.

3. Jolly A. Lemur social behavior and primate intelligence. *Science* 1966; 153:501–506.

4. Byrne RW. Why are animals cognitive? *Current Biology* 2006:16:445–448.

5. Silk J, Cheney D, Seyfarth R. A practical guide to the study of social relationships. *Evol Anthropol.* 2013 SepOct; 22(5):213–25. doi: 10.1002/evan.21367.

6. Jolly A. Lemur social behavior and primate intelligence. *Science* 1966; 153: 501–506.

7. Humphrey N K. Growing Points in Ethology (eds) Bateson PPG, Hinde, RA. Cambridge University Press, Cambridge, UK, 1976.

8. Byrne RW, Whiten A. Marchiavellian intelligence: Social expertise and bathe evolution of intellect in monkeys, apes and humans. Oxford 1988.

9. Reader SM, Laland KN. Social intelligence, innovation, and enhanced brain size in primates. *PNAS* 2002; 99:3336–4441.

10. Brady ST, Siegel GJ, Albers RW, Price DL (Eds). Basic Neurochemistry, Eighth edition, Elsevier Academic Press, New York 2012.

11. Young LJ, Lim MM, Gingrich B. Cellular mechanisms of social attachment. *Hormones and Behavior* 2001; 40:133–138.

12. Lim MM, Murphy AZ, Young LJ. Ventral striatopallidal oxytocin and vasopressin V1a receptors in the monogamous prairie vole (Microtus ochrogaster). *J Comp Neurol* 2004; 468:555–570.

13. Lim MM, Zang Z, Olazabal DE, Ren X, Terwilliger EF, Young LJ. Enhanced partner preference in a promiscuous species by

manipulating the expression of a single gene. *Nature* 2004; 429:754–757.

14. Dolen G, Darvishzadeh A, Huang KW, Malenka RC. Social reward requires coordinated activity of nucleus accumbens oxytocin and serotonin. *Nature* 2013; 502:179–1184 and doi:10.1038/nature 12518.

15. Dunbar IM. Bridging the bonding gap: the transition from primates to humans *Philosophical Transactions of the Royal Society B.* 2012; 367:1837–1846.

16. Mithen S. The Prehistory of the Mind. Thames and Hudson, London, 2003.

17. Opie C, Atkinson QD, Shultz S. The evolutionary history of primate mating systems. *Commun Integr Biol* 2012; 5:458–461.

18. Shultz S, Dunbar RIM. The evolution of the social brain: anthropid primates contrast with other vertebrates. *Proc Biol Sci* 2007; 274:2429–2436.

19. Finger EC, Mackinley J, Blair M et al. Oxytocin for frontotemporal lobe dementia. A randomized dose finding study of safety and tolerability. *Neurology* 2015; 84:174–181.

20. Pelphrey KA, Viola RJ, McCarthy G. When strangers pass: processing of mutual and averted social gaze in the superior temporal sulcus. *Psychol Sci.* 2004; 15:598–603.

21. Kandel ER. The Age of Insight. Random House Publishing House, 2012 New York.

22. Tsao GY, Friedwald WA, Tootell RB, Livingston MS. A cortical region consisting entirely of face-selective cells. *Science* 2006; 311:670–674.

23. Jellema T, Baker CI, Wicker B, Perrett DI. Neural representation for the perception of the intentionality of actions. *Brain and Cognition* 2000; 44:280–302.

24. Kawashima R, Sugiura M, Kato T, Nakamura A, Hatano K, Ito K, Fukuda H, Kojima S, Nakamura K. The human amygdala plays an important role in gaze monitoring. A PET study. *Brain.* 1999; 122:779-8.

25. Cheney DL, Seyfarth RM. Baboon Metaphysics. University of Chicago Press, Chicago, 2008.

26. Hitti FL, Siegelman SA. The hippocampal CA2 region is essential for social memory. *Nature* 2014; 508:88–92.

27. Boden Albala B et al. Social isolation and outcomes post stroke. *Neurology* 2005; 64:1888-1892.

28. Ikeda A, Iso H, Kawachi I et al. Social support and stroke and coronary artery disease: the JPHC study cohorts II. *Stroke* 2008; 39:768.

29. Spiegel D, Sephton SE. Psychoneuroimmune and endocrine pathways in cancer: effects of stress and support. *Semin Clin Neurospychiatry* 2001; 6:252–265.

30. Strating MMH, Suurmeijer TPBM, Van Schuur WH. Disability, social support and distress in rheumatoid arthritis: Results from a thirteen year prospective study. *Arthritis Care Res* 2006; 55:736–744.

31. Cohen SD, Sharma T, Acquaviva Keet al. Social support and chronic kidney disease: an update. *Adv Chronic Kidney Dis* 2007; 14:335–344.

32. Weil ZM, Normal GJ, Barker JM et al. Social isolation potentiates cell death and inflammatory responses after global ischemia. *Mol Psychiatry* 2008; 13:913–915.

33. Karelina K, Stuller KA, Jarrett B, Zhang N, Wells J, Norman GJ, Courtney DeVries A. Oxytocin mediates social neuroprotection after cerebral ischemia. *Stroke* 2011; 42:3606–3611.

34. Wang HX, Karp A, Winblad B, FratiglioniL. Late life engagement in social and leisure activities is associated with a decreased risk of dementia: a longitudinal study from the Kungsholmen project *Am J Epidemiol* 2002; 155:1081–1087.

35. Nowak M. Super-Cooperators: Altruism, Evolution and Why We Need Each Other to Succeed. Simon and Shuster, New York 2011.

36. Hauser OP, Rand DG, Peysakhovich A, Nowak MA. Cooperating with the future *Nature* 2014; 511:220–223.

37. Wuchty S, Jones BF, Uzzi B. The increasing dominance of teams in production of knowledge. *Science.* 2007; 316(5827):1036–9.

38. Uzzi B, Dunlap S. How to build your network. *Harv Bus Rev.* 2005; 83:53–60.

39. Uzzi B. A social networks changing statistical properties and the quality of human innovation. *Journal of Physics A: Mathematical and Theoretical* 2008; 41:224023.

40. Grau C, Ginhoux R, Riera A et al. Conscious Brainto-Brain Communication Humans using Non Invasive Technologies. *PLOS ONE* 2014; 9:1–6. e105225.

41. Dunbar RI. Neocortex size as a constraint on group size in primates. *Journal of Human Evolution* 1992; 22:469–493.

42. Gamble C, Gowlett J, Dunbar R. Thinking Big. How Evolution of Social Life Shaped the Human Mind. Thames and Hudson 2014, London.

43. Norenzayan A, Shariff AF. The origin and evolution of religious prosociality. *Science* 2008; 322; 58–62.

44. Valladas H Clottes J, Geneste JM, Garcia MA, Arnold M. Cachier H, Tisnerat-Laborde N. Paleolithic Paintings: Evolution of Prehistoric Art. *Nature* 2001; 413:479.

45. Koscik TR, Tranel D. Brain evolution and human neuropsychology: the inferential brain hypothesis. *J Int Neuropsychol Soc.* 2012 May; 18(3):394–401. doi: 10.1017/ S1355617712000264

46. Pollet T, Robers SG, Dunbar RI. Use of social network sites and instant messaging does not lead to increased offline social network size, or to emotionally closer relationships with offline network members. *Cyberpsychol Behav Soc Netw* 2011; 14:253–258.

47. Ekman P. Emotions revealed. Recognizing faces and feelings to improve communication and emotional life. St Martin's Griffin, New York 2003.

48. Dobson SD. Socioecological correlates of facial mobility in non-human anthropoids. *Am J Phys Anthropol* 2009; 139:413–420

49. Lebel C, Beaulieu C. Longitudinal development of human brain wiring continues from childhood into adulthood. *J Neurosci* 2011; 31:10937–10947.

50. Von Der Heide R, Skipper LM, Kobusicky E, Olsen IR. Dissecting the uncinate fasciculus: disorders, controversies and a hypothesis. *Brain* 2013; 136:1692–1707.

6

Cognitive Exercise and Cognitive Reserve

A wide variety of activities that involve some degree of mental activity, thought, planning, or engagement in a task have been shown to improve cognition, and delay the onset of mild cognitive impairment and dementia. This has been demonstrated for both younger as well as elderly individuals.[1] Any activity that engages the brain rewires, to a greater or lesser extent, with effects on synapses, be it creating new synapses, facilitation of long-term potentiation, or long-term depression or via epigenetic mechanisms.

Hobbies and Leisure Activities Slow Cognitive Decline and Dementia

In a prospective community cohort study by Hall et al. (Bronx Aging Study), a number of leisure-related cognitive activities were evaluated and people followed for over fifteen years. The specific leisure activities included board games, card games, crossword puzzles, group discussions, reading, writing, and playing music. A scale was devised, which was by self-report, and gave one point for each activity the person engaged in per day per week. For an individual activity, a person would receive seven points if the activity was performed daily for one week, four points if engaged in several days per week, one point for once-a-week participation, and zero if only occasional or no activity performed during the week.

Neuropsychological tests were performed and the DSM III criteria used to evaluate for incident dementia. Of 488 initially healthy people with normal cognition (aged seventy-five to eighty-five years), 101 subsequently developed memory decline as assessed by a memory test, the Buschke selective reminding test, that was specifically not used in the initial diagnostic memory evaluation. The results revealed that every additional activity day (participation in one activity for one day in a week) resulted in a 0.18 year (~66 days) delay in the beginning of what was termed accelerated memory decline. The importance of this study was in the demonstration of the beneficial effects of late-life cognitive activity that was not influenced by education earlier in life.[2]

Hobbies and Leisure Activities Slow Cognitive Decline and Dementia in Other Cultures

A French study that examined the effects of travel, knitting, and performing odd jobs was associated with decreased risk of developing dementia.[3] Similarly a Chinese community study of gardening activities correlated with a decrease in incident dementia. [4]

A Wide Range of Hobbies and Leisure Activities Slow Cognitive Decline

In a New York–based study of initially nondemented elderly people, Scarmeas et al. used a self-reported questionnaire for evaluating participation in thirteen different leisure-based activities that included the following:

1. Reading magazines, newspapers, or books
2. Attending a synagogue temple or church
3. Visiting relatives or friends
4. Listening to music
5. Knitting
6. Physical conditioning
7. Going to movies, restaurants, or sporting events
8. Watching television or listening to the radio
9. Performing unpaid community or volunteer work

10. Playing cards, bingo, or other games
11. Attending a club
12. Attending classes
13. Walking for pleasure or excursion

The results revealed that those who had a high activity involvement (>6) as opposed to those with low (<6) had a marked decrease (38%) in the risk of developing subsequent dementia.[5]

Intellectual and Scholarly Activity and Amount of Education Slow Cognitive Decline and Development of Dementia

In a study of elderly people in New York City that were not demented at study onset, a correlation was found with increased rates of literacy and a more gradual decline in cognitive functions such as memory, executive ability, and language.[6] In a prospective study of 801 clergy (nondemented) and their intellectual activity, a one-point score of increase in their particular intellectual activity correlated with a 33% decrease in the likelihood of Alzheimer's disease development.[7]

Sociality and Learning a Second Language Are Also Protective Against Cognitive Decline and Dementia

A Swedish study that studied extensive social networks that people had showed that this too was protective for developing dementia.[8] Alladi et al. in a study examining bilinguism and polyglot ability (speaking several languages) reported delays in the development of dementia were noted in the three most common dementia syndromes, namely Alzheimer's disease, frontotemporal lobe dementia, and vascular dementia. Being able to speak a third language did not result in any additional benefit over bilinguism. The mechanism has been ascribed to the frequent need for activating one language circuit and suppressing another, which taxes and develops the primary executive functions (attention, inhibition, working memory) of the brain.[9]

Computerized Games Build and Improve
Cognitive Performance in the Elderly

Computer-based and smart phone–based electronic games have become very popular as a mode of cognitive entertainment and engagement particularly among younger generations. However, in a study involving the older generations (mean age 81.8 years) in retirement communities, cognitive evaluations were recorded for immediate and delayed memory as well as language tests, which were noted at baseline and at subsequent intervals of two and six months. A group using a computerized game (Brain Fitness, Dakim Inc., Santa Monica, CA) that they played five days per week for approximately twenty to twenty-five minutes per day was compared to a control group. Those who managed to play forty or more sessions over a six-month period improved significantly in all three cognitive test domains.[10]

Brain Building Occurs with Cognitive Activities: White Matter Structural Changes in Response to Cognitive Activities

Every action, sensation, and even thoughts leave a neural trace. The brain changes itself through experience, activities, and medications. Gray matter structural changes in response to learning new skills are due to cellular processes such as dendritic arborization and synaptogenesis.[11, 12]

A study of brain changes as measured by an MR diffusion tensor imaging (DTI), which measures the integrity of fiber tracts in response to learning juggling, was performed in twenty-four healthy people (juggling group) and twenty-four control subjects over a six-week period. The requirement for juggling success included the ability to perform the sequence of two continuous cycles of three ball cascades. The DTI scans were performed at baseline after six weeks and ten weeks. A significant increase in the FA (fractional anisotropy) in the white matter of the right posterior intraparietal sulcus in the training group was shown, which persisted in the final scan at ten weeks.[13]

Possible neurobiological mechanisms proposed include what has been termed activity dependent myelomodulation (the axon controls its myelination over the training period) and an increase in axon diameter.[14]

Brain glial cells, which include astrocytes, microglia, and oligodendrocytes, have many key roles in the brain. They discern neuronal activity, modulate and control it, and are involved in diverse cognitive processes, such as memory formation, and play a key role in cerebral injury of all kinds, as well as nerve fiber myelin formation. They are much more numerous than neurons, outnumbering them ~6:1 (figure 6.1).

Fig. 6.1. Glial cells outnumber neurons ~6:1 and modulate many activities from blood brain barrier to neural transmission: Hippocampal neurons (blue), astrocytes (red), oligodendrocytes (green) Figure credit with permission: Fields DR. Map the other brain. Nature Sept 2013; 501:25–27.

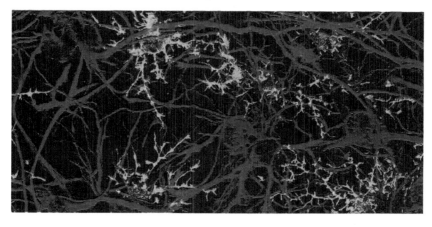

A fourth type of glial cell, termed NG2 cells, may represent a kind of sleeper cell that is capable of transforming into not only new glial cells but also neurons. This dynamic nature of the brain and its remodeling capability have only recently been appreciated.[15]

Learning a Second Language in Adults Builds Cognitive Reserve Associated with a Structural, Measurable Brain White Matter Change

A study of eleven people (English) who undertook a new language, learning course (Chinese) as well as a control group, were monitored by MRI-DTI scans over a nine-month period. Those who learnt the new language showed a progressive alteration in the fiber tracts of both hemispheres, specifically in the language circuitry of the left hemisphere as well as similar right hemisphere regions and the genu of the corpus callosum in the frontal region. The significance of these underscore the plasticity that adults can undergo with certain cognitive experiences.[16]

The Concept of Cognitive Reserve

In clinical memory and cognitive centers, the report by people of memory impairment, lack of multitasking, or another facet within the mild cognitive impairment spectrum is frequent. Not infrequently neuropsychological scores may be normal, yet surrogate markers of incipient dementia by positron emission computed tomography (PET) and quantitative MRI may suggest more profound disease sometimes with a marked clinicoradiological disparity. In some, autopsy findings have shown extensive disease (plaques and tangles) at a time that cognition was normal or near normal. A number of cohort studies have confirmed these impressions with some people having advanced dementia yet behave normally and may have normal neuropsychological tests when formally tested. In addition their brain scans (anatomical) such as MRI may be normal or show little abnormality in the form of atrophy or shrinkage.[17]

Yaakov Stern noted this clinicopathological disparity and conceptualized the entity of cognitive reserve encompassing both brain reserve (larger brains more synapses, more brain cells) and cognitive reserve (increased brain circuitry, compensatory brain circuits, alternative brain circuitry). Cognitive reserve might be due to neural reserve or brain circuitry less prone to disruption and more robust, or due to neural compensation. In the latter category, in the setting of brain damage, alternate or compensatory brain networks may be engaged (figure 6.2).[18]

Fig. 6.2. Brain reserve and cognitive reserve
1. Neural reserve – inherent inter-individual differences with respect neural efficiency or processing ability
2. Neural compensation interindividual differences in ability to counteract in the face of pathology

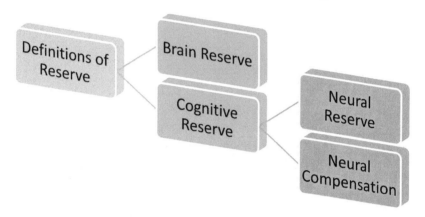

Several lifetime experiences such as education, occupation, intellectually stimulating activities, physical exercise, and socioeconomic status have been found to delay the onset of dementia by improving cognitive reserve.[19]

Table 6.1. Epidemiological studies have delineated several cognitive reserve factors

1. Education in years
2. Hobbies – various
3. Socioeconomic status
4. Degrees of literacy
5. Occupation
6. Intelligence quotient
7. Bilinguism

Table 6.2. Hypothetical components of brain/cognitive reserve capacity

1. Brain reserve (analogy of the hard drive)
2. Cognitive reserve (analogy of software, which can be updated, changed)

3. Neural reserve (more robust brain circuitry)
4. Neural compensation (using alternative brain circuits)

Neuroimaging Studies Support the
Concept of Cognitive Reserve

Resting studies initially with regional blood flow by PET scans have shown an inverse relationship between blood flow and education level, occupational level and leisure activities[20-22] that was subsequently confirmed by autopsy data.[23] These findings were interpreted as supporting the cognitive reserve hypothesis. This hypothesis posits that people with better cognitive reserve are able to tolerate more Alzheimer pathology as well as relatively decreased cerebral blood flow at any particular disease level. In short, they are better able to compensate for brain diseases.

The neurobiological processes underlying cognitive reserve against dementia was hypothesized to take two forms—neural reserve and neural compensation.[24] The innate efficiency of a particular individual's network may be a factor in their durability in the face of dementing illness. In addition, using alternate (compensatory) networks in people developing Alzheimer's pathology, compared to healthy individuals who do not use alternate networks, underlies the concept of neural compensation.[25-27] Functional magnetic resonance imaging studies and cognitive testing with the letter Sternberg task (a letter memory recognition task) suggested two networks that were involved as the task increased in difficulty. One network used by younger and older adults involved the working memory circuitry, and a second was associated with parahippocampal activation used only in the elderly group, the latter who had a worse performance. This was interpreted as the neurobiological representation of neural compensation circuitry as part of the cognitive reserve model.[28]

Two individuals with identical neuropsychological and cognitive ability (for example both have MCI) may have markedly different degrees of Alzheimer's pathology. This has tremendous importance for the clinical diagnosis, especially in the mild cognitive impairment categories. This variability is attributed to the cognitive reserve that each may have, and biomarkers, whether by neuroimaging (PET metabolism or tracer studies) or CSF analysis (amyloid beta 1–42, total tau, phosphorylated tau), need to complement the clinical evaluation. Furthermore, even in those with incipient cerebral pathology, there is a period of time during which even sensitive or demanding neuropsychological or other clinical testing reveals no cognitive impairment. Additionally, the rate of decline, after becoming clinically apparent in those with high cognitive reserve, is much more precipitous. This will dramatically impact clinical trials that depend on rate of decline comparisons of treatment versus control groups.[29]

Strategies to Improve Cognitive Reserve and Impede Worsening

More importantly, interventions whether through physical exercise, appropriate nutrition, cognitive training, or pharmacotherapeutic avenues should be engaged in the quest for improving an individual's cognitive reserve. The results from the Mayo Clinic Study of Aging supported intellectual lifestyle enrichment programs as a dementia preventative measure. The study, a longitudinal population-based study of 1,995 people with either normal cognition or MCI who followed an intellectual enrichment program, showed that midor late-life engagement in such cognitive activities were associated with increased levels of cognition that would likely delay onset of cognitive deterioration.[30] This is supported by studies that have correlated cognitive engagement with measurement of cerebral amyloid deposition.[31, 32]

However, strategies to hinder worsening are viewed as equally important. Mounting evidence implicates small vessel cerebrovascular disease in dementia syndromes. This was evident in studies using network analysis. Using DTI tractography network connectivity imaging, Lawrence et al. showed that in those with small vessel disease, the cerebral networks were significantly less efficient and less dense.[33] This corroborates closely with the findings by Deschaintre et al. five years earlier that treating cerebrovascular risk factors in people even without Alzheimer's disease delayed the onset of the dementia[34] (figure 6.3).

Fig. 6.3. Treatment of vascular risk factors is associated with slower decline in Alzheimer's disease with no cerebrovascular disease.
Vascular risk factor (VRF) treatment is recorded in conjunction with Mini-mental score examination (MMSE) on the y-axis and time in months on the x-axis
Figure credit with permission: Deschaintre Y, Richard F, Leys D, Pasquir F. Neurology 2009; 73:674–680.

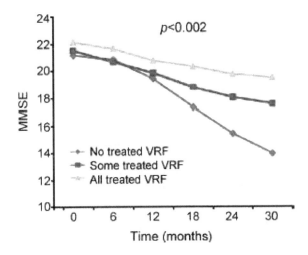

Interventions and experiences impact cognitive reserve during all stages of life, importantly in the mid and late life as well. However, of all interventions studied, the most effective of these appears to be aerobic exercise.[35, 36] An exercise prescription and close monitoring and reconciliation should therefore form part of the treatment plan.

Quantification and Molecular Signatures of Cognitive Reserve Will Be Critical in Future Dementia Research

A brain magnetic resonance imaging study of the two most common brain aging processes, Alzheimer's disease and cerebrovascular disease, showed that education counteracts the detrimental effects of Alzheimer's disease and cerebrovascular disease. This underscores the need for cognitive reserve quantification in studies of dementia.[37] Perhaps molecular studies will provide further refinements. In a postmortem study and specific analysis of pre-synaptic protein subtypes, Honer et al. showed that increasing amounts of vesicle membrane proteins—namely complexin I, complexin II, and SNAP 25/syntaxin interaction—correlated with a lower likelihood of having dementia.[38]

Cognitive Health Effects: Meditation, Transcendence, and Spirituality Evolutionary Insights: Evidence for Spiritual/Religious Circuitry in Human Brains

So-called higher order consciousness, creativity, mysticism, and spirituality are considered apical neural activities of humans.[39, 40] With evidence from neuroarcheological and neuropsychological perspectives, researchers have inferred that the human brain circuitry is wired to be spiritual and mystical. The various and specific cultural interpretations of these experiences subsequently led to formal religions as we know them today.[41–43] Some insights have been gleaned from the French and Spanish cave art, which are regarded as the initial (as far as we know) attempts at communicating abstract thinking that likely included pondering the afterlife and spirituality. The Lascaux painting depicting the phallic bird-man, disemboweled bison, and bird on a stick could be interpreted as a mere adverse hunting experience. However, it is regarded as a metaphorical manifestation of trance, death, transformation, and mystical flight (figure 6.4).

Fig. 6.4. Lascaux painting. Prostate man with a bird's head and a bison that has been disemboweled: Trance, death and mystical flight.

Figure credit with permission: Whitley DS. Cave Paintings and the human spirit. The origin of creativity and belief. Prometheus Books, New York, 2009.

This form of communication is therefore imagistic, and it preceded modern language. Art solidified groups for survival and so enhanced survival of the group. It was a means of social unification, and those bereft of this were less proficient in coping with a constantly changing environment (Neanderthals).[44] The cave art in other regions (Africa, North America, Australia) of depictions of visual hallucinatory images include both simple types such as spirals, parallel lines, filigrees, crescent shapes, navicular shapes, zigzag lines to complex ones such as animals and scenes (figure 6.5).

Fig. 6.5. Categories of different simple geometric, visual hallucinations (entoptics) occurring in the first stage during a trance (left). In stages 1, 2 and 3, the visual hallucinations range from simple shapes, to construals (culturally specific) to complex imagery (right)
Figure credits with permission: Whitley DS. Cave Paintings and the Human Spirit. The Origin of Creativity and Belief. Prometheus Books. New York 2009 and Lewis-Williams D, Dowson TA. Signs of the times. Entoptic phenomena in Upper Paleolithic Art. Current Anthropology 1988; 29:201–245.

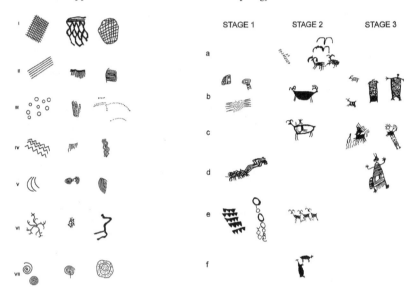

Such images are also reported in migraineurs and may occur after occipital lobe or temporal lobe lesions or, in association with seizures, provide the neurological bridge or underlying neurobiological predisposition for these. These are interpreted as normal neurobiological events in people that purposely pursued a transcendental state. This varied from one culture to another, and some of the initiating practices include sensory deprivation, audio-driving such as with prolonged drumming, sustained rhythmic dancing, prolonged flashing light exposure, chanting meditation, contemplative prayers, meditation, fatigue, fasting, and controlled breathing (figure 6.6).[45-48]

Fig. 6.6. Spirituality, mysticism, and religion

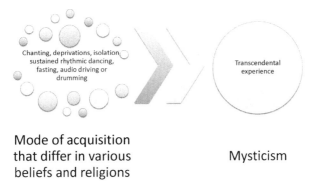

Chanting, deprivations, isolation, sustained rhythmic dancing, fasting, audio driving or drumming

Transcendental experience

Mode of acquisition that differ in various beliefs and religions

Mysticism

The normal human brain responds to these stimuli in a stereotyped manner with various levels of hallucinations. The achievement of a transcendental state is a goal common to many religions. The neurological bridge hypothesis is a theory based on the concept of the intensified consciousness trajectory that entails three stages of hallucinatory experiences as opposed to the normal conscious spectrum proposed by David Lewis Williams and Jean Clottes (figure 6.7).

Fig. 6.7. The intensified consciousness trajectory and neurological bridge hypothesis
Modified from Lewis-Williams D. The Mind in the Cave. Thames & Hudson, London 2001

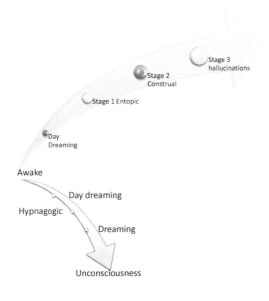

This helps explains the universal neurobiological responses that are triggered by the stimuli that transform the mind along the intensified consciousness trajectory and explain the cave art imagery.[49]

Religion and not agriculture may have spawned culture, with the latter interpreted as a by-product of the requirements of social gatherings.[50] The recent archeological discovery of the first temple, Göbekli Tepe in Turkey dated to ~11,000 years ago at a time when no evidence of agriculture was recorded gave rise to the theory of ideology before subsistence.[51] and temples before cities by the discoverer, Schmidt.[52] Cave art and spirituality or early religion are therefore probably closely related and appeared relatively suddenly in human evolution. Neuro-archeological data suggests that a number of other concurrent brain developments occurred during this time, such as an expansion of working memory capacity, early language, social intelligence, episodic memory, and mental time travel ability. The interaction of these advanced brain faculties forms the basis of the ensemble hypothesis proposed by Kellogg whereby the emergence of these faculties and their interaction are regarded as multiplicative.[53] The spectrum of spirituality from a neurobiological point of view includes both religious and atheistic feelings, and the concept of the afterlife in humans may be a default state.

Spiritual and religious impairments due to a number of brain lesions and circuitry abnormalities have been described. For example, damage to the left and right inferior posterior parietal regions may induce self-transcendence.[54] Profound and prolonged analytical activity has been postulated to precipitate religious disbelief in otherwise religious people.[55] A relatively unusual but well-known neurological condition seen with epilepsy and stroke called Geschwind Gastaut syndrome comprises of a constellation of findings that include increased interpersonal viscosity (excessively prolonged discourse), nascent philosophical interests, hypergraphia (excessive writing), hyposexuality, and hyperreligiosity.[56] Ecstatic seizures and mystical seizures have been described with temporal lobe epilepsy (TLE).[57] Furthermore, there are also reports of nonbelievers having religious experiences during a seizure.[58] Both religious and atheistic feelings are viewed as part of the neurobiological circuitry of the human brain. From an evolutionary psychology perspective, the evolving human mind became inclined toward supernatural ideology, which included concept of an afterlife and the belief in divine beings. This in turn may have stemmed from our theory of mind ability that allowed us to ponder the minds of others. In addition there are societal advantages. As human group size expanded, there developed increasing impersonality and anonymity among people. Supernatural belief functioned as a kind of community surveillance or the feeling of being monitored.[59, 60] In Bering's and Boyer's views, the concept of the afterlife in humans is a default state.[61, 62]

Functional neuroimaging (SPECT) of meditating Buddhist monks that reported mystical experiences as well as Franciscan nuns while engaged in intense prayer showed left superior parietal hypoperfusion (implying brain underactivity) as well as bilateral prefrontal cortex hyperperfusion (implying increased brain activity). One of the known neurological functions of the posterior superior parietal area concerns orientation and establishing the border between the self and the environment. Neurobiologically, this posterior brain region may be an important hub in the circuitry that mediates the common perception of the self as endless and connected with many others and the world, a common mystical experience.[63-65]

Both general medical and cognitive health benefits have been correlated to those who regularly engage in spiritual practices. Overall, epidemiological studies support many general medical and cognitive health benefits for those who engage in spirituality and religion practices.[66] An extensive review of studies, including several meta-analyses, of physical and mental health in relation to spirituality and religion was performed by Mayo Clinic researchers.

Their analyses revealed that most of the studies that qualified for assessment were associated with improved quality of life meaures, improved health outcomes, and increased longevity.[67]

Studies involving a broad range of race-ethnicity groups have revealed beneficial effects of spirituality/religion in health measures pertaining to cardiac disease, hypertension, stroke, cancer, cirrhosis, renal failure, mortality as well as a likelihood toward longevity.[68, 69]

Purported mechanisms include a number of possibilities such as advantageous lifestyle adjustments—for example, smoking cessation, alcohol curtailment—that may be enhanced by religious affiliation. Socialization provided by the community gatherings and the religious emphasis of positive emotions are other possible factors.[70] A

biochemical study revealed supporting evidence that religious practice was associated with a lowering C-reactive protein and therefore
chronic inflammation, translating into cardioprotection, among
others.[71]

The Environment, Biophilia, and Forest Bathing (Nature Therapy)

Biophilia, a term first used in nineteenth century and later modified
by Wilson, refers to "our integral affiliation with nature and its atten-
dant health-promoting effects."[72] Since 1987, however, recreation in
the natural environment has decreased by about 25% in the USA,
attributed primarily to indoor electronic entertainment of various
kinds.[73] Despite this, new evidence suggests that we may have a particularly unique affinity for aquatic-based environments such as the
lacustrine (lake) and marine shores. This is ascribed to the evolutionary necessity for both constant hydration as well as fish and shellfish
consumption.[74]

The attentional brain network, with the prefrontal cortex as a
major hub, is engaged during tasks requiring external focus and especially during attention shifting, which is also metabolically expensive.
When not attentive, we are invariably in a mode that involves the
idling brain circuit or default mode network, which may be viewed
as reinvigorating the brain and fostering creativity, for example.
Multimedia electronic usage engages the attentional network and
disengages the default mode network.[75, 76] The attention restoration
theory posits that exposure to the natural environment promotes
revitalizing processes to the attentional brain circuitry, of which the
prefrontal cortex is a key component, which are taxed during multitasking type activities (so-called attention fatigue) typical of our
technology-based society.[77]

An innovative study by Ruth Ann Atchley employed a creative test, the remote associates test (RAT), during hiking excursions
lasting up to six days in various wilderness regions in the western
United States. Compared to the control group (test administered
to pre-hike group), the hike group, were tested with an abbreviated
tenitem RAT test after the fourth day and recorded a 50% improvement in performance (mean 4.14, SD 0.46 versus 6.08 SD 0.39, p <

0.01). Although difficult to extricate the significant influence of the physical exercise component in this study, proposed mechanisms of the natural environment to brain health include the switching and engagement of the default mode network and introspection as well as exposure to stimuli that elicit positive emotions together with relatively low arousal.[78]

Cognitive-, cardiovascular-, and immune-based studies on people after walking in Japanese forests have shown improvements in neuropsychological scores, lowering of blood pressure and pulse rates, and alleviation in anxiety and depressive symptoms. For example, Li et al. studied sixteen men after two-hour morning and afternoon hikes in suburban Tokyo forests as well as excursions in the Tokyo suburbs. The forest hikes significantly reduced blood pressure, urinary levels of adrenaline and dopamine as well as serum DHES (dehydroepiandrosterone sulfate) levels indicating beneficial cardiovascular and sympathetic nervous system effects.[79]

Studies conducted while walking in a forest environment by Li et al. correlated with increased numbers (40% increase) and activity of natural killer cell activity. Phytoncides (aromatic volatile substances released by trees) were proposed as possible candidate mechanisms, and this was subsequently studied in a controlled setting. Phytoncide (alpha-pinene and beta-pinene, limonenes) exposure was correlated with significantly increased natural killer cell NK activity. Using a different approach with the aid of the mobile application called Mappiness that incorporated GPS tracking, MacKerron and Mourato tracked the location of people whether in natural surroundings or not. At intervals they were sent questionnaires that were rated on a scale of 1 to 100 for happiness, which supported increased contentment when outdoors.[80]

Wallace Nichols wrote a compelling book, *Blue Mind*, about our affinity with water and in particular the ocean. He weaves both personal and many individual anecdotes, neuropsychological studies, and some neurophysiological evidence supporting the unique relationship between us and water and its cognitive and emotional health-promoting effects.[81] Evolutionary insights support this claim and can be substantiated by our evolutionary origins that include lacustrine and riverine evolution in the African Rift Valley in the last few million years.[82]

Further support relates to the human near extinction and survival at Pinnacle Point, South Africa, thanks to the unique seafood availability, tubers, and ocean-side caves during the marine isotope stage 6 Ice Age.[83] The beachcomber express theory of the exodus from Africa by walking along the coastline to Asia and beyond to Australia further underscore our special and close relationship with the ocean and shoreline. [84]

Proposed Mechanistic Actions of Biophilic Engagement

Possible mechanisms include epigenetic-related DNA methylation with alteration in gene expression.[85] Forest bathing or Shinrin-Yoku has been promoted in Japan since 1982 with forty-four so-called forest therapy base locations at the time of writing.[86]

With respect to cognitive effects, the decreased blood flow to the prefrontal cortex as measured by the surrogate of hemoglobin concentrations by near infrared time-resolved spectroscopy, in the forest as opposed to the city environment, has been proposed but remains to be evaluated further.[87]

Animals, Animal-Assisted Intervention, Animal-Assisted Therapy

We evolved in an ecological system of plants, microbes, and animals. We are already aware of the tremendous importance of our two hundred trillion microbes that live within our bodies and how they influence our mind, immune system, overall health and contribute to our epigenetic evolution. It should come as no surprise that there is considerable emerging evidence for a health-promoting association with the environment, both plants and animals (figure 6.8). Our first recorded (imagistic) communication, the artwork of the horses, reindeer, mammoths, and buffalo in the caves of France and Spain dating back about forty thousand years are testimony to the esteem with which we regarded these animals. The many different representations, configurations, and associations depicted are thought to connote spiritual incidents with the impressive artwork at the time representing the method of communicating the ideas of humans at the time. About fourteen thousand years ago we developed a mutually beneficial relationship with wolves, the predecessors of domesticated dogs. A number of factors may have led to this symbiosis, including assistance with hunting by tracking game together and sharing. Soon thereafter the domestication of wildcats (~11,000–4,000 years ago) followed. However, in an interesting mitochondrial DNA study, Driscoll et al. hypothesized that wildcats sought humans out, rather than the other way around, in a case of opportunistic animals venturing into the early human communes.

Fig. 6.8. Ecology of human health and the biosphere

Thereafter followed the domestication of aurochsen that later evolved into domesticated cattle, the bezoars that evolved into goats, the mouflon that evolved into sheep, and the wild boar that evolved into pigs.[88] Genetic studies indicated that all cattle evolved from about eighty wild oxen (aurochsen) in the Near East approximately 10,500 years ago.[89]

The mismatch between us and our environment was elegantly outlined by a number of captivating examples by Rob Dunn. For example, he cited the pronghorn principle: the pronghorn antelope can run almost as fast as a cheetah because twelve thousand years ago they had to run from North American cheetahs, now extinct. He also reflected on the efficacy of restoring worms to our guts to help fight autoimmune disease and the "innate fondness for nature and restoring nature to our lives makes us healthier and happier," termed *biophilia*.[90]

Interacting and Being Associated with Nonthreatening Animals Pays Dividends in Both Health and Disease

So far there are many studies suggesting a benefit from animal-assisted activities and animal-assisted therapies. Scientific rigor provided by randomized, controlled, double-blinded trials, however, is lacking so far, with blinding in animal therapy not possible.[91] Pets decrease depression, stress, anxiety, posttraumatic stress disorder, facilitate sociality and emotional health, and owners with pets are more likely to exercise.[92] Many animals have been studied, with implied positive effects on health, including aquarium fish.[93] A minimeta-analysis of eighteen studies of animal-assisted interventions in people with various neuropsychiatric conditions including dementia detailed a number of positive outcomes such as promoting social interaction and agitation reduction.[94] The many reported animal-assisted activity studies in dementia patients have included robotic animals. The Australian PARO study used a robotic seal, which was constructed to be responsive to both voice as well as being able to display emotion. Furthermore, the robotic seal required minimal maintenance, was safe to use and devoid of infection.[95]

In otherwise healthy but obese children, dogs have demonstrated value in providing motivation for exercise and assist with weight reduction.[96] Horses can provide both psychological therapy for posttraumatic stress disorder (PTSD) and autism spectrum conditions. Hippotherapy is a horse-activity-related therapy whereby people with various kinds of musculoskeletal abnormality including paraplegia, hemiparesis, congenital abnormalities, and cerebral palsies gain mobility and exercise through riding. For example, in the Saratoga warhorse project, veterans were evaluated with the Beck Depression Inventory-II, Posttraumatic Stress Disorder Checklist, and other measures and significant improvements were noted over a three-month period with PPCL-C improving by 58%.

At the time of writing, the many preliminary case studies, case series, and randomized controlled studies were subjected to more formal review by the Cochrane database reviewers. Of the randomized controlled trials available during 2013, identification of eleven randomized controlled trials involving cats, dogs, dolphins, birds, rabbits, cows, guinea pigs, and ferrets were analyzed. A meta-analysis was not possible because of the variability of animals used and wide range of cognitive and neuropsychiatric conditions of the people studied.[97]

Neurobiological Basis: Oxytocin Release and Prefrontal Cortex Activity Modulation May Be Part of the Neurochemical Explanation

Preliminary findings point to oxytocin release, when petting a dog for example, which occurs in both humans as well as the petted dog, and has also been shown for primates and rodents.[98] Using near-infrared spectroscopy for evaluation of frontal cortical activity in mood disorders in patients whom the activity is often low, animal-assisted therapy was shown to increase activity in study patients.[99]

Metacognition, Plasticity, and Meditation Meditation

There are reports of a group of people named the Upanishads who voluntarily relinquished their families and homes and sought a solitary existence in the forests of India about 800 y BCE (before the common era). They practiced meditation that enabled transcendence. Soon thereafter Buddhism, Jainism in the Indian subcontinent and adjacent regions, and Taoism in China emerged, all using different methods in achieving states of transcendence.[100]

Neurobiology of Meditation

In contradistinction to animals (we think), humans engage in stimulus-independent thought for a large part of the waking day, also termed mind wandering. The thoughts concern contemplation of the future and what may or may not happen and has been determined to be the default mode of functioning of the brain. From an evolutionary point of view, it enabled humans to engage in mental time travel, to plan, reason, and role-play scenarios. A downside to this may be the emotional and neuropsychiatric conditions that plague humans, with meditation being proposed as a possible solution to mind wandering, to live in the moment. Using an iPhone-based application, Killingsworth and Gilbert constructed a database of five thousand people and twenty-two activities with a happiness rating scale of 0 to 100. They found that people's minds wandered frequently (about 50% of awake time), and when their minds wandered, they were relatively less happy, hence their article entitled "A Wandering Mind Is an Unhappy Mind."[101]

The importance of the default mode network (DMN) and its relevance to meditation mind-wandering neural activity has been shown to correlate with the activity of the DMN (figure 6.9).

**Fig. 6.9. Default mode network (orange/ yellow)
and attentional network (blue)**

Abbreviations: PCC posterior cingulate cortex, dACC – dorsal anterior cingulate cortex, mPFC – medial prefrontal cortex, MTL – medial temporal lobe, SPL-IPS – superior parietal lobe, inferior parietal lobe, FEF – frontal eye field, DLPFC – dorsolateral prefrontal cortex, pIPL – posterior inferior parietal lobe, MT or VS – medial temporal lobe

Figure credit with permission: Carhart-Harris RL, Friston KJ. The default mode, ego functions and free energy: a neurobiological account of Freudian ideas. Brain 2010; 133:1265–1283.

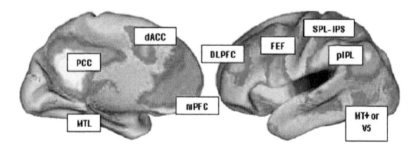

The DMN, or resting activity of the brain, without stimulation or specific engagement, can be imaged by functional magnetic resonance imaging, and major hubs include medial parietal cortex, dorsal cingulate cortex, medial prefrontal cortex, lateral parietal area, and lateral temporal cortex that consume approximately 60–80% of the total energy used by the brain.

Furthermore, Alzheimer's disease may be viewed as a DMN disease, as interestingly the brain regions affected in this dementia syndrome follow closely those of the DMN.[102, 103] Mindfulness meditation involves the maintenance of attention on the immediate experiences at hand, together with an acceptance of this. A number of different procedures are used, such as choiceless awareness, focusing attention on random conscious experiences; loving-kindness, promoting acceptance of others; and self-concentration, attention on an object or activity such as breathing.[104]

In a functional magnetic resonance imaging and connectivity analysis study, Brewer et al. noted less activity in two of the major hubs of the DMN (PCC, medial prefrontal cortex) as well as particular connectivity patterns in meditators versus controls. The implications are that activation and connectivity of the DMN differ in meditators that engage in mindfulness training. In addition, the observation report that meditators have less mind wandering supports the DMN alterations that are associated with mind-wandering reduction. Overall, these findings shed light on the neurobiology of meditation and that DMN differences by connectivity analysis may be correlated with decreased mind wandering.[105]

In a meta-analysis of twenty-one neuroimaging studies derived from three hundred meditation practitioners, looking at the brain microstructural changes in response to meditation, Fox et al. found a number of brain regions to be predictably altered.[106]

These included the following:

1. The frontopolar cortex that is linked to metacognition
2. The hippocampus (memory consolidation)
3. The anterior cingulate region
4. The orbitofrontal cortex implicated in emotional regulation

Several medical conditions have been reported to benefit from mindfulness training and include depression, anxiety, and chronic pain conditions.[107–109]

Bornman et al. has successfully used the mantram repetition program to treat posttraumatic stress disorder (PTSD) in veterans. A mantra refers to a silent repetition of a phrase, a short prayer, or sometimes only a word that is repeated at periods during the day in an attempt to quiet the mind and body. The study group of veterans with PTSD received either usual care plus mantram meditation or only usual care. In the mantram intervention group, a significant reduction in PTSD symptoms as per the CAPS scale was noted with 24% of veterans experiencing a meaningful improvement, compared to 12% improvement in the control group.[110, 111] The beneficial role of meditation in stress, such as PTSD, was supported by another using a different meditation method, namely transcendental meditation (TM). TM was used in Congolese refugees using a Posttraumatic Stress Disorder Checklist – Civilian. A beneficial outcome was reported within ten days and subsequent further improvement within thirty days.[112] Aside from medical conditions, meditation may improve creativity. In a Chinese student study reported by Ding et al., whose subjects meditated daily, for thirty minutes per day, creativity was evaluated (in addition to mood), with the Torrance test of creative thinking, and a significant improvement in the divergent thinking task was reported.[113] Different types of meditation may influence different brain circuits. This was supported by a study by Xu et al. looking at nondirective versus concentrative methods using f-MRI. The nondirective in comparison to concentrative method showed elevated right parahippocampal and amygdala activity, areas concerned with explicit memory formation and emotional tasking.[114] The enzyme telomerase, through its influence on telomere length, is viewed as a measure of life expectancy and aging. The enzyme telomerase is measurable as a blood test. Mindfulness meditation was associated with increased mononuclear cell telomerase activity.[115]

Metacognition: Our Most Supreme Intelligence and Its Plasticity

Metacognition refers to our internal ability to arbitrate about our own judgments and memory as well as our compensatory ability on realizing our deficiencies. This ability to introspect has been correlated byfunctional imaging and diffusion tensor imaging (DTI) studies with the frontopolar cortex (Broca's area 10 or anterior prefrontal cortex) gray matter. In addition, the white matter fiber tracts that connect to this area (BA10) as well as the orbitofrontal prefrontal cortex (BA13) were shown by a diffusion tensor imaging study using fractional anisotropic (FA) analysis to correlate with introspective ability.[116] Further studies have delineated that the anterior and dorso-lateral PFC are implicated in the accuracy of *retrospective* evaluation of a performance, whereas the medial prefrontal cortex is concerned with the *prospective* evaluation of a performance (figure 6.10).[117]

Fig. 6.10. Metacognitive ability correlated with gray-matter volume in the right frontopolar cortex (red positive correlation) and left inferior temporal gyrus (blue negative correlation)
Figure credit with permission: S. M. Fleming and R. J. Dolan. Review. Neural basis of metacognition. Phil. Trans. R. Soc. B (2012) 367, 1338–1349

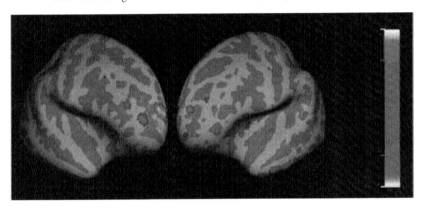

Metacognitive ability is regarded as a precondition for success in all cognitive domains and previously, in our hominin past, as a critical survival competence. Augmentation of these cerebral networks has been investigated pharmacologically and electrically. Methylphenidate (in healthy people), clozapine (in schizophrenics), and transcranial magnetic stimulation have so far shown positive preliminary results in the different study groups.[118] However, because of its ease of use, lack of side effects, and widespread applicability, meditation has been extensively investigated with respect to augmenting the neuroplasticity of the metacognitive circuitry. In the first randomized controlled trial, fifty students were subjected to a two-week meditation program that incorporated a focused attention procedure. A control group was engaged in a nutritional education program. The accuracy of introspection was augmented for the memory component, but not a sensory task in the meditation group.[119]

Meditation and Brain Building

Experienced meditators have neuroimaging evidence of both increased structural (gray matter) as well as functional connectivity (white matter) of the medial frontopolar cortex.[120, 121] Other brain regions considered part of the circuitry also show volume increases. These include increases in the hippocampal volume, inferior parietal lobe, and posterior cingulate cortex following meditation courses over eight weeks for example.[122] Experienced meditators also have larger hippocampal volumes. Mindfulness training with induced neuroplasticity in these brain regions may be correlated with the objective improvements in metacognition.[123, 124]

The method of loving-kindness meditation was evaluated and showed increased gray matter volume in the right anterior insular region that is concerned with interoceptive awareness as well as the left inferior temporal gyrus and right hippocampus. These regions are known to be activated during meditation, and the practice itself appears to be causing structural changes in these regions.[125, 126]

Short-term meditation (eleven hours), for example integrative body-mind training (IBMT), a tradition of Chinese medicine, was shown to increase fractional of anisotropy (FA) white matter connections of the corona radiata to the anterior cingulate gyrus (figure 6.11). The anterior cingulate gyrus is a key component of the circuitry for self-regulation, the connectivity of which increases with development during childhood. Impaired activation has been reported in conditions such as schizophrenia, addiction, depression, and attention deficit disorder. Buttressing the anterior cingulate gyrus and its connections may be an important method of upgrading self-regulation as well as a possible preventative and therapeutic tool in the future for these conditions.[127]

Fig. 6.11. Meditation "brain builds": White matter connectivity to the anterior cingulate gyrus increases in efficiency and integrity. FA increases (all significant) in the superior corona radiata (purple), body of the corpus callosum (red), genu of the corpus callosum (blue) and left anterior corona radiata (green). Figure credit with permission: Tang Y-Y, Lu Q, Gen X, Stein EA, Yang Y, Posner MI. Short-term meditation induces white matter changes in the anterior cingulate. PNAS 2010; 107:15649–15652.

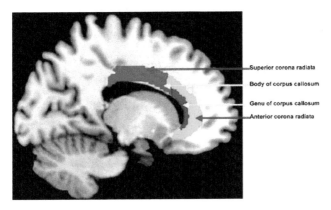

Closely related to the circuitry of meditation is that of the condition known as eudaimonic well-being. Eudaimonia refers to the quality giving importance to the pursuit of intellectual activities, virtuosity, and personal fulfillment distinguished from hedonic well-being that is related to positive emotional status. Eudaimonic well-being has, for example, been correlated with lower risk for cardiovascular disease and depression.[28] A positive association was recorded with eudaimonic well-being, as assessed by a forty-two-item Ryff scale of psychological well-being and right insular cortical gray matter volume.[129] This is noteworthy insofar as a negative association previously noted between depression and insula.[130]

The Arts as Emotional Templates and Potential Therapies

The arts in general (music, poetry dance performances, paintings, storytelling) may be conceived of as providing and interpreting imaginative experience. This may be regarded as the most important aspect of the arts and works of art may kindle emotional responses.[131] Pretend play that is universal among children beginning around the age of two and fiction in adults are, for example, instances of entering the imaginative world. In Carroll's view, art and its fictional representations, provides us with templates or mental maps for coping and understanding emotional life.[132]

Music has primordial origins and regarded as one of our most fundamental hominin brain circuitries. Evidence for this is derived from multiple disciplines. For example, music can generate emotions, enhance emotion, communicate emotions to others, as well as promoting social emotion and cooperation. These are compelling reasons for existence and evolution of music. However, music is the most abstract of the human arts and because of its ephemeral nature, places strong demands on auditory working memory. As an example, a protracted melody or lengthy sentence or discourse places demands on working memory to enable deciphering of the overall message or meaning.[133, 134] The neurobiological substrates involve the primary auditory cortex from which emanate the inferior stream to the anterior temporal lobes and a posterior dorsal stream to the parietal lobes, both of these in turn converge on the three main frontal cortical regions, the inferior prefrontal, the dorsolateral prefrontal and premotor cortex. The connectivity between the auditory cortex and inferior prefrontal regions in the right hemisphere has been supported by functional neuroimaging studies. The mammalian mesolimbic reward system reinforces important biological operations such as foraging, reproduction, nurturing offspring and strong emotions by way of dopamine release within the mesolimbic striatum. Emotions can be triggered by music with concomitant mesolimbic dopamine.[135]

The earliest archeological evidence we have at present dates back some forty thousand years, evidenced by the findings of vulture bone flutes with a string of longitudinally incised holes, found in the Danube valley. Undoubtedly, musicality must have existed for many thousands of years prior to that. That music evolved before language and probably occurred before the Neanderthal *Homo sapiens* split, five hundred thousand to two hundred thousand years ago, supported by convergent evidence from several disciplines.[136, 137] The connectivity of motor cortices with auditory association cortices underscores the intimate link of the temporal component within music and movement. When did musicality emerge among hominins? Neural oscillations that underlie rhythm in the brain of humans, may be relatively unique as they connect motor output to auditory stimuli. Although evidence for biomusicality has been shown in certain animals such as songbirds, parrots and sea lions, the switch from arboreal to terrestrial locomotion and bipedality may have been facilitated by the intrinsic neural rhythm.[138] Rhythm is a critical component of music and is also innate to efficient walking and running. Neuroarcheological evidence suggests that music came long before language. Mithen's language evolution model posits that infant directed speech, a method of emotional and social regulation was a possible precursor of language. His musical protolanguage model is summarized in the acronym hmmmmm—holistic, mimetic, multimodal, manipulative, mimetic, musical.[139]

Projections of both the cochlear and vestibular nuclei terminate within the reticular formation. The vestibular nucleus also connects to the parabrachial nucleus where a merger of autonomic, visceral and vestibular fibers that likely explain the arousal associated with music, as well as movement, explaining the human tendency to move to music and rhythms.[140–142] Modern human musicality was likely a result of enhanced working memory that also led to the improved communication between the various types of intelligences.[143] The global work space model of Dehaene describes a similar hypothesis.[144] With regard to the neurobiology of musicality in hominin evolution, this is supported by the profound increase in connectivity particularly of the inferior parietal and anterior temporal regions which are markedly enlarged in humans relative to macaques.[145]

Benefits of Musicality

Music based treatment for aphasia has been successful in clinical trials, administered in the form of melodic intonation therapy (MIT). Singing a words or short phrases according to a basic melody improves expressive language, probably by engaging the right hemisphere which controls movement in relation to vocalization supported by functional MRI studies.[146]

Music and motion are intertwined at a neural circuit level and the synchronization of rhythm in those with sensorimotor systems disorders such as Parkinson's disease and stroke, have been responsive to rhythmic beats and tapping. The use of rhythmic auditory stimulation (RAS) or walking in response to a rhythm, the tempo of which can be increased over time, has been correlated with improvements in the speed of gait, stride length and cadence.[147-149] Other areas in which music therapy has shown positive results include a lowering of the risk of developing various forms of dementia and in people with autism spectrum condition, the latter promoting social interaction with improved language and motor skills.[150, 151]

Aside from assisting those with neurological impairments, in normal people, music can help with working memory, attention, emotional well-being and sociality. For example, long-term music training, such as occurs in accomplished musicians, has been correlated with visual and auditory working memory improvements, as measured by behavioral and event related potential (ERP) evaluations.[152] Music modulates activity in neural components that are part of the known emotional circuitry such as the amygdala, hippocampus, insula, nucleus accumbens, orbitofronal prefrontal cortex and the anterior and posterior cingulate cortex (figure 6.12).[153]

Fig. 6.12. Musicality and the brain: Principal circuits mediating autonomic and neuromuscular effects of music.
Abbreviations: OFC – orbitofrontal cortex, ACC –anterior cingulate cortex, RCZ – rostral cingulate zone, MCC – middle cingulate zone, NAc – nucleus accumbens, AMYG – amygdala, VN – vestibular nuclei, CN – cochlear nuclei, IC – inferior colliculus, M1 – primary motor cortex, MGB – medial geniculate body, AC – auditory cortex.
Figure with permission: Koelsch S. Brain correlates of music-evoked emotions Nature Reviews Neuroscience 2014; 15:170–180.

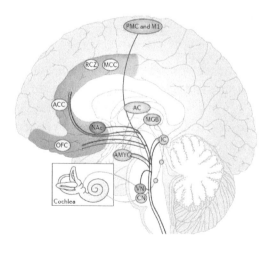

Koelsch stressed the importance of the social role of music (the 7 Cs), whereby people making music, initiate contact with each other. This, in turn, leads to social cognition whereby the listener tries to discern the intention of the melodist or songwriter. Making music leads to the formation of a copathy (social function of empathy) that facilitates interindividual empathy. Communication, coordination of actions, and cooperation among those making music lead to an overall increased social cohesion in a group.[154] Hence these functions of music assist with the feeling of belonging such as a particular group. This has been shown to improve health, longevity, and relieve anxiety.[155, 156]

Art as a Neurological Tool and Therapy

During the course of becoming human, the archeological record documents both cave art as well as portable art forms dating to about 40 kya. The neuroarcheological interpretation of this art includes a means of social coalition and unifying groups for survival. Those with no representational art, such as the Neanderthals who lived in present day Europe at the same time, were considered less likely to cope with the changing climactic and environmental conditions and indeed they did not survive. This form of art persisted for about twenty thousand years and represented the imagistic form of communication of ideas and abstractions at the time.[157]

From a neurobiological point of view, a work of art stimulates diverse brain circuits. The texture, color, body postures, facial and emotional expressions depicted by a painting stimulate disparate brain circuits synchronously. For example, the occipitotemporal region that mediates color interpretation is stimulated by fauvism (a style of art characterized by color and vibrancy) and art of people in motion activates the parietal motion area.[158] In a very insightful speculation of the brain-art interaction, Nobel laureate (2000) in physiology or medicine, Eric Kandel, in his remarkable book of neuroscience and art, described five neurotransmitter modulatory changes that may be taking place in our brain, depending of course on the viewer, in response to viewing a painting such as *Judith* by the Austrian artist Gustav Klimt (1862–1918).[159]

1.   The luminous gold surface, soft rendering of the body, harmonious colors activate pleasure circuits dopamine release.
2.   Judith's smooth skin and exposed breast trigger endorphins.
3.   The violence of Holoferne's decapitated head and Judith's sadistic gaze could trigger release of norepinephrine.
4.   The soft brushwork and repetitive almost meditative patterning may stimulate serotonin release.
5.   The acetylcholine release to the hippocampus contributes to storing the image in viewer's memory.
6.   The image complexity and the activation of conflicting signals results in complex emotional signals in the brain.

In Ramachandran's perspective, artists may strive not so much to depict reality but to transcend it through their artistic portrayals.[160] There are a number of neurological conditions, which may be associated with enhanced artistic ability. These include frontotemporal lobe degeneration and dementia, Alzheimer's disease, stroke, Parkinson's disease, autism, savant conditions, epilepsy and traumatic brain injury. Artwork can be used, not only to diagnose a change in brain function but can also help monitor the condition in an objective manner, not available by any other means.[161]

However artistic endeavor may also serve in a therapeutic role. Viewing art results in complex neurophysiological responses that is considered to exercise our emotional, theory of mind and empathic abilities. Art is regarded as a critical human trait that had survival value and is important for us to this day.[131, 159] Formal clinical trials of art therapy are sparse,[162] but a recent novel application for conveying the complex emotional and neuropsychiatric sequelae of traumatic brain injury and post-traumatic stress disorder using face mask painting was reported from the National Intrepid Center of Excellence (NICOE) art and mask project.[163]

A Proposal for Brain Building (Cognitive Exercises)

A long list of activities have been shown to be of benefit and many others not mentioned may qualify:

1. Computerized exercises such as Posit, Lumosity, Brain Age. These yield a number of different scores that can track improvement or worsening over time.
2. Board games, such as chess and Stratego. These two in particular have inherent attributes that stimulate thinking many moves ahead. This specific ability may be one of the earliest indicators of incipient cognitive failure in people as they age.
3. Card games
4. Sudoku
5. Book clubs and discussion groups
6. Learning an additional language
7. Pursuing a qualification, diploma or degree
8. Engagement in educational courses for example the Great Courses programs
9. Biophilic engagement outdoor exercise, interaction with nature (Japanese forest therapy)
10. Animal companionship or pet assisted therapy
11. Meditation, spirituality. Meditation does not require monitoring. However a recently launched EEG and smart phone based device (Melon) may allow efficacy or efficiency tracking.
12. Literary arts – reading, writing, poetry
13. Culinary arts – cooking or baking classes
14. Visual arts – viewing museum paintings or engaging inn art production or therapy
15. Music or performing arts/dance – listening, producing or participating

References

1. Valenzuela MJ, Sachdev P, Wen W, Chen X, Brodaty H. Lifespan mental activity predicts diminished rate of hippocampal atrophy. *Plos One* 2008; 3:e2598.
2. Hall CB, Lipton RB, Sliwinksi K, Katz MJ, Derby CA, Verghese J. Cognitive Activities delay onset of memory decline in persons who developed dementia. *Neurology* 2009; 73:356–361.
3. Fabriguole C et al. Social and leisure activities and risk of dementia. A prospective longitudinal study. *J Am Geriatric Soc* 1995; 43:485–490.
4. Wang H-X et al. Late life engagement in social and leisure activities is associated with a decreased risk of dementia: a longitudinal study from the Kungsholmen project. *Am J Epidemiol* 2002; 155:1081–1087.
5. Scarmeas N et al. Influence of leisure activity on the incidenceof Alzheimer Disease *Neurology* 2001; 57:2236–2242.
6. Manly JJ et al. Cognitive decline and literacy among ethnically diverse elders. *J Geriatric Psychiatry Neurol* 2005; 18:213–217.
7. Wilson RS et al. Participation in cognitively stimulating activities and in risk of incident Alzheimer's disease. *J Am Med Assoc* 2002; 287:742–748.
8. Fratiglioni L et al. Influence of social network on occurrence of dementia: a community based longitudinal study. *Lancet* 2000; 355:1315–1319.
9. Alladi S, Bak TH, Duggirala V, Surampudi B, Shailaja M, Shukla AK, Chaudhuri JR, Kaul S. Bilingualism delays age at onset of dementia, independent of education and immigration status. *Neurology* 2013; 81:1938–1944.
10. Miller KJ, Dye RV, Kim J, Jennings JL, O'Toole E, Wong J, Siddarth P. Effect of a computerized brain exercise program on cognitive performance in older adults. *Am J Geriatr Psychiatry.* 2013; 21:655–63.
11. Volkmar FR, Greenough WT. Rearing complexity affects branching of dendrites in the visual cortex of the rat. *Science.* 1972; 176:1445–1447.
12. Turner AM, Greenough WT. *Brain Res.* 1985; 329:195–203

13. Scholz J, Klein MC, Behrens TE, Johansen-Berg H. Training induces changes in white matter architecture. Training induces changes in white-matter architecture. *Nature Neuroscience* 2009; 12:1367–1368.

14. Fields RD. White matter in learning, cognition and psychiatric disorders. *Trends Neurosci* 2008; 31:361–370.

15. Fields DR. Neuroscience: Map the other brain. *Nature* 2013; 501:25–27.

16. Schlegel AA1, Rudelson JJ, Tse PU. White matter structure changes as adults learn a second language. *J Cogn Neurosci.* 2012; 24(8):1664–70.

17. Katzman R et al. Development of dementing illnesses in an 80 year old volunteer cohort. *Ann Neurol* 1989; 25:307–324.

18. Stern Y. Cognitive Reserve. *Alzheimer Dis Assoc Disorders* 2006; 20:112–117.

19. Valenzuela MJ, Sachdev P. Brain reserve and dementia: A systematic review. *Psychol Med* 205; 25:1–14.

20. Friedland RB, Brun A, Budinger TF. Pathological and positron emission tomographic relations in Alzheimer's disease. *Lancet* 1985; 325:228.

21. Stern Y, Alexander GE, Prohovnik I, Mayeaux R. Inverse relationship between education and parietotemporal perfusion deficit in Alzheimer's disease. *Ann Neurol* 1992; 32:371–375.

22. Scarmeas N, Zarahn E, Anderson KE et al. Association of life activities and cerebral blood flow in Alzheimer's disease: implications for the cognitive reserve hypothesis. *Arch Neurol* 2003; 60:159–165.

23. Bennett DA, Wilson RS, Schneider JA et al. Education modifies the relation of AD pathology to level of cognitive function in older persons. *Neurology* 2003; 60:1909–1915.

24. Stern Y, Habeck C, Moeller J et al. Brain networks associated with cognitive reserve in healthy young adults and old adults. *Cereb Cortex* 2005; 15:394–402.

25. Stern Y, Moeller JR, Anderson KE, et al. Different brain networks mediate task performance in normal aging and AD: defining compensation. *Neurology* 2000; 55:1291–1297.

26. Scarmeas N, Zarahn E, Anderson KE et al. Cognitive reserve mediated modulation of PET activation during memory tasks in AD. *Arch Neurol* 2004; 61:73–78.

27. Kemppainen NM, Aalto S, Karrasch M, Nagren K, Savisto N, Oikonen V, Viitanen M, Parkkola R, Rinne JO. Cognitive Reserve Hypothesis: Pittsburgh Compound B and Fluorodeoxyglucose Position Emission Tomography in Relation to Education in Mild Alzheimer's Disease. *Ann Neurol* 2008; 63:112–118.

28. Zahran E, Rakitin B, Abela D, Flynn J, Stern Y. Age related changes in brain activation during a delayed item recognition task. *Neurobiol Aging* 2007; 28:784–798.

29. Stern Y. Cognitive Reserve in ageing and Alzheimer's disease. *Lancet Neurology* 2012; 11:1006–1012.

30. Vemuri P, Lesnick TG, Przybelski SA et al. Association of lifetime intellectual enrichment with cognitive decline in the older population. *JAMA Neurol* 2014; 71:1017–1024.

31. Landau SM, Marks SM, Jagust WJ et al. Association of lifetime cognitive engagement and low Beta amyloid deposition. *Arch Neurol* 2012; 69:623–629.

32. Jagust WJ, Mormino EC. Lifespan brain activity, beta amyloid and Alzheimer's disease. *Trends Cogn Sci* 2011; 15:520–526.

33. Lawrence AJ, Chung AW, Morris RG Markus HS, Barrick TR. Structural network efficiency is associated with cognitive impairment in small vessel disease. *Neurology* 2014; 83:304–311.

34. Deschaintre Y, Richard F, Leys D, Pasquir F. Treatment of Vascular Risk Factors is associated with slower decline in AD with no CVD. *Neurology* 2009; 73:674–680.

35. Angevaren M, Aufdemkampe G, Verhaar H, Aleman A, Vanhees L. Physical activity and enhanced fitness to improve cognitive function in older people without known cognitive impairment. *Cochrane Database Syst Rev* 2008; 2:CD005381.

36. Kramer AF, Hahn S, Cohen NJ et al. Ageing, fitness and neurocognitive function. *Nature* 1999; 400:418–419.

37. Murray AD, Staff RT, McNeil CJ, Salarirad S, Ahearn TS, Mustafa N, Whalley LJ. The balance between cognitive reserve and brain imaging biomarkers of cerebrovascular and Alzheimer's diseases. *Brain*. 2011; 134:3687–96.

38. Honer WG, Barr AM, Bennett DA et al. Cognitive reserve, pre-synaptic proteins and dementia in the elderly. *Transl Psychiatry* 2012; 2(5):e114.

39. Mellars P. Cognitive changes and the emergence of modern humans in Europe. *Cambridge Archeological Journal* 1991; 1:63–76.

40. Renfrew C, Morely I (Eds). Becoming Human. Innovation in Prehistoric Material and Spiritual Culture. Cambridge University Press, Cambridge 2009.

41. Niels G et al. Genetic and Environmental Influences on Religious Interests, Attitudes and Values: A Study of Twins Reared Apart and Reared Together. *Psychological Science* 1990; 1:138–141.

42. Newberg A and d'Aquili E. Why God won't go away: Brain Science and biology of believing. NewYork: Balantine Books 2001.

43. Renfrew C. Situating the creative explosion: universal or local? In: Renfrew C, Morely I (Eds). Becoming Human. Innovation in Prehistoric Material and Spiritual Culture. Cambridge University Press, Cambridge 2009.

44. Whitley DS. Cave Paintings and the Human Spirit. The Origin of Creativity and Belief. Prometheus Books. New York 2009 and Curtis G. The Cave Painters. Probing the mysteries of the world's first artists. Anchor Books, New York 2006.

45. Lewis-Williams D, Dowson TA. Signs of the times. Entoptic phenomena in Upper Paleolithic Art. *Current Anthropology* 1988; 29:201–245.

46. Barrett Jl. Exploring the natural foundations of religion. Trends in *Cognitive Sciences* 2000; 4:29–34.

47. Atkinson QD, Whitehouse H. the cultural morphospace of ritual form: Examining modes of religiosity cross culturally. *Evolution and Human Behavior* 2011; 32:50–62.

48. James W. Varieties of Religious Experience (1893), 1963. New York: University Books.

49. Lewis Williams JD. Neuropsychology and Upper Paleolithic art: observations on the progress of altered states of consciousness. *Cambridge Archeological Journal* 2001; 14:107–111.

50. Norenzayan A, Shariff AF. The origin and evolution of religious prosociality. *Science* 2008; 322; 58–62.

51. Robson D. Civilization's true dawn. *New Scientist* 2013, Oct 5: 32–37.

52. Scham S. The World's First Temple. *Archeology Archive* 2008; 61(6)archive.archaeology.org/0811/abstracts/turkey. Htm.

53. Kellogg R. The making of the mind. Prometheus Books, New York, 2013.

54. Urgesi C, Aglioti SM, Skrap M, Fabbro F. The Spiritual Brain: Selective cortical lesions modulate human self-transcendence. *Neuron* 2010; 65:309–319.

55. Gervais WM, Norenzayan A. Analytic Thinking Promotes Disbelief. *Science* 2012; 336:493–496.

56. Trimble M, Freeman A. An investigation of religiosity and the Geschwind Gastaut Syndrome in patients with temporal lobe epilepsy. *Epilepsy Behav* 2006; 9:407–414.

57. Devinsky O, Lai G. Spirituality and religion in epilepsy. *Epilepsy and Behavior* 2008; 12:636–643.

58. Dewhurst K, Beard AW. Sudden religious conversion in temporal lobe epilepsy. *British Journal of Psychiatry* 1970; 117:497–507

59. Ysseldyk R, Matheson K, Anisman H. Religiosity as indentity: toward an understanding of religion from a social identity perspective. *Pers Soc Psychol Rev* 2010; 14:60–71.

60. Bering JM. The folk psychology of souls. *Behavioral Brain Science* 2006; 29:453–462.

61. Bering JM. The cognitive psychology of belief in the supernatural. *American Scientist* 2006; 94:142–149.

62. Boyer P. Religion explained: the evolutionary origins of religious thought. New York, Basic Books, 2001.

63. Newberg A, Alavi A, Baime M, Pourdehnad M, Santanna J, d'Aquili E. The measurement of regional cerebral blood flow during the complex cognitive task of meditation: a preliminary SPECT study. *Psychiatry Res.* 2001; 106(2):113–22.

64. Newberg A, Pourdehnad M, Alavi A, d'Aquili EG. Cerebral blood flow during meditative prayer: preliminary findings and methodological issues. *Percept Mot Skills.* 2003; 97(2):625–30.

65. Khalsa DS, Amen D, Hanks C, Money N, Newberg A. Cerebral blood flow changes during chanting medita-

tion. *Nucl Med Commun.* 2009; 30:956–61. doi: 10.1097/MNM.0b013e32832fa26c.

66. Seybold KS, Hill PC. The role of religion and spirituality in mental and physical health. *Current Directions in Psychological Science* 2001; 10:21–24.

67. Mueller PS, Plevak DJ, Rummans TA. Religious involvement, spirituality, and medicine: implications for clinical practice. *Mayo Clin Proc.* 2001; 76:1225–35.

68. Larson DB, Swyers JP, McCullough ME (Eds). Scientific research on spirituality and health: a consensus report. National Institutes of Healthcare Research. Rockville, MD, 1998.

69. Levin JS, Vanderpool HY. Religious factors in physical health and in the prevention of illness. In Pargament KI, Maton KI, Hess RE (Eds). Religion and prevention of in mental health: Research, vision and action. Haworth Press, New York 1992.

70. Sethi S, Seligman MEP. Optimism and fundamentalism. *Psychological Science* 1993; 4:256–259.

71. Ferraro KF, Kim S. Health benefits of religion among Black and White older adults? Race, religiosity, and C-reactive protein. *Soc Sci Med.* 2014; 120:92–99. doi: 10.1016/j.socscimed.2014.08.030.

72. Kellert SR, Wilson EO. The Biophilia Hypothesis. Shearwater Book, Washington DC, 1984.

73. Pergrams ORW, Zaradic PA. Evidence for a fundamental and pervasive shift away from nature-based recreation. *Proc Natl Acad Sci* 2008; 105:2295–2300.

74. Finlayson C. The Water Optimization Hypothesis and the Human Occupation of the Mid-Latitude Belt in the Pleistocene. *Quaternary International* 2013; 300:22–31.

75. Immordino-Yang MH, Christodoulou JA, Sing V. Rest is not Idleness. *Perspectives on Psychological Science* 2012; 7:352–364.

76. Van Den Heuvel MP, Stam CJ, Kahn RS, Pol HEH. Efficiency of functional brain networks and intellectual performance. *The Journal of Neuroscience* 2009; 29:7619–7624.

77. Kaplan S. the restorative benefits of nature. Toward an integrative framework. *Journal of Environmental Psychology* 1995; 15:169–182.

78. Atchley RA, Strayer DL, Atchley P. Creativity in the Wild: Improving Creative Reasoning through Immersion in Natural Settings. *PLOS ONE* 2012; 7:1–3 e51474.

79. Li Q, Otsuka T, Kobayashi M, Wakayama Y et al. Acute effects of walking in forest environments on cardiovascular and metabolic parameters. *Eur J Appl Physiol.* 2011; 111:2845–53.

80. MacKerron G, Mourato S. Happiness is greater in natural environments. *Global Environmental Change* 2013; 23:992–1000.

81. Nichols WJ. Blue Mind. Little Brown & Co, New York 2014.

82. Broadhurst CL, Cunnane SC, Crawford MA. Rift Valley lake fish and shellfish provided brain-specific nutrition for early Homo. *Br J Nutr.* 1998; 79:–21.

83. Marean CW, Bar-Matthews M, Bernatchez J et al. Early human use of marine resources and pigment in South Africa during the Middle Pleistocene. *Nature.* 2007 Oct 18; 449(7164):905–8.

84. Ridley M. Out of Africa, but when? Mind and Matter. *Wall Street Journal,* February 05, 2012.

85. Li Q, Kobayashi M, Wakayama Y et al. Effect of phytoncide from trees on human natural killer cell function. *Int J Immunopathol Pharmacol.* 2009; 22(4):951–9.

86. Selhub EM Long AC. Your Brain on Nature. Wiley, Mississauga ON, Canada, 2012.

87. Tsunetsugu Y, Miyazaki Y. Measurement of absolute hemoglobin concentrations of prefrontal region by near-infrared time resolved spectroscopy: examples of experiments and prospects. *J Physiol Anthropol Appl Human Sci* 2005; 24:469–472.

88. Driscoll CA, Macdonald DW, O'Brien SJ. From wild animals to domestic pets, an evolutionary view of domestication. *PNAS* 2009; 106:9971–9978.

89. Bollongino R, Burger J, Powell A, Mashkour M, Vigne JD, Thomas MG. Modern taurine cattle descended from a small number of near-eastern founders. *Journal of Molecular Biology and Evolution* 2012; 29:2101–2104.

90. Dunn P. The Wild Life of our Bodies. Predators, parasites and partners that shape who we are today. Harper-Collins Publishers, New York, 2011.

91. Burton A. Dolphins, dogs, and robot seals for the treatment of neurological disease. *Lancet Neurol.* 2013; 12:851–2.

92. McConnell AR, Brown CM, Shoda TM, Stayton LE, Martin CE. Friends with benefits: on the positive side consequences of pet ownership. *Journal of Personality and Social Psychology* 2011; 101:1239–1252.

93. Levinson BM. The aquarium as a therapeutic aid. *Pyschol Report* 1979; 45:577–578.

94. Bernabei V, De Ronchi D, La Ferla T, Moretti F, Tonelli L, Ferrari B, Forlani M, Atti AR. Animal-assisted interventions for elderly patients affected by dementia or psychiatric disorders: a review. *J Psychiatr Res.* 2013; 47:762–73.

95. Shibata T, Wada K. Robot therapy: a new approach for mental healthcare of the elderly – a mini review. *Gerontology* 2013; 57:378–386.

96. Wohlfarth R, Mutschler B, Beetz A, Kreuser F, KorstenReck U. Dogs motivate obese children for physical activity: key elements of a motivational theory of animal-assisted interventions. *Front Psychol.* 2013; 29:796. doi: 10.3389/ fpsyg.2013.00796.

97. Kamioka H, Okada S, Tsutani K et al. Effectiveness of animal-assisted therapy: A systematic review of randomized controlled trials. Complement Ther Med. 2014; 22(2):371–90.

98. Rehn T, Handlin L, Uvnås-Moberg K, Keeling LJ. Dogs' endocrine and behavioral responses at reunion are affected by how the human initiates contact. *Physiol Behav* 2014; 124:45–53.

99. Aoki J, Iwahashi K, Ishigooka J, Fukamauchi F, Numajiri M, Ohtani N, Ohta M. Evaluation of cerebral activity in the prefrontal cortex in mood affective disorders during animal-assisted therapy (AAT) by near-infrared spectroscopy (NIRS): a pilot study. *Int J Psychiatry Clin Pract.* 2012; 16:205–13.

100. Radhakrishnan S. The Principal Upanishads. Allen and Unwin, London 1969.

101. Killingsworth MA, Gilbert DT. A wandering mind is an unhappy mind. *Science* 2010; 330: 932.

102. Petrella JR, Sheldon FC, Prince SE, Calhoun VD, Doraiswamy PM. Default mode network connectivity in stable vs progressive mild cognitive impairment. *Neurology* 2011; 76:511–517

103. Buckner RL, Andrews-HannaJR, Schacter DL. The brain's default network: Anatomy, function and relevance to disease.

In: Kingstone A, Miller MB (eds). The Year in Cognitive Neuroscience 2008. Blackwell Publishing Malden MA, 2008.

104. Gunaratana H. Mindfulness in Plain English. Wisdom Publications, Somerville MA, 2002.

105. Brewer JA, Worhunsky PD, Gray JR, Tang Y-Y, Weber J, Kober H. Meditation experience is associated with differences in default mode network activity and connectivity. *PNAS* 2011; 108:20254–20259.

106. Fox KC, Nijeboer S, Dixon ML, Floman JL, Ellamil M, Rumak SP, Sedlmeier P, Christoff K. Is meditation associated with altered brain structure? A systematic review and meta-analysis of morphometric neuroimaging in meditation practitioners. *Neurosci Biobehav Rev* 2014; 43:48–73.

107. Teasdale JD, Segal ZV, Williams JM, Ridgeway VA, Soulsby JM, Lau MA. Prevention of relapse/recurrence of major depression by mindfulness-base cognitive therapy. *J Consult Clin Psychol 2000*; 68:615–623.

108. Kabat-Zinn J, Lipworth L, Burney R. The clinical use of mindfulness meditation for the self-regulation of chronic pain. *J Behav Med* 1985; 8:163–190.

109. Goldin P, Ramel W, Gross J. Mindfulness training and self referential processing in social anxiety disorder: Behavioral and neural effects. *J Cogn Psychother* 2009; 23:242–257.

110. Bormann, J. E., Thorp, S. R., Wetherell, J. L., Golshan, S., & Lang, A. J. (2012, March 12). Meditation-based mantram intervention for veterans with posttraumatic stress disorder: A randomized trial. Psychological Trauma: Theory, Research, Practice, and Policy 2012 doi: 10.1037/ a0027522.

111. Bormann JE, Hurst S, Kelly A. Responses to Mantram Repetition Program from Veterans with posttraumatic stress disorder: a qualitative analysis. J Rehabil *Res Dev.* 2013; 50(6):769–84.

112. Rees B, Travis F, Shapiro D, Chant R. Significant reductions in posttraumatic stress symptoms in Congolese refugees within 10 days of Transcendental Meditation practice. *J Trauma Stress.* 2014; 27(1):112–5.

113. Ding X, Tang YY, Tang R, Posner MI. Improving creativity performance by short-term meditation. *Behav Brain Funct.* 2014; 10(1):9. doi: 10.1186/1744-9081-10-9.

114. Xu J, Vik A, Groote IR, Lagopoulos J, Holen A, Ellingsen O, Håberg AK, Davanger S. Nondirective meditation activates default mode network and areas associated with memory retrieval and emotional processing. *Front Hum Neurosci.* 2014; 26; 8:86. doi: 10.3389/ fnhum.2014.00086.

115. Schutte NS, Malouff JM. A meta-analytic review of the effects of mindfulness meditation on telomerase activity. *Psychoneuroendocrinology.* 2014;4 2:45–8.

116. Fleming SM, Weil RS, Nagy Z, Dolan RJ, Rees G. Relating introspective accuracy to individual differences in brain structure. *Science* 2010; 329:1541–1543.

117. Fleming SM Dolan RJ. The neural basis of metacognitive ability. *Philosophical Transactions of The Royal Society B.* 2012; 367:1338–1349.

118. Fleming SM. The Power of Reflection. *Scientific American Mind* 2014, Sept/Oct:31–37.

119. Baird B, Mrazek MD, Phillips DT, Schooler JW. Domainspecific enhancement of metacognitive ability following meditation training. *Journal of Experimental Psychology: General* 2014. doi. org/10.1037/a0036882.

120. Kang DH, Jo HJ, Jung WH, The effect of meditation on brain structure: cortical thickness mapping and diffusion tensor imaging. *Soc Cogn Affect Neurosci.* 2013; 8:27–33. doi: 10.1093/ scan/nss056.

121. Hasenkamp W, Barsalou LW. Effects of meditation experience on functional connectivity of distributed brain networks. *Front Hum Neurosci.* 2012; 6:38. doi:10.3389/ fnhum.2012.00038.

122. Holzel BK, Carmody J, Vangel M et al. Increases in regional brain gray matter density. *Psychiatry Research: Neuroimaging* 2011; 191:36–43.

123. Holzel BK, Ott U, Hempel H et al. Differential engagement of anterior cingulate and adjacent medial frontal cortex in adept meditators and nonmeditators. *Neuroscience Letters* 2007; 421:16–21.

124. Luders E, Toga AW, Leore N, Gaser C. The underlying anatomical correlates of long term meditation: larger hippocampal and frontal volume of gray matter. *Neuroimage* 2009; 45:672–678.

125. Holzel BK, Ott, U, Gard T et al. Investigation of mindfulness meditation practitioners with voxel-based morphometry. *Social Cognitive and Affective Neuroscience* 2008; 3:55–61.

126. Lutz A, Greischar LL, Perlman DM, Davidson RJ. (2009). BOLD signal in insula is differentially related to cardiac function during compassion meditation in experts vs. novices. *NeuroImage* 2009; 47:1038–46.

127. Tang Y-Y, Lu Q, Gen X, Stein EA, Yang Y, Posner MI. Short-term meditation induces white matter changes in the anterior cingulated. *PNAS* 2010; 107:15649–15652.

128. Ryff CD, Singer BH, Dienberg Love, G. Positive Health: connecting well being with biology. *Philosophical Transactions of the Royal Society of London Series B: Biological Sciences* 2004; 359:1383–1394.

129. Lewis GJ, Kanai R, Rees G, Bates TC. Neural correlates of the good life: eudaimonic well being is associated with insular cortex volume. *Scan* 2014; 9:615–618.

130. Hwang JP, Lee TW, Tsai SJ et al. Cortical and subcortical abnormalities in late onset depression with history of suicide attempts investigated with MRI and voxel based morphometry. *Journal of Geriatric Psychiatry and Neurology* 2010; 23:171–184.

131. Dutton DD. The Art Instinct: Beauty, Pleasure and Human Evolution. Bloomsbury Press, New York 2009.

132. Carroll J. Literary Darwinism: Evolution, Human Nature and Literature. Routledge, 2004, New York.

133. Hauser MD. The evolution of the music faculty: A comparative perspective. *Nature Neuroscience* 2003:6:663–668.

134. Walin N, Merker B, Brown S. The origins of music. MIT Press 2000, Cambridge.

135. Zatorre RJ, Salimpoor VN. From perception to pleasure: Music and its neural substrates. *PNAS* 2013; 110:10430–10437.

136. Fitch T. Evolution of language. Cambridge University Press, London 2010.

137. Wynn T, Coolidge FL. Beyond Symbolism and Language. An Introduction to Supplement 1, Working Memory. *Current Anthropology* 2010; 51:S5–S16.

138. Patel AD. The Evolutionary Biology of Musical Rhythm: Was Darwin Wrong? *PLOS Biology* 2014; 12:1–6.

139. Mithen S. The Singing Neanderthals. The Origins of Music, Language Mind and Body Phoenix, Orion Books Ltd, London, 2007.

140. Todd NPM, Cody FW. Vestibular responses to loud dance music: a physiological basis of the "rock and roll threshold"? *J Acoustic Soc Amer* 2000; 107:496–500.

141. Kandler K, Herbert H. Auditory projections from the cochlear nucleus to pontine and mesencephalic reticular nuclei in the rat. *Brain Research* 1991; 562:230–242.

142. Phillips-Silver J, Trainor LJ. Feeling the beat: movement influences infant rhythm perception. *Science* 2005; 308; 1430.

143. Mithen S. The Prehistory of the Mind. Phoenix, Orion Books Ltd, London, 2003.

144. Dehaene S, Kerszberg M, Changeux JP. A neuronal model of a global workspace in effortful cognitive tasks. *Proc Natl Acad Sci U S A.* 1998; 95:14529–34.

145. Van Essen DC, Lewis JW, Drury HA et al. Mapping visual cortex in monkeys and humans using surface based atlases. *Vision Research* 2001; 41:1359–1378.

146. Schlaug G, Marchina S, Norton A. From Singing To Speaking: Why Singing May Lead to Recovery of Expressive Language Function in Patients with Broca's Aphasia. *Music Perception* 2008; 25:315–323.

147. Thaut MH, McIntosh KW, McIntosh GC, Hoernberg V. Auditory rhythmicity enhances movement and speech motor control in patients with Parkinson's disease. *Functional Neurology* 2001; 16:163–167.

148. Hurst CP, Rice RR, McIntosh GC, Thaut MH. Rhythmic auditory stimulation in gait training for patients with traumatic brain injury. *Journal of Music Therapy* 1998; 35:228–241.

149. Thaut MH, McIntosh GC, Rice RR. Rhythmic facilitation of gait training in hemiparetic stroke rehabilitation. *Journal of Neurological Sciences* 1997; 151:207–212.

150. Hsieh S, Hornberger M, Piquet O, Hodges JR. Neural basis of music knowledge: evidence from the dementias. *Brain* 2011; 134:2523–2534.

151. Allen R, Heaton P. Autism, music and the therapeutic potential of music in alexithymia. *Music Perception* 2010; 27:251–261

152. George EM, Coch D. Music training and working memory: an ERP study. *Neuropsychologia.* 2011; 49:1083-94.

153. Koelsch S. Brain correlates of music-evoked emotions. *Nature Reviews Neuroscience* 2014; 15:170–180.

154. Koelsch S. Brain and Music. Wiley, New York, 2012.

155. Caciopp JT, Patrick W. Loneliness: Human Nature and the Need for Social Connection. W.W Norton and Company 2008, New York.

156. House JS. Social isolation kills, but how and why? *Psychosomatic Med* 2001; 63:273–274.

157. Lewis-Williams D. The Mind in the Cave. Thames and Hudson 2002 London.

158. Zeki S. Inner vision: an exploration of art and the brain. Oxford University Press, New York, 2000.

159. Kandel ER. The Age of Insight Random House Publishing, New York 2012.

160. Ramachandran VS. The Artful Brain. Fourth Estate, New York, 2005.

161. Schott GD. Pictures as a neurological tool: lessons from enhanced and emergent artistry in brain disease. *Brain* 2012; 135:1947–1963.

162. Schouten KA, Niet GJ, Knipscheer JW et al. The Effectiveness of Art Therapy in the Treatment of Traumatized Adults: A Systematic Review on Art *Therapy and Trauma. Trauma Violence Abuse.* 2014 Nov 16 doi:10.1177/1524838014555032.

163. Alexander C, Johnson L. The invisible war on the brain. *National Geographic* February 2015:30–53

7

Putting It All Together: What May Be the Benefits of Adhering to All Five Components of Brain Health?

A recent publication looking at several lifestyle factors showed an astounding 86% reduction in cardiac infarcts in men. This was achieved by adhering to five basic tenets that included physical activity for forty minutes per day or more, formal exercise for one hour or more per week, avoiding a waistline greater than 95 cm, following a prudent diet, not smoking, but using small amounts of daily alcohol.[1] The five major components of this brain health regimen provide further neural and vascular protection well beyond those featured in the study by also including attention to sociality, sleep, and cognitive exercise programs. It is quite possible therefore that even more disease prevention is achievable.

The Realm of Personalized Medicine

We are used to seeing a string of notification lights and computer monitoring alerts light up every time we turn a car's ignition, but we generally don't do the same for our brain and bodies—the most complex of all devices. Rather than wait for syndromes (dementia, hypertension, diabetes, cancer, obesity) to emerge within our bodies that are then recognized by people and their doctors with the appropriate intervention often late or too late. A better way would be more precise monitoring and (nipping things in the bud.) Simple maneuvers that take a few seconds such as checking resting pulse rate may be the earliest indicator of impending viral illness or infections that should preclude any strenuous athletic activity for example.[2]

Ischemic stroke is the second most common cause of global mortality and atrial fibrillation one of the most common causes of stroke. Currently prevalent rates of atrial fibrillation are ~3 million people in the United States, and up to 25% of people are likely to be impacted during their life span.[3] Furthermore, atrial fibrillation is associated with cognitive impairment, both due to intermittent or chronic cerebral hypoperfusion, also due to vascular cognitive impairment secondary to cardioembolic strokes. The former has been shown to be reversed by successful ablation therapy for example.[4] Lone atrial fibrillation and intermitent atrial fibrillation may be diagnosed by monitoring with a device such as Alivecor facilitating early diagnosis, prevention of stroke, and incipient dementia and cognitive impairment.

Prospective studies are under way incorporating not only easily measurable physiological variables but also including microbiome, genome sequence, and immune activity analysis. The Hundred Person Wellness Project is one such study, a pilot project by Hood of the Institute of Systems Biology in Seattle that incorporates intensive monitoring and feedback to their subjects with daily, weekly, and monthly monitoring on a dashboard of body indicators.[5]

Table 7.1. Personalized medicine: The Hundred Person Wellness Project

Organ, metabolic cellular system	Measurements
Brain	Sleep patterns
Heart	Pulse, activity levels
Colon	Microbiome ecology, stool samples
Liver, lungs, brain, and heart	100 proteins tracked thrice monthly (blood)

Lymphatic system	Immune cell activity, thrice monthly (blood)
Insulin sensitivity	Blood glucose thrice monthly
Chromosomes	Whole genome sequence at enrolment
Epigenetics	DNA methylation reflecting environmental exposure

The Brain Box: Taking Responsibility for Your Own Health

Constructing your own dashboard of monitors for your body and brain and taking responsibility for your own health can be done using some or all the following suggested devices (figure 7.1):

Fig. 7.1. Brain box dashboard

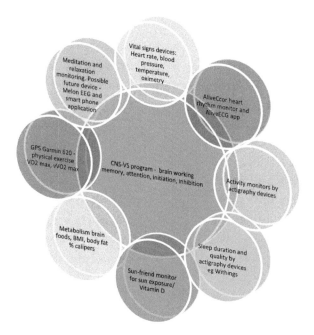

1. Vital signs

   Blood pressure (BP)—wrist BP devices, easier to use, calibrate with arm devices

   Pulse—by new BP devices and new Apple watch and Garmin Forerunner 225 devices for example, at the time of writing, were the first to provide wrist, optical sensor based, continuous heart rate monitoring.

   Temperature—infrared devices

   Oximetry—finger device for oxygen saturation

2. Cardiac arrhythmia detection

   AliveCor device with electrocardiographic recording using smartphone AliveECG application (http://www.alivecor.com).

   Irregular heart rate detection also recorded by many BP devices

3. General twenty-four-hour activity monitors Actigraphic devices

   These devices have smartphone graphic displays that can visualize daily, weekly, or monthly trends that can be shared with your health care providers.

4. Sleep actigraphic devices

   Monitor sleep with simple, unobtrusive, actigraphic devices. These give robust data about sleep quality and duration. Once sleep patterns and characteristics have been determined, various interventions and changes can be implemented and the device used for assessing efficacy the intervention—for example, curtailing evening alcohol use and early morning wakings and sleep quality. Sleep wrist actigraphy has been successfully used in evaluating astronaut sleep quality on the International Space Station and Shuttle crews for example.[6] These devices have smart phone graphic displays that can visualize daily, weekly, or monthly trends that can be shared with your health care providers.

5. Sun exposure

   Maximize vitamin D synthesis and minimize harmful radiation effects. Consider the SunFriend monitoring device.

6. Brain foods and metabolism
   Legacy diet guidelines
   Body mass index (BMI) – maintain at 20 to 25, refer to
        Web -based height/weight BMI calculator
   Percentage body fat using caliper device
7. Physical exercise monitoring
        GPS devices such as Garmin 620 measure VO2 max
   and vVO2 max
8. Attention, focus, meditation, relaxation monitoring may
   prove useful by recently marketed Melon EEG based
   headband and iPhone application (http://www. think-
   melon.com)
9. Brain health monitoring
        Computerized neuropsychological testing for the
   core frontal system networks responsible for brain output
   of all kinds in general working memory, attention, initiation, and inhibition. These can be tested by the CNS-VS
   (http://www.cnsvitalsigns.com) program for example, but
   others such as lumosity and brain age give scores that can
   track progress, whether adverse or improving.
10. Monitoring of deleterious and potentially harmful
    lifestyles.
        Alcohol is advocated as beneficial among some diets
    such as the Mediterranean diet. However, because alco-
    hol is used so frequently and is a major factor in motor
    vehicle accidents, breath analyzers are a useful, relatively
    cheap, commercially available tool to estimate dangerous
    alcohol levels.

The concept of the five principal domains that govern our brain
health, physical activity, brain foods, cognitive activity, sociality, and
sleep hygiene represent our evolutionary heritage and, to some extent
also relatively recently, our cultural heritage. There are some that are
nonnegotiable, such as sleep duration and timing, the need for physical activity and the requirements of essential food items. Sleep cycles
were ultimately determined by astrophysical forces. However, there
is leeway among others, such as the type of cognitive stimulation and
the various proportions of macronutrient intake (figure 7.2).

Fig. 7.2. Natural rhythms ranges from direct control, encompassed by brain fitness components, to factors that made us human, to no control at all

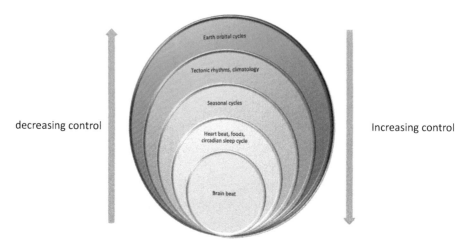

decreasing control

Increasing control

Our bodies were literally honed by fire (volcanism, tectonics, and climate changes) and ice (Ice Ages and consequently forced dietary changes) and in the course of evolution our neural circuitry entrained the systems that allow us to associate the right activities, foods, and experiences with brain health. This has been mediated by the dopaminergic, nucleus accumbens reward system of the brain. We are addicted to certain foods—such as fats, sugars, and salt— because they ensured our survival. However, nowadays, the excess of these components in many of our foods as well as the concept of making foods hyperpalatable by combining two or three of these in one particular food item is simply making us fat and prone to ill health. Another downside of this reward system is its propensity to addiction as well as the proclivity as a species to be afflicted by neuropsychiatric (depression, bipolar disease, anxiety, schizophrenia) conditions. The study by Akesson et al[7] of the dramatic reduction to 86% in heart attack rate and the study by Larsson et al. demonstrating a 68% reduction in stroke[8] should inject great enthusiasm for adhering to these lifestyle recommendations. These reductions exceed dramatically reductions achieved by drugs. The additional lifestyle factors promoted in this book, such as sociality, cognitive exercises, and appropriate time and duration of sleep should boost brain health even more.

References

1. Akesson A, Larsson SC, Discacciatti A, Wolk A. LowRisk Diet and Lifestyle Habits in the Primary Prevention of Myocardial Infarction in Men. A Population-Based Prospective Cohort Study. *Journal of American College of Cardiology* 2014; 64:1299–1306.

2. Ferrer R, Artigas A. Physiologic parameters as biomarkers: what can we learn from physiologic variables and variation? *Crit Care Clin.* 2011; 27:229–40. doi: 10.1016/j. ccc.2010.12.008.

3. Naccarelli GV, Varker H, Lin J, Schulman KL. Increasing prevalence of atrial fibrillation and flutter in the United States. *Am J Cardiol* 2009; 105:1534–1539.

4. Efimova I, Efimova N, Chernov V, Popov S, Lishmanov YAblation and pacing: improving brain perfusion and cognitive function in patients with atrial fibrillation and uncontrolled ventricular rates. *Pacing Clin Electrophysiol.* 2012 Mar; 35(3):320–6. doi: 10.1111/j.1540–8159.2011.03277.x.

5. Gibbs WW. Medicine gets up close and personal. *Nature* 2014; 506:144–145.

6. Barger LK, Flynn-Evans E, Kubey et al. Prevalence of sleep deficiency and use of hypnotic drugs in astronauts before, during and after spaceflight: an observational study. *Lancet Neurology* 2014; 13:904–912.

7. Akesson A, Larsson SC, Discacciatti A, Wolk A. LowRisk Diet and Lifestyle Habits in the Primary Prevention of Myocardial Infarction in Men. A Population-Based Prospective Cohort Study. *Journal of American College of Cardiology* 2014; 64:1299–1306.

8. Larsson SC, Akesson A, Wolk A. Healthy diet and lifestyle and risk of stroke in a prospective cohort of women. *Neurology* 2014; 83:1699–1704.

Index

AA. *See* arachnoidic acid
Acanthostega 31
acne vulgaris 195
ADHD. *See* attention-deficit
 hyperactivity disorder
African Rift Valley 21, 23, 39,
 178
AIM model 280, 281
Akt 146
alcohol 204, 205
 anticarcinogenic properties of
 209
 beneficial effects of 207, 209
 clinical 205, 208
 deleterious effects of 207, 209
 metabolism and action of 207
 neurological effects of 208
Alvarez bolide impact theory 35
Alzheimer's disease 321
Alzheimers disease 96, 108, 112,
 201, 270, 335
AMOC. *See* Atlantic meridional
 overturning circulation
amphioxi 29
AMY1 45
animal-assisted therapy 330, 331,
 332

anoneirognosis 282
antioxidants 213, 214
aphasia 23
arachidonic acid 169, 170, 171,
 177
argenine vasopressin. *See* AVP
arts, the 339, 340, 341, 343, 344
as angiogenesis 128
ASPM 45
Atchley, Ruth Ann 328
atherosclerosis 173, 174
 common sites of 174
Atlantic meridional overturning
 63, 65, 67, 69
attention-deficit hyperactivity
 disorder 180
australopithecines 23, 38, 42, 99,
 190, 191
 fat and neat diets of 190
 habitat of 178
 tuber diet of 158, 178
Australopithecus
 afarensis 38, 130
 africanus 22, 376
 paranthropus 191
 robustus 191
autonoesis 52, 53

AVP 295
Bacteroidetes 166
Band-Aid effect 20
BDNF 146, 148
berries. *See* antioxidants
bilaterians 29
biophilia 328, 330, 332
bipedalism 22, 38, 41, 96, 100
Blue Mind 329
BMP2 46
BMP7 46
BO10. *See* 10 under Broddmann
 area
BO13. *See* 13 under Broddmann
 area
body mass index 193
Bond events 67
brain
 enlargement of 34, 40
 climactic change 40
 factors affecting health of 218
 lesions of 23, 24, 25, 26, 27
 size of 22, 30, 37, 38, 41, 45,
 79, 156, 157, 175, 177,
 178, 183, 184, 192, 294,
 298
brain box dashboard 362, 363,
 364
brain-derived neurotrophic factor.
 See BDNF
Brocas area *10* 25, 336
Broddmann area
 10 51
 13 51
Buschke selective reminding test
 313
Calvin, William 67
carbon elimination process 70
CDK5RAP2 45
celiac disease 197
Charcots variant 282

chase hunting 101
Chicxulub asteroid impact 73
chrons 72
circadian rhythms 17, 257
climate change 72
cognitive decline 312, 313
cognitive exercises 345
cognitive reserve 317, 318, 319,
 320, 321
communication 305
cooking 191
Crawford, Michael 186
crown mammalia 34
Dart, Raymond 22, 73
Darwinius masillae 37
default mode network 334, 335
dementia 109, 312, 313, 318,
 321
DHA. *See* docosahexanoic acid
diabetes mellitus 192
diet 182, 221, 222
 ancestral 162
 Atkins 202, 220
 DASH 212
 deleterious categories for 224
 flexibility of 157
 food beneficial categories for
 223
 food categories for 223
 fruits and vegetables 203
 legacy 220, 223
 Mediterranean 162, 201, 220
 Okinawa 202, 220
 Paleo 150, 151, 158, 162, 201,
 220
 primordial 180
 quality of 157
 recommendations for 204
 Rosedale 203, 220
 Western 165, 180
dirt archeology 22

DISP1 46
diversive curiosity 80
DLX1 46
DLX2 46
DLX5 46
DLX6 46
DMN. *See* default mode network
docosahexanoic acid 146, 176,
     177, 178, 179, 183, 184
  benefits of 187
dopamine 100, 101
dreams 279, 280, 281
  benefits of 281
drunken monkey hypothesis 205
Dudley, Robert 205
Dunkleosteus 30, 31
echolalia 25
echopraxia 25
Ediacarans 28
EI. *See* emotional intelligence
electronic games 315
El Niño 40, 69
emotional intelligence 54
enamel 190
endocannabinoid 103
enteric nervous system 161
environmental dependency syn-
     drome 24, 25
epigenetics 78
eudaimonia 339
evolution
  humans 22, 23, 27
  primates 36, 73
executive functions 47, 48, 49,
     52, 101
exercise 104
  aerobic 101, 109, 111, 124
  amount of 119
  anaerobic 124
  benefits of 107, 108, 109, 111,
     113, 114, 115, 116, 123

intensity of 120
  moderate 115
  screening before 124
  strength training as 124
  strenous 115
Facebook 305
fasting 217
fencing 127
fire 191
Firmicutes 166
fishapods 31, 32
foraminfera 68
forest bathing 328, 329
FOXP2 45
frontopolar cortex 25
G-6PD gene deficiency 160
gaze detection 294
general intelligence 38
geomagnetic reversal 72
  Brunhes-Matumaya 72
  Gothenburg 72
  Lake Mungo 72
  Laschamp 72
  Mono Lake 72
glial cells 78, 316
gluten
  illnesses related to 198
  sensitivity to 197
glycolysis 122
Gondwanaland 32
Gothenburg magnetic excursion
     72
great oxygen event, the 177
HACNS1 45
hafting 44
hallucinations 54
Hangenberg event 31
herbs. *See* antioxidants
Hobson, Allan 280
holobiont 218, 219
hologenome 218, 219

hologenome theory of evolution 218

Homo
  erectus 41, 42, 43, 99, 182, 191
  habilis 99
  heidelbergensis 43
  heidelbergensis 48
  sapiens 18, 44, 178
honey 198, 199
  benefits of 200
hormesis 205
hots pots. *See* hub vulnerability hypothesis
hub vulnerability hypothesis 79
Hundred Person Wellness Project 361, 362
hunter-gatherers 151, 157, 163, 165, 305
hyperphasia, forced 25
hyperthermophile 27
Ice Ages 62, 63
  records of 68
ice sheet formation 58, 59, 60, 61, 62
Instagrams 305
interglacial periods 63
Isbell, Lynne 36
Jarman-Bell relationship 154
Jefferson, Richard 218
Judith 343
Jurassic period 32
Kalenjin 164
kayaking 125
ketones 187, 188
  clinical uses of 188, 189
Klimt, Gustav 343
KT event 35
lactate threshold 122, 123, 124
Laetoli footprints 23, 38, 97
language
  development of 43

evolution of 54
La Niña 40, 70
Lascaux painting 322, 323
Leakey, Mary 23
leisure-based activities 313
leptin 144
leukoaraiosis 110
limnic eruptions 37
Lion Man 52
lycopenes 214
Lyon Heart Study 142
macronutrients 148, 151, 162, 166
  carbohydrates
    complex 196
    grains 196
    sugars 189
  deterioration of 165
  fats 167
    cerebrovascular disease relationship with 171, 172
    cholesterol 168, 173
    classification of 167
    consumption of 181
    coronary heart disease relationship with 171, 172, 173
    eicosanoids 168
    role in human evolution 175, 176
  fava beans 160
  lactase 160
  maize 159
  proteins 166, 167
  salivary amylase 158, 159
malaria 160
mammals 34
Mappiness 329
Marchiavellian intelligence hypothesis 294
Masai 163

meditation 333, 335, 336, 338, 339
MEF2A 46
megadontia quotient 191
megalodon 31
memory
  episodic 52, 53, 54, 301
  working 37, 45, 46, 47, 48, 53, 101
mental time travel. *See* autonoesis
metabolic syndrome 192, 194
metacognition 51, 336, 337
metazoans 28, 29
microbiome 142, 161, 219
microcephalin 1 45
micronutrients 148
  deficiencies of 152
  subtypes of 152, 153, 154
Milankovitch, Milutin 62
mirror neuron system 24, 25, 50
mirror test 293
MNS. *See* mirror neuron system
musicality 341, 342, 343
myelin 30
MyFitnessPal app 222
MYH16 45
mysticism 325
NaCl. *See* salt
narcolepsy 267
Neanderthals 44, 48
neuroarcheology 23
neurogenesis 104, 105, 106, 107, 113, 114, 126, 128
neurology 23
Nichols, Wallace 329
nonrapid eye movement. *See* NREM
NREM 273, 279
obesity 150, 193
  causes of 193, 194
OTX2 46

overeating 150
oxidants
  cacao 216
  coffee 215
  teas
    black 216
    green 216
oxytocin 295, 298, 333
Paleocene-Eocene thermal maximum 36
Panderichthys 31
pastoralists 157, 164
PCDH11X 45
PCDH11Y 45
pellagra 159
Permian-Triassic extinction event 32
PETM. *See* Paleocene-Eocene thermal maximum
photosynthesis 28
placoderms 30
polypill 123
polyunsaturated fatty acids 171, 185, 186
postagricultural communities 151
posttraumatic stress disorder 282
power scavenging 101
prairie voles 296, 297
Proconsul 38
psychiatric disorders
  attention-deficit hyperactivity 50
  bipolar 49, 71
  depression 49, 71
  obsessive-compulsive 25, 49
  Tourettes syndrome 25, 50
psychobiome 219
PUFA. *See* polyunsaturated fatty acids
rabbit starvation 166
Randall, Lisa 73

rapid eye movement. *See* REM
Reece, Matthew 73
refined sugar 196
REM 265, 268, 273, 279
remote associates test 328
resveratrol 209
rimonabant 150
RNF213 45
Romers gap 31
Rosenberg, Zilber 218
runners high 102
running 96, 98, 100, 102, 103,
    121
RUNX2 45
Sahara pump theory 69, 70
salt 209
    biochemistry of 211
    food content of 211
    hypertension in relationship
        with 212
    intake variation of 211
    trading of 210
SDB. *See* sleep breathing disorder
    syndromes
sensorimotor integration 34
Shubin, Neil 17, 31
sleep
    disorders of
        hypersomia 267
        insomia 268, 269
        REM 268
    effects of deprivation of 269,
        270, 271, 272
    evolutionary insights of 272
    functions of 277
    molecular mechanisms of 278
    neurobiological overview of
        259, 260, 261, 262, 263
    neurological disorders of 265
    physics of 283
    problems of

causes of 258
    epidemiology of 257
    scope of 258
    recommendations for improved
        283, 284
    restorative functions of 278
    stages of 273
sleep apnea
    central 267
    obstructive 267
sleep breathing disorder syn-
    dromes 266, 267
snake detection theory 36
social behavior
    neurobiological insights into
        294
    neurochemical insights into 294
social brain circuitry 305
social intelligence 38, 294
social interaction 127, 294, 297,
    298, 302, 306
socialization 306
sodium 210, 211
sodium chloride. *See* salt
soft drinks 195
solar storms 71
Southern Ocean gateway opening
    58
spices. *See* antioxidants
spirituality 54, 322, 323, 325,
    326, 327
SRGAP2 45
starch 158
Stern, Yaakov 317
superconnections 303
supercooperators 302
swimming 124
synapsids 32, 34
taste senses 148, 149
TB. *See* tuberculosis
tectonic plates 57

tectonic uplift 70

thermohaline circulation 65

The Universe Within Us 17

Tibetan Plateau formation 70

Tiktaalik 31, 116

Torrance test of creative thinking
    336

TSC1 46

tuberculosis 219

Twitter 305

two-mile time machine 67

urbilaterian 29

USF1 45

vagus nerve 145

vasopressin 297. *See* AVP

visual streams 42

vitamin supplemetation 217

VITATOPS 143

VO2 max 120, 124, 125
    concept of 121
    measuring of 121
    training use of 122

volume of oxygen uptake maxi-
    mum. *See* VO2max

Walker circulation 40

West Side Story 303

Willbrands variant 282

xanthohumol 209

yoga 124

Zelig-like syndrome 25

zonulin 197

About the Author

Michael Hoffmann obtained his medical degree (MBBch) at the University of Witwatersrand, Johannesburg, South Africa, famous for the triadic doyens of human evolution, Raymond Dart, Robert Broom and Philip Tobias, discoverers of several species of *Australopithecus africanus*, the "missing link." He was fortunate to have had Phillip Tobias as both his anatomy professor and dean of medicine during his formative medical training. Under his tutelage in anatomy were included site visits to the adjacent Cradle of Humankind, the UNESCO world heritage Sterkfontein caves where many australopithecine fossils have been found and continue to be found. Subsequent neurology specialty training ensued at the University of Kwa-Zulu Natal with neurology certification, FCP(SA) awarded by the Colleges of Medicine of South Africa, and later in his career, a clinical senior medical doctorate (MD) was obtained followed by a PhD in behavioral medicine. Further neurological subspecialty fellowship training in stroke and cerebrovascular disease occurred at Columbia University in New York City. His main areas of research have concerned cognitive disorders after stroke and more recently his research has focused on factors pertaining to improved brain health and preventative aspects derived through human evolutionary insights.

He is currently a Professor of Neurology with the University of Central Florida and University of Florida (courtesy) and director of the stroke and cognitive neurology divisions at the Orlando VA Medical Center. He is a cognitive neurology consultant at the Roskamp Neuroscience Institute in Sarasota, Florida, where he focuses on mild cognitive impairment, traumatic brain illness, and neurotoxicological syndromes such as Gulf War illness. His popular human evolution seminars are testimony to the burgeoning fascination with this discipline.

CPSIA information can be obtained
at www.ICGtesting.com
Printed in the USA
LVOW01s0909110316

478680LV00024B/152/P